AN AMERICAN SHORT STORY SURVEY

An American Short Story Survey

Edited by

ROGER PENN CUFF

Professor of English
Central Michigan College

THE STACKPOLE COMPANY
HARRISBURG, PENNSYLVANIA

Printed in the U. S. A.

By

THE TELEGRAPH PRESS

Established 1831

Harrisburg, Pennsylvania

To my wife

ELEANOR FRAZIER CUFF

my loyal helper for a quarter century

CONTENTS

PART II: MATTER

HUMOR

LOVE

SURPRISE

DETECTIVE

ADVENTURE

INTRODUCTION

FOR artistry in its short story product, America probably holds top rank among the nations of the world, with France a close second, and with Russia, Germany, and England not far behind. So popular is the short-length fiction as a tool for reflecting a writer's observation of life and his philosophy and for providing entertainment and vicarious experience that stories are read voraciously today by many persons both inside and outside college.

Ever since about 1910 courses of study in the short story have been offered in American institutions of higher learning. Today one would probably have difficulty in finding very many liberal-arts-college curricula that do not include among the English-department offerings one or more courses in the short story. The popularity of this type of literature indicates a demand that may need to be supplied.

I. THE PURPOSES OF THIS ANTHOLOGY

This new collection of stories provides opportunity for a comparative study of classics and of contemporary work of high quality. The Comparison Exercises are designed to stimulate this kind of study. They suggest that attention be given to similarities and dissimilarities of content and method between the two stories of each pair representing the types: plot, character, setting, theme, atmosphere, humor, love, surprise, detective, and adventure. This comparative study can be applied to such story elements as tempo of action, sharpness of climax, play of fancy, techniques of characterization, relationship of background to plot, devices for depicting setting, realistic or romantic approach, emotional appeal, quality of humor, methods of making a love story dignified and attractive, the use of suspense in a story that ends with a surprise as well as in a story of detection, the use of other detective-story devices, and the quality of the diction employed.

The stimulating of comparative study is only one of the aims of

1

this book. Another purpose of the anthology is to help meet the widespread interest the reading public has in the short-story branch of literature. The volume is planned to serve either as the basic reading matter for a college course in short-length fiction or as a guide to techniques in a course of short-story writing. Twenty selected stories, representing ten types, two stories to the type—one drawn from the nineteenth century, the other from the twentieth—will furnish ample brief narratives to meet the needs of many a college class interested in either gaining appreciation of the short story as a literary form or developing story-writing ability. When desirable, the stories in this volume may be supplemented by choices from the list of Recommended Readings. Procedures, useful to students and teachers alike, for developing short-story appreciation are outlined in the Plan for Studying a Short Story.

A third aim of this new collection, as already intimated, is to stimulate an interest in story-writing and to offer help in the use of those techniques which story analysts and theorists and critics usually regard as successful. The three aims can hardly be separated and placed in absolutely distinct compartments; neither can the means of achieving these aims. Some help toward story-writing ability may be obtainable from intelligent story-reading, from complying with the directions given in the Study Notes, and from doing the comparative studies suggested in the Comparison Exercises. The most highly focused attempts that this book makes, however, to guide a person's story-writing propensities appear in the Suggestions on How to Write a Story and in the Writing Suggestions (one assignment at the end of each pair of stories).

II. A PLAN FOR STUDYING A SHORT STORY

It is only natural that anyone who has not yet had a wide experience in the reading of short stories should wonder how he might proceed in order to obtain the appreciation and mastery which he desires. Numerous techniques for the study of the short narrative have been proposed by various anthologists.[1] The following plan is presented as one useful procedure—one method of attack that may help the student to escape from his feeling of inexperience and may

---

[1] E. A. Cross, for example, set forth a short-story study outline in *A Book of the Short Story*, New York: American Book Company, 1934, pp. 62-4.

stimulate him to be sufficiently critical to become fond of at least some of the stories he may read.

A PLAN OF SHORT-STORY STUDY

1. The author's name and the title of the story.
2. The dates of the author's birth and death (only the birth date, of course, if the author is living).
3. The facts of first publication of the story.
   a. The title of the magazine, newspaper, or book in which the story first appeared.
   b. (1) The volume number, date, and page reference for the magazine, or
      (2) The date and page reference for the newspaper, or
      (3) The place of publication, the name of the publisher, and the date of publication for the book.
4. The name of the type to which the story belongs (see Heydrick, *Types of the Short Story,* for a list of names of story classifications).
5. The time (year or season or era or whatever method of designation the narrative itself employs) within which the action is represented as having occurred.
6. The scene of the action—the locale to which the events are assigned.
7. A brief summary of the plot—arranging in 1-2-3 order the main threads of action (the most important incidents), usually about five.
8. The climax (the most exciting and decisive event) or, in the case of the mystery story, the solution of the mystery.
9. The author's contributions to short-story style and method (this listing may be based on the statements of critics or may be only the student's conclusions or may be both; perhaps preferably should include some of his own generalizations).
10. Suggestions on how to teach this particular story (these helpful hints may be drawn from books of teaching methods or may merely present the student's own best judgment).

An application of the above study plan to Irving's "Adalantado of the Seven Cities" would yield a set of answers approximating those here given.

3

INTRODUCTION

A Written Report on a Short Story

1. Washington Irving; "The Adalantado of the Seven Cities."
2. 1783-1859.
3. a. *The Knickerbocker.*
   b. (1) XIV (July, 1839), 28-38.
4. Adventure (with a love element).
5. A century, beginning in the early 1400's.
6. Lisbon, Portugal; the legendary "Island of the Seven Cities," St. Brandan; and Palma, one of the Canaries.
7. (1) In the days of Prince Henry of Portugal, another navigator, who had recently returned to Lisbon, told of having seen the "Island of the Seven Cities."

   (2) Don Fernando de Ulmo, a Portuguese cavalier, decided he would lead an expedition to the island, and he received from the king a commission authorizing the project.

   (3) Fernando busied himself with the necessary preparations, purchasing ships and supplies, and at evenings conversing with his bethrothed, Serafina Alvarez, from beneath her balcony window, despite her father's desire to keep the two lovers apart.

   (4) Finally, the lovers pledged mutual constancy and the ships sailed on their expedition to the "Island of the Seven Cities," where Fernando arrived, after having been tossed about by a violent storm.

   (5) At the island he was treated with very great respect as the "Adalantado," participated in a festival for what he thought was just one night (but which he later was informed was a full century), and made love to the alcayde's daughter.

   (6) Upon his return to Lisbon, after having been rescued in an unconscious condition from a wreck at sea, he hurried to the Alvarez mansion and there found a woman whom he supposed was his betrothed Serafina; but was he told that she was Serafina's great-granddaughter.

   (7) He reported to the office of the Minister of Marine, but could not convince the clerk that Fernando was the self-same man who had undertaken the expedition a hundred years earlier.

   (8) Not being able to finance another expedition to search for the phantom island, Fernando sailed for Palma, one of the Canaries; and from a promontory he daily scanned the horizon in the hope of again seeing St. Brandan; but he died on the promontory one day with this hope unfulfilled.

8. Maria's informing Fernando that she was the great-granddaughter of Serafina.
9. (1) An entertaining rather than a propagandizing purpose.
   (2) A rich atmosphere (in this story, Spanish and Portuguese).
   (3) Excellent characterization (in this story, Don Fernando and Serafina and her father, Don Ramiro, are well drawn).
   (4) A strikingly original fancy.
   (5) A lucid, attractive style.
10. (1) Request the student to investigate and explain the historical elements of the story.
    (2) Consider the extent to which the story is legendary and the extent to which it is original.

Perhaps students may find in the following suggestions, which on first publication were aimed primarily at teachers of the short-story survey course, some help toward interpreting and evaluating the stories which this volume contains. "(1) Begin the readings by assigning a story in the anthology chosen for the course, requesting that the story be read by the next class meeting, and then at that next session having the students take turns and taking turns with them at reading the story aloud. (2) Note the purpose of the story—whether to entertain with imagination or whimsy, to serve as a sugar coating or an embellishment for moralizing, or to arouse pity or fear or sympathy and admiration. (3) State the theme and indicate the situation or the type of character out of which the theme grows. (4) Connect the short story with the author's life to the extent that making such a connection is feasible, noting the preparation that the writer had received for producing this type of work and the reasons, so far as they can be discovered, why the author wrote this particular kind of story. (5) Consider the content—the setting, the characterization, and the action . . . (6) Give some attention to techniques and style—to the deviousness or directness, the obviousness or subtlety, of the craftsmanship and to the relevancy of materials and to the use of diction and dialogue, of imagery and emotion. (7) Use other effective devices for helping the students to understand the essentials of the short story as a form of literature, such methods as requesting written composition, stimulating oral discussion, or instituting a comparison of the type of story written by one author with that created by some other writer. (8) Encourage, by thought-provoking questions, the use of the library for reference as a source of information concerning the story writer, the particular narrative being studied, and the type or types of his total short story product. (9) Encourage the reading of stories in contemporary and current magazines and the applying to these stories of knowledge, already acquired in the course, concerning the techniques of story writing. (10) Build a summary, with the help of the students, of the salient features of the course, when the course is nearing the end." [2]

III. SUGGESTIONS ON HOW TO WRITE A STORY

Any discussion of the story-writer's craft might well begin with a hard-to-take piece of advice: Work like a horny-handed son of toil. No substitute can equal hard and honest labor as a means of obtaining the material of a story plot and making of this material a beautifully finished narrative. Effective stories are seldom, if ever, born except at the cost of toil and travail. The idea that belles-lettres are usually brought into being by a sudden and effortless surge of inspiration is an exploded myth.

Writing techniques possess certain indispensable characteristics. Many of these techniques can be learned. The mechanics of story writing can be taught. There is no way ever to know them except to learn them. The *craft* of story writing may be obtained from instruction and study. The *art* of story writing, depending upon individual temperament, training, and philosophy, is somewhat unpredictable, and one may well question whether the rich fancy and the highly polished urbanity that make some stories attractive can really be taught. In large measure, however, story-writing ability (at least the craft and perhaps in some degree also the art) can be acquired. The suggestions here given may help the student to add to his personal equipment such parts of short-narrative technique as are subject to the learning process.

1. Find a theme that will make the story really significant.

Although some stories can hardly be said to have a theme, it is probably usually best to build a story around a motif. The theme unifies the action. The range of possible motifs is not large. Among the major fields of human activity are adventure, business, love,

---

[2] R. P. Cuff, "Modernizing the Short Story Survey," *Peabody Journal of Education* (May, 1946). Reprinted by permission of the *Journal.*

politics, mystery-solving, and character-building. Among the worthy motives which stir the heart are bravery, courtesy, faith, friendship, honor, hope, loyalty, and even a willingness to sacrifice one's own interests for the sake of a cause. From these activities and motives themes may be obtained. Once a theme is found, it should be allowed to affect the plot and the characters.

2. Place the characters in a conflict-producing situation—the kind of pressure that will force them into action.

If the characters are delineated concretely, the story is almost sure to be more widely admired than if the actors are undifferentiated and unlifelike. As the narration of the conflict progresses, one should use effective methods of characterization, relying mainly upon the objective devices. The chief techniques of character portrayal that have been employed by writers are (1) description of physical appearance, (2) analysis, by the author, of the character's inward experiences—thoughts and emotions and motives, (3) the writing of dialogue that is important for the light it throws upon character, and (4) assigning to a character actions that harmonize with the personality that the story author wishes to portray. Dialogue and action are the most frequently used and the most effective of these methods.

Good dialogue is difficult to write. One should study its handling by the masters. Dialogue should be spontaneous and seem natural. It may throw into bold relief the habits of illiterate speech—such habits as the use of colloquialism and slang and even profanity or other vulgarisms. Dialogue should be dramatic—therefore highly condensed and marked by stoppages or changes in the smooth flow of thought, interruptions that dashes may indicate. Dialogue should serve two main purposes: reveal personality and carry the action forward. It should contribute to both the plot and the characterization.

The characters should be made true to life and their personalities should be closely related to the development of the plot. All the methods of characterization should employ a rich measure of concrete language. The reader should be caused to picture as flesh-and-blood persons all the actors delineated. Concrete portrayal is the kind that holds the interest.

3. Plot the action from the initial situation to the denouement.

In fairness to the beginning story writer, a caution should be given: Avoid plots that are tabooed by many persons—such plots as those based on miraculous coincidence; those involving suicide; those which reward crime; those which display religious bigotry, political partisanship, sectionalism, or race prejudice; and those which deal with such unpleasant subjects as insanity attributed to the main character. The narrator will increase his chances of success if he will treat of adventure or mystery or romance, provided he will steadfastly refuse to supercharge the love stories with sex.

To obtain legitimate and attractive plot materials, the story writer will need to observe life closely, to read voraciously, and to have a wide range of experience. Observation of life is a fruitful source of narrative materials. Almost any time or anywhere might be observed a person, a place, or an event which by the alchemy of inventiveness could result in an intriguing plot. Reading may uncover suggestions for plot in the news items of the daily newspaper, in some short story, or in almost any published work wherein a fertile mind may find odd facts or fictions which the imagination may use as the germ of a new narrative. The best stories are likely to be well rooted in experience—to originate from personal first-hand knowledge. The imagination may either create a whole plot or may add to some suggestion already in hand—perhaps to a few factual details—the portions that need to be supplied to produce an interesting complication.

4. Make the story dramatic.

One way to dramatize the action is to narrate much of the story by scenes—moments of crisis each of which has its own background of time and place. Many a story could hardly, however, be cast completely in scenic form. Usually straight narrative (consisting of analysis and explanation—of summary, and interpretation, of action) appears between the scenes.

Another way to dramatize a story is to use devices of suspense. Facing the leading character with oppositions which keep the reader uncertain whether the character will win or lose is one effective device. A second technique of suspense is the building of the story up to a climax through a series of actions, each of which is more exciting than the one preceding.

5. Maintain the narrative point of view that seems most suitable for the story being told.

Two kinds of focus—that of a diary or a series of letters and that of the story within a story—are so objectionable or difficult that the amateur writer would better avoid them. Both these points of view are likely to produce a verbose and incoherent style and to cause the action to move at too slow a tempo.

The three other main types of narrative angle—the ones that are most useful to the story writer—are the omniscient point of view (third-person), the chief character's point of view (first-person), and a minor character's point of view (first-person). The first-named is impersonal and external. It represents action as seen by the author, who is not one of the characters participating in the plot. The remaining two are personal and internal. They represent action as seen by participants. The main-character angle narrates events as viewed by the hero or the heroine. The minor-character focus recounts the incidents as known to and told by a subsidiary person, who is nevertheless a participator.

Each point of view has its own values. In the full-fledged omniscient angle (there does exist, of course, the also possible point of view of limited omniscience, in which the author, writing in the third person, assumes mind-reading power toward only one or a small group of the characters—not toward all), the author assumes an absolute knowledge of all the characters—an ability to read their thoughts and feelings. Because of the free range of mental analysis that this fully omniscient focus makes possible, the device is particularly useful in psychological stories. Any story that deals primarily with subjective experience should be told from the omniscient point of view. The main-character angle is especially useful in stories heavy with action. This is the kind of focus that most frequently appears in short stories. When this point of view is taken, the leading character must be portrayed through his own utterances and actions. Subjective analysis cannot be used for delineating his personality. This main-character point of view is, however, a vivid method of narration and one that readily contributes to unity and coherence. The minor-character kind of focus is commonly used in mystery stories which employ a detective's foil, a Dr. Watson, as the narrator. The foil knows no more as the story unfolds than does the reader. The device is effective for creating suspense.

6. Picture the setting within which the characters interact.

The setting is the physical environment of action, especially the time and place within which an incident is represented as having occurred. Setting may include such other externals as climate and social surroundings and the effect of these externals upon the appearance of the locale of the action or upon the psychological reaction of the characters.

The scene of action has sometimes been depicted so skillfully that its dominance in a story is not objectionable. More often, however, the setting serves as a backdrop for action or characterization either of which may loom larger than the environment itself. Such description of the milieu as does appear should take the form of small portions well distributed in the story rather than of one extensive passage.

7. Follow the fundamental principles of structure.

The creative process when applied to short-story writing should conform to certain rhetorical principles, such as unity, order, compactness, and proportion. The story should present one main action, have no subplots. It is also helpful for a brief narrative to have unity of time and place and mood. The materials should be so arranged as to create suspense and reveal existing cause-and-effect relationships. As early as 1885 Brander Matthews in a published article, "The Philosophy of the Short-Story," named compression as one of the laws that should govern the writing of short-length fiction. This law of compactness requires that only such descriptions, conversations, scenes, and explanations may be included as depict the setting, advance the action, or directly contribute to the characterization. Proportion requires that description, dialogue, scenic action, and straight narrative appear in such balance as leaves the reader impressed with the effectiveness of the story. The action must not be impeded by too much description or explanation.

8. Infuse into the writing the essential elements of artistic style.

The word, *style,* though technical and difficult to define with thoroughness, does signify artistic quality in literature. The student, and the writer, of short stories should give serious thought to the artistry of literary narration. Clearly, the person who is being exposed to a survey of the short story should wait no longer to obtain at least a tyro's acquaintance with the meaning of style and a sense of how to impart artistic quality to literary work.

A minimum acceptable standard of short-story style must demand precision in the choice of words, a mastery of sentence form (including syntax), a knowledge of the essential elements of plot, and probably some reflection of the writer's attitude toward life. Among the essentials of literary art that even a beginning short-story writer should apply are clearness and concreteness. Vague sentences indicate haste, ignorance, or slovenliness. Inescapable is the story-maker's obligation to express his narrative in understandable language. Since narration depends more heavily upon imagery than do some other forms of discourse, the creator of fiction also has a responsibility to employ a high percentage of concrete phrasing—not neglecting the pictorial adjectives and verbs.

9. Use all necessary legitimate devices to make the story interesting.

Besides using the structural and stylistic and dramatic techniques that have been named, a writer may enhance the interest of a story by utilizing certain helpful devices in the beginning and in the ending.

Some of the suitable methods of beginning are the statement of a theme, the description of the setting, the delineation of character, and the presenting of action through either dialogue or straight narrative. Whatever the device used, the opening should seize the reader's interest and cause him to desire further acquaintance with the story. The introductory part should give the reader some information on all of the story elements that inhere within the materials—on the time setting, the place setting, the characters, and the action. The beginning should answer the four questions, *When? Where? Who?* and *What?*

Some of the interesting devices for terminating the story are the climax, the statement of a surprise, a needed explanation, an author or a character coment, and a statement echoing something said at the beginning. The concluding part should answer all the questions that, in order to give a "totality of effect," should be resolved, so that the reader will not feel disappointed or imposed

11

INTRODUCTION

upon. Usually a story should have been so well written that by the time the climax is reached few loose threads will remain to be tied. By that time, the action will be at an end or definitely very near. Regardless of the device employed, the ending should produce in the reader the effect of gratification and finality, a sense that the story is finished rather than abruptly broken off, that the unit of action with which the narrative proposed to deal has been completed.

PART I: MANNER

PERSONS interested in creating short stories may profitably consider the concrete elements of which stories are made, that is, the structural principles by which brief narratives are written. Primarily to help would-be story writers, Part I presents examples of five structural types: plot, character, setting, theme, and atmosphere. It is probably impossible to divide all short narratives into two absolutely distinct categories named MANNER and MATTER; perhaps no story belongs fully in one of these classes to the exclusion of the other. Technique and content cannot (at least should not) be completely divorced. Some stories, however, place a stronger emphasis upon manner than upon matter; others exhibit the matter more clearly than the manner. The classification of short fictions into two groups, those of method and those of content, has, though, some value. Stories of plot, character, and setting rather obviously emphasize form or technique; and by examining these types of writing the student can comparatively easily discover the principles by which such pieces of writing are constructed. The student may also notice the structural principles employed in stories of theme and atmosphere, although perhaps not quite so readily as in the examples in which plot, character, and setting predominate. Stories of theme and atmosphere may belong to the borderline between manner and matter. Structure seems less predominant in thematic and atmospheric stories than in those of plot, character, and setting. All five of the types illustrated in Part I, however, provide opportunity for the study of concrete story elements. These concrete structural elements are explained in detail in the individual "introductions" to the five pairs of stories in Part I.

PLOT

Introduction to Plot-Dominated Stories

STORIES with fascinating plot and vividly drawn characters are more in demand than any other kind. A story of plot deals with a problem and its outcome, with the achievement of a definite purpose despite difficulty.

Plot is a series of probable events which lead to an important change in the life of at least one character, a sequence of actions in which causality operates. One incident logically produces a second, and the cause-and-effect relationship exists throughout the whole set of occurrences that comprise the narrative.

Conflict is essential to plot. Some force opposes another. The chief character is the protagonist, and his obstacle or opposing force is the antagonist. The obstacle may take the form of an internal fault or of external circumstance or fate or inanimate object but is most often another person or persons (in short stories most likely one person, because the brevity of this form of writing permits the presentation of only a few characters in the total action).

The structural elements of short-story plot have usually been named introduction, complication, climax, and denouement. Occasionally, in a brief narrative, a small amount of falling action may appear between the climax and the denouement, but not always, and when such a plot division is present, it is usually quite brief. In fact, not only do some short stories have no falling action except the denouement itself, but some of them have no separate denouement but end with the climax.

Though analysis, designed to help someone read a story critically, may focus attention on the introduction as if that division of plot were strictly separable from the rising action, in reality the introduction is a part of the complication and should not be a lecture, a list of characters, a lengthy description, or anything else disjointed from

15

the action proper. The very first sentence might well start the conflict. The first paragraph should certainly arouse the reader's interest.

The introductory part of the story, sometimes called the *exposition,*
should apprise the reader of facts needed for comprehending the
action that follows. This exposition usually presents one or two of
the most important characters, often the hero or heroine and sometimes the antagonist. The opening paragraph usually suggests the
time-and-place setting and initiates the action with some occurrence
sufficiently startling and dramatic to pique the reader's curiosity to
continue to peruse the story. The introduction may also contain dialogue hinting of future action.

The complication, which is the major part of the action of the
story, may be defined as the series of incidents that comprise the
dramatic conflict, or as all the entanglements of plot, beginning with
the so-called exciting force (the event that unbalances the quiescence
and equilibrium, the natural course of life which is present in the
initial part of the story), and continuing with increasing emphasis
and suspense through the climax.

Though the crisis is, strictly speaking, the apex of the rising action,
analysis of story structure frequently lists the climax separately because this element is particularly important. The climax is the point
of highest interest to the reader and of decisive conflict between the
major opposing forces. Unless the crisis is worthy and well motivated, the story will be a failure.

The denouement, when one exists, is usually only a very brief dis-
entanglement following the climax, making final disposal of any
character of whose fate the reader may not have been already informed. The skilful story writer does not usually risk dragging the
plot into anticlimax after having reached the culminating event.

THE ADALANTADO OF THE SEVEN CITIES[1]
(1839)

WASHINGTON IRVING

IN the early part of the fifteenth century, when Prince Henry of Portugal, of worthy memory, was pushing the career of discovery along the western coast of Africa, and the world was resounding with reports of golden regions on the mainland, and new-found islands in the ocean, there arrived at Lisbon an old bewildered pilot of the seas, who had been driven by tempests, he knew not whither, and raved about an island far in the deep, upon which he had landed, and which he had found peopled with Christians, and adorned with noble cities.

The inhabitants, he said, having never before been visited by a ship, gathered round, and regarded him with surprise. They told him they were descendants of a band of Christians, who fled from Spain when that country was conquered by the Moslems. They were curious about the state of their fatherland, and grieved to hear that the Moslems still held possession of the kingdom of Granada. They would have taken the old navigator to church, to convince him of their orthodoxy; but, either through lack of devotion, or lack of faith in their words, he declined their invitation, and preferred to return on board of his ship. He was properly punished. A furious storm arose, drove him from his anchorage, hurried him out to sea, and he saw no more of the unknown island.

This strange story caused great marvel in Lisbon and elsewhere. Those versed in history remembered to have read, in an ancient chronicle, that, at the time of the conquest of Spain, in the eighth century, when the blessed cross was cast down, and the crescent erected in its place, and when Christian churches were turned into Moslem mosques, seven bishops, at the head of seven bands of pious exiles, had fled from the peninsula, and embarked in quest of some ocean island, or distant land, where they might found seven Christian cities, and enjoy their faith unmolested.

The fate of these saints-errant had hitherto remained a mystery,

---

[1] First published in *The Knickerbocker* (July, 1839) and later included in *Wolfert's Roost and Other Papers* (1855). The story has the subtitle, "A Legend of St. Brandan." The imaginary island, St. Brandan, was long thought to exist about two hundred leagues westward from the Canaries.

and their story had faded from memory; the report of the old tempest-tossed pilot, however, revived the long-forgotten theme; and it was determined by the pious and enthusiastic, that the island thus accidentally discovered was the identical place of refuge whither the wandering bishops had been guided by a protecting Providence, and where they had folded their flocks.

This most excitable of worlds has always some darling object of chimerical enterprise. The "Island of the Seven Cities"[2] now awakened as much interest and longing among zealous Christians as has the renowned city of Timbuctoo among adventurous travelers, or the Northeast passage among hardy navigators; and it was a frequent prayer of the devout, that these scattered and lost portions of the Christian family might be discovered and reunited to the great body of Christendom.

No one, however, entered into the matter with half the zeal of Don Fernando de Ulmo, a young cavalier of high standing in the Portuguese court, and of most sanguine and romantic temperament. He had recently come to his estate, and had run the round of all kinds of pleasures and excitements when this new theme of popular talk and wonder presented itself. The Island of the Seven Cities became now the constant subject of his thoughts by day, and his dreams by night; it even rivalled his passion for a beautiful girl, one of the greatest belles of Lisbon, to whom he was betrothed. At length his imagination became so inflamed on the subject, that he determined to fit out an expedition, at his own expense, and set sail in quest of this sainted island. It could not be a cruise of any great extent; for, according to the calculations of the tempest-tossed pilot, it must be somewhere in the latitude of the Canaries; which at that time, when the New World was as yet undiscovered, formed the frontier of ocean enterprise. Don Fernando applied to the crown for countenance and protection. As he was a favorite at court, the usual patronage was readily extended to him; that is to say, he received a commission from the king, Don Ioam II, constituting him Adalantado, or military governor, of any country he might discover, with the single proviso, that he should bear all the expenses of the discovery, and pay a tenth of the profits to the crown.

---

[2] This imaginary island, conceived of as existing somewhere in midocean and often confused with St. Brandan, had by the name *Antilla* been placed upon some of the maps current in Columbus's time.

Don Fernando now set to work in the true spirit of a projector. He sold acre after acre of solid land, and invested the proceeds in ships, guns, ammunition, and sea-stores. Even his old family mansion in Lisbon was mortgaged without scruple, for he looked forward to a palace in one of the Seven Cities, of which he was to be Adalantado. This was the age of nautical romance, when the thoughts of all speculative dreamers were turned to the ocean. The scheme of Don Fernando, therefore, drew adventurers of every kind. The merchant promised himself new marts of opulent traffic; the soldier hoped to sack and plunder some one or other of those Seven Cities; even the fat monk shook off the sleep and sloth of the cloister, to join in a crusade which promised such increase to the possessions of the Church.

One person alone regarded the whole project with sovereign contempt and growing hostility. This was Don Ramiro Alvarez, the father of the beautiful Serafina, to whom Don Fernando was betrothed. He was one of those perverse, matter-of-fact old men, who are prone to oppose every thing speculative and romantic. He had no faith in the Island of the Seven Cities; regarded the projected cruise as a crack-brained freak; looked with angry eye and internal heart-burning on the conduct of his intended son-in-law, chaffering away solid lands for lands in the moon; and scoffingly dubbed him Adalantado of Cloud Land. In fact, he had never really relished the intended match, to which his consent had been slowly extorted by the tears and entreaties of his daughter. It is true he could have no reasonable objections to the youth, for Don Fernando was the very flower of Portuguese chivalry. No one could excel him at the tilting-match, or the riding at the ring; none was more bold and dexterous in the bull-fight; none composed more gallant madrigals in praise of his lady's charms, or sang them with sweeter tones to the accompaniment of her guitar; nor could any one handle the castanets and dance the bolero with more captivating grace. All these admirable qualities and endowments, however, though they had been sufficient to win the heart of Serafina, were nothing in the eyes of her unreasonable father. O Cupid, god of love! why will fathers always be so unreasonable?

The engagement to Serafina had threatened at first to throw an obstacle in the way of the expedition of Don Fernando, and for a time perplexed him in the extreme. He was passionately attached to the young lady; but he was also passionately bent on this romantic enterprise. How should he reconcile the two passionate inclinations? A simple and obvious arrangement at length presented itself—marry Serafina, enjoy a portion of the honeymoon at once, and defer the rest until his return from the discovery of the Seven Cities!

He hastened to make known this most excellent arrangement to Don Ramiro, when the long-smothered wrath of the old cavalier burst forth. He reproached him with being the dupe of wandering vagabonds and wild schemers, and with squandering all his real possessions in pursuit of empty bubbles. Don Fernando was too sanguine a projector, and too young a man, to listen tamely to such language. He acted with what is technically called "becoming spirit." A high quarrel ensued; Don Ramiro pronounced him a madman, and forbade all further intercourse with his daughter until he should give proof of returning sanity, by abandoning this madcap enterprise; while Don Fernando flung out of the house, more bent than ever on the expedition, from the idea of triumphing over the incredulity of the graybeard, when he should return successful. Don Ramiro's heart misgave him. Who knows, thought he, but this crack-brained visionary may persuade my daughter to elope with him, and share his throne in this unknown paradise of fools? If I could only keep her safe until his ships are fairly out at sea!

He repaired to her apartment, represented to her the sanguine, unsteady character of her lover and the chimerical value of his schemes, and urged the propriety of suspending all intercourse with him until he should recover from his present hallucination. She bowed her head as if in filial acquiescence, whereupon he folded her to his bosom with parental fondness and kissed away a tear that was stealing over her cheek, but as he left the chamber quietly turned the key in the lock; for though he was a fond father and had a high opinion of the submissive temper of his child, he had a still higher opinion of the conservative virtues of lock and key, and determined to trust to them until the caravels should sail. Whether the damsel had been in any wise shaken in her faith as to the schemes of her lover by her father's eloquence, tradition does not say; but certain it is, that the moment she heard the key turn in the lock she became a firm believer in the Island of the Seven Cities.

20

The door was locked; but her will was unconfined. A window of the chamber opened into one of those stone balconies, secured by iron bars, which project like huge cages from Portuguese and Spanish houses. Within this balcony the beautiful Serafina had her birds and flowers, and here she was accustomed to sit on moonlight nights as in a bower, and touch her guitar and sing like a wakeful nightingale. From this balcony an intercourse was now maintained between the lovers, against which the lock and key of Don Ramiro were of no avail. All day would Fernando be occupied hurrying the equipments of his ships, but evening found him in sweet discourse beneath his lady's window.

At length the preparations were completed. Two gallant caravels lay at anchor in the Tagus ready to sail at sunrise. Late at night, by the pale light of a waning moon, the lover had his last interview. The beautiful Serafina was sad at heart and full of dark forebodings; her lover full of hope and confidence. "A few short months," said he, "and I shall return in triumph. Thy father will then blush at his incredulity, and hasten to welcome to his house the Adalantado of the Seven Cities."

The gentle lady shook her head. It was not on this point she felt distrust. She was a thorough believer in the Island of the Seven Cities, and so sure of the success of the enterprise that she might have been tempted to join it had not the balcony been high and the grating strong. Other considerations induced that dubious shaking of the head. She had heard of the inconstancy of the seas, and the inconstancy of those who roam them. Might not Fernando meet with other loves in foreign ports? Might not some peerless beauty in one or other of those Seven Cities efface the image of Serafina from his mind? Now let the truth be spoken, the beautiful Serafina had reason for her disquiet. If Don Fernando had any fault in the world, it was that of being rather inflammable and apt to take fire from every sparkling eye. He had been somewhat of a rover among the sex on shore, what might he be on sea?

She ventured to express her doubt, but he spurned at the very idea. "What! he false to Serafina! He bow at the shrine of another beauty? Never! never!" Repeatedly did he bend his knee and smite his breast, and call upon the silver moon to witness his sincerity and truth.

21

MANNER

He retorted the doubt: "Might not Serafina herself forget her plighted faith? Might not some wealthier rival present himself while he was tossing on the sea; and, backed by her father's wishes, win the treasure of her hand?"

The beautiful Serafina raised her white arms between the iron bars on the balcony, and, like her lover, invoked the moon to testify her vows. Alas! how little did Fernando know her heart. The more her father should oppose, the more would she be fixed in faith. Though years should intervene, Fernando on his return would find her true. Even should the salt sea swallow him up (and her eyes shed salt tears at the very thought), never would she be the wife of another! Never, *never,* NEVER! She drew from her finger a ring gemmed with a ruby heart, and dropped it from the balcony, a parting pledge of constancy.

Thus the lovers parted with many a tender word and plighted vow. But will they keep those vows? Perish the doubt! Have they not called the constant moon to witness?

With the morning dawn the caravels dropped down the Tagus, and put to sea. They steered for the Canaries, in those days the regions of nautical discovery and romance, and the outposts of the known world, for as yet Columbus had not steered his daring barks across the ocean. Scarce had they reached those latitudes when they were separated by a violent tempest. For many days was the caraval of Don Fernando driven about at the mercy of the elements; all seamanship was baffled, destruction seemed inevitable, and the crew were in despair. All at once the storm subsided; the ocean sank into a calm; the clouds which had veiled the face of heaven were suddenly withdrawn, and the tempest-tossed mariners beheld a fair and mountainous island emerging as if by enchantment from the murky gloom. They rubbed their eyes and gazed for a time almost incredulously, yet there lay the island spread out in lovely landscapes, with the late stormy sea laving its shores with peaceful billows.

The pilot of the caravel consulted his maps and charts; no island like the one before him was laid down as existing in those parts; it is true he had lost his reckoning in the late storm, but, according to his calculations, he could not be far from the Canaries; and this was not one of that group of islands. The caravel now lay perfectly becalmed off the mouth of a river, on the banks of which, about a

22

league from the sea, was described a noble city, with lofty walls and towers, and a protecting castle.

After a time, a stately barge with sixteen oars was seen emerging from the river, and approaching the caravel. It was quaintly carved and gilt; the oarsmen were clad in antique garb, their oars painted of a bright crimson, and they came slowly and solemnly, keeping time as they rowed to the cadence of an old Spanish ditty. Under a silken canopy in the stern, sat a cavalier richly clad, and over his head was a banner bearing the sacred emblem of the cross.

When the barge reached the caravel, the cavalier stepped on board. He was tall and gaunt; with a long Spanish visage, moustaches that curled up to his eyes, and a forked beard. He wore gauntlets reaching to his elbows, a Toledo blade strutting out behind, with a basket hilt, in which he carried his handkerchief. His air was lofty and precise, and bespoke indisputably the hidalgo. Thrusting out a long spindle leg, he took off a huge sombrero, and swayed it until the feather swept the ground, accosted Don Fernando in the old Castilian language, and with the old Castilian courtesy, welcoming him to the Island of the Seven Cities.

Don Fernando was overwhelmed with astonishment. Could this be true? Had he really been tempest-driven to the very land of which he was in quest?

It was even so. That very day the inhabitants were holding high festival in commemoration of the escape of their ancestors from the Moors. The arrival of the caravel at such a juncture was considered a good omen, the accomplishment of an ancient prophecy through which the island was to be restored to the great community of Christendom. The cavalier before him was grand chamberlain, sent by the alcayde to invite him to the festivities of the capital.

Don Fernando could scarce believe that this was not a dream. He made known his name and the object of his voyage. The grand chamberlain declared that all was in perfect accordance with the ancient prophecy, and that the moment his credentials were presented, he would be acknowledged as the Adalantado of the Seven Cities. In the meantime the day was waning, the barge was ready to convey him to the land, and would as assuredly bring him back.

Don Fernando's pilot, a veteran of the seas, drew him aside and expostulated against his venturing, on the mere word of a stranger, to land in a strange barge on an unknown shore. "Who knows, Señor, what land this is, or what people inhabit it?"

Don Fernando was not to be dissuaded. Had he not believed in this island when all the world doubted? Had he not sought it in defiance of storm and tempest, and was he now to shrink from its shores when it lay before him in calm weather? In a word, was not faith the very cornerstone of his enterprise?

Having arrayed himself, therefore, in gala dress befitting the occasion, he took his seat in the barge. The grand chamberlain seated himself opposite. The rowers plied their oars, and renewed the mournful old ditty, and the gorgeous but unwieldy barge moved slowly through the water.

The night closed in before they entered the river, and swept along past rock and promontory, each guarded by its tower. At every post they were challenged by the sentinel.

"Who goes there?"

"The Adalantado of the Seven Cities."

"Welcome, Señor Adalantado. Pass on."

Entering the harbor, they rowed close by an armed galley of ancient form. Soldiers with crossbows patrolled the deck.

"Who goes there?"

"The Adalantado of the Seven Cities."

"Welcome, Señor Adalantado. Pass on."

They landed at a broad flight of stone steps, leading up between two massive towers, and knocked at the water-gate. A sentinel, in ancient steel casque, looked from the barbican.

"Who is there?"

"The Adalantado of the Seven Cities."

"Welcome, Señor Adalantado."

The gate swung open, grating upon rusty hinges. They entered between two rows of warriors in Gothic armor, with crossbows, maces, battle-axes, and faces old-fashioned as their armor. There were processions through the streets, in commemoration of the landing of the seven Bishops and their followers, and bonfires, at which effigies of losel Moors expiated their invasion of Christendom by a kind of *auto-da-fe*. The groups round the fires, uncouth in their attire, looked like the fantastic figures that roam the streets in Carnival time. Even the dames, who gazed down from Gothic bal-

24

conies hung with antique tapestry, resembled effigies dressed up in Christmas mummeries. Every thing, in short, bore the stamp of former ages, as if the world had suddenly rolled back for several centuries. Nor was this to be wondered at. Had not the Island of the Seven Cities been cut off from the rest of the world for several hundred years; and were not these the modes and customs of Gothic Spain before it was conquered by the Moors?

Arriving at the palace of the alcayde, the grand chamberlain knocked at the portal. The porter looked through a wicket, and demanded who was there.

"The Adalantado of the Seven Cities."

The portal was thrown wide open. The grand chamberlain led the way up a vast, heavily moulded, marble staircase, and into a hall of ceremony, where was the alcayde with several of the principal dignitaries of the city, who had a marvelous resemblance, in form and feature, to the quaint figures in old illuminated manuscripts.

The grand chamberlain stepped forward and announced the name and title of the stranger-guest, and the extraordinary nature of his mission. The announcement appeared to create no extraordinary emotion or surprise, but to be received as the anticipated fulfilment of a prophecy.

The reception of Don Fernando, however, was profoundly gracious, though in the same style of stately courtesy which everywhere prevailed. He would have produced his credentials, but this was courteously declined. The evening was devoted to high festivity; the following day, when he should enter the port with his caravel, would be devoted to business, when the credentials would be received in due form, and he inducted into office as Adalantado of the Seven Cities.

Don Fernando was now conducted through one of those interminable suites of apartments, the pride of Spanish palaces, all furnished in a style of obsolete magnificence. In a vast saloon, blazing with tapers, was assembled all the aristocracy and fashion of the city—stately dames and cavaliers, the very counterpart of the figures in the tapestry which decorated the walls. Fernando gazed in silent marvel. It was a reflex of the proud aristocracy of Spain in the time of Roderick the Goth.

The festivities of the evening were all in the style of solemn and

25

antiquated ceremonial. There was a dance, but it was as if the old tapestry were put in motion, and all the figures moving in stately measure about the floor. There was one exception, and one that told powerfully upon the susceptible Adalantado. The alcayde's daughter—such a ripe, melting beauty! Her dress, it is true, like the dresses of her neighbors, might have been worn before the flood, but she had the black Andalusian eye, a glance of which, through its long dark lashes, is irresistible. Her voice, too, her manner, her undulating movements, all smacked of Andalusia, and showed how female charms may be transmitted from age to age, and clime to clime, without ever going out of fashion. Those who know the witchery of the sex, in that most amorous part of amorous old Spain, may judge of the fascination to which Don Fernando was exposed, as he joined in the dance with one of its most captivating descendants.

He sat beside her at the banquet! such an Old-World feast! such obsolete dainties! At the head of the table the peacock, that bird of state and ceremony, was served up in full plumage on a golden dish. As Don Fernando cast his eyes down the glittering board, what a vista presented itself of odd heads and headdresses; of formal bearded dignitaries and stately dames, with castellated locks and towering plumes! Is it to be wondered at that he should turn with delight from these antiquated figures to the alcayde's daughter, all smiles and dimples, and melting looks and melting accents? Besides, for I wish to give him every excuse in my power, he was in a particularly excitable mood from the novelty of the scene before him, from this realization of all his hopes and fancies, and from frequent draughts of the wine-cup presented to him at every moment by officious pages during the banquet.

In a word—there is no concealing the matter—before the evening was over Don Fernando was making love outright to the alcayde's daughter. They had wandered together to a moon-lit balcony of the palace, and he was charming her ear with one of those love-ditties with which, in a like balcony, he had serenaded the beautiful Serafina.

The damsel hung her head coyly. "Ah! Señor, these are flattering words; but you cavaliers, who roam the seas, are unsteady as its waves. Tomorrow you will be throned in state, Adalantado of the Seven Cities, and will think no more of the alcayde's daughter."

26

Don Fernando in the intoxication of the moment called the moon to witness his sincerity. As he raised his hand in adjuration, the chaste moon cast a ray upon the ring that sparkled on his finger. It caught the damsel's eye. "Signor Adalantado," said she, archly, "I have no great faith in the moon, but give me that ring upon your finger in pledge of the truth of what you profess."

The gallant Adalantado was taken by surprise; there was no parrying this sudden appeal; before he had time to reflect, the ring of the beautiful Serafina glittered on the finger of the alcayde's daughter.

At this eventful moment the chamberlain approached with lofty demeanor, and announced that the barge was waiting to bear him back to the caravel. I forbear to relate the ceremonious partings with the alcayde and his dignitaries, and the tender farewell of the alcayde's daughter. He took his seat in the barge opposite the grand chamberlain. The rowers plied their crimson oars in the same slow and stately manner to the cadence of the same mournful old ditty. His brain was in a whirl with all that he had seen, and his heart now and then gave him a twinge as he thought of his temporary infidelity to the beautiful Serafina. The barge sallied out into the sea, but no caravel was to be seen; doubtless she had been carried to a distance by the current of the river. The oarsmen rowed on; their monotonous chant had a lulling effect. A drowsy influence crept over Don Fernando. Objects swam before his eyes. The oarsmen assumed odd shapes as in a dream. The grand chamberlain grew larger and larger, and taller and taller. He took off his huge sombrero, and held it over the head of Don Fernando, like an extinguisher over a candle. The latter cowered beneath it; he felt himself sinking in the socket.

"Good-night! Señor Adalantado of the Seven Cities!" said the grand chamberlain.

The sombrero slowly descended—Don Fernando was extinguished!

How long he remained extinct no mortal man can tell. When he returned to consciousness he found himself in a strange cabin, surrounded by strangers. He rubbed his eyes and looked round him wildly. Where was he? On board a Portuguese ship, bound to Lisbon. How came he there? He had been taken senseless from a wreck drifting about the ocean.

27

MANNER

Don Fernando was more and more confounded and perplexed. He recalled, one by one, every thing that had happened to him in the Island of the Seven Cities, until he had been extinguished by the sombrero of the grand chamberlain. But what had happened to him since? What had become of his caravel? Was it the wreck of her on which he had been found floating?

The people about him could give no information on the subject. He entreated them to take him to the Island of the Seven Cities, which could not be far off; told them all that had befallen him there; that he had but to land to be received as Adalantado, when he would reward them magnificently for their services.

They regarded his words as the ravings of delirium, and in their honest solicitude for the restoration of his reason, administered such rough remedies that he was fain to drop the subject and observe a cautious taciturnity.

At length they arrived in the Tagus, and anchored before the famous city of Lisbon. Don Fernando sprang joyfully on shore, and hastened to his ancestral mansion. A strange porter opened the door, who knew nothing of him or his family; no people of the name had inhabited the house for many a year.

He sought the mansion of Don Ramiro. He approached the balcony beneath which he had bidden farewell to Serafina. Did his eyes deceive him? No! There was Serafina herself among the flowers in the balcony. He raised his arms toward her with an exclamation of rapture. She cast upon him a look of indignation, and, hastily retiring, closed the casement with a slam that testified her displeasure.

Could she have heard of his flirtation with the alcayde's daughter? But that was mere transient gallantry. A moment's interview would dispel every doubt of his constancy.

He rang at the door; as it was opened by the porter he rushed upstairs, sought the well-known chamber, and threw himself at the feet of Serafina. She started back with affright, and took refuge in the arms of a youthful cavalier.

"What mean you, señor," cried the latter, "by this intrusion?"

"What right have you to ask the question?" demanded Don Fernando fiercely.

"The right of an affianced suitor!"

28

Don Fernando started and turned pale. "Oh, Serafina! Serafina!" cried he, in a tone of agony, "is this thy plighted constancy?"

"Serafina? What mean you by Serafina, señor? If this be the lady you intend, her name is Maria."

"May I not believe my senses? May I not believe my heart?" cried Don Fernando. "Is not this Serafina Alvarez, the original of yon portrait, which, less fickle than herself, still smiles on me from the wall?

"Holy Virgin!" cried the young lady, casting her eyes upon the portrait. "He is talking of my great-grandmother!"

An explanation ensued, if that could be called an explanation which plunged the unfortunate Fernando into tenfold perplexity. If he might believe his eyes, he saw before him his beloved Serafina; if he might believe his ears, it was merely her hereditary form and features, perpetuated in the persosn of her great-granddaughter.

His brain began to spin. He sought the office of the Minister of Marine, and made a report of his expedition, and of the Island of the Seven Cities, which he had so fortunately discovered. Nobody knew anything of such an expedition, or such as island. He declared that he had undertaken the enterprise under a formal contract with the crown, and had received a regular commission, constituting him Adalantado. This must be matter of record, and he insisted loudly, that the books of the department should be consulted. The wordy strife at length attracted the attention of an old gray-headed clerk, who sat perched on a high stool, at a high desk, with iron-rimmed spectacles on the top of a thin, pinched nose, copying records into an enormous folio. He had wintered and summered in the department for a great part of a century, until he had almost grown to be a piece of the desk at which he sat; his memory was a mere index of official facts and documents, and his brain was little better than red tape and parchment. After peering down for a time from his lofty perch, and ascertaining the matter in controversy, he put his pen behind his ear, and descended. He remembered to have heard some thing from his predecessor about an expedition of the kind in question, but then it had sailed during the reign of Don Ioam II, and he had been dead at least a hundred years. To put the matter beyond dispute, however, the archives of the Torre de Tombo, that sepulchre of old Portuguese documents, were diligently searched, and a record was found of a contract between the crown and one Fernando de Ulmo, for the discovery of the Island of the Seven Cities, and of a commission secured to him as Adalantado of the country he might discover.

"There!" cried Don Fernando, triumphantly, "there you have proof, before your own eyes, of what I have said. I am the Fernando de Ulmo specified in that record. I have discovered the Island of the Seven Cities, and am entitled to be Adalantado, according to contract."

The story of Don Fernando had certainly what is pronounced the best of historical foundation, documentary evidence; but when a man, in the bloom of youth, talked of events that had taken place about a century previously, as having happened to himself, it is no wonder that he was set down for a madman.

The old clerk looked at him from above and below his spectacles, shrugged his shoulders, stroked his chin, reascended his lofty stool, took the pen from behind his ear, and resumed his daily and eternal task, copying records into the fiftieth volume of a series of gigantic folios. The other clerks winked at each other shrewdly, and dispersed to their several places, and poor Don Fernando, thus left to himself, flung out of the office, almost driven wild by these perplexities.

In the confusion of his mind, he instinctively repaired to the mansion of Alvarez, but it was barred against him. To break the delusion under which the youth apparently labored, and to convince him that the Serafina about whom he raved was really dead, he was conducted to her tomb. There she lay, a stately matron, cut out in alabaster; and there lay her husband beside her, a portly cavalier in armor; and there knelt, on either side, the effigies of numerous progeny, proving that she had been a fruitful vine. Even the very monument gave evidence of the lapse of time; the hands of her husband, folded as if in prayer, had lost their fingers, and the face of the once lovely Serafina was without a nose.

Don Fernando felt a transient glow of indignation at beholding this monumental proof of the inconstancy of his mistress; but who could expect a mistress to remain constant during a whole century of absence? And what right had he to rail about constancy, after what had passed between himself and the alcayde's daughter? The unfortunate cavalier performed one pious act of tender devotion;

he had the alabaster nose of Serafina restored by skilful statuary, and then tore himself from the tomb.

He could now no longer doubt the fact that, somehow or other, he had skipped over the whole century, during the night he had spent at the Island of the Seven Cities; and he was now as complete a stranger in his native city as if he had never been there. A thousand times did he wish himself back to that wonderful island, with its antiquated banquet halls, where he had been so courteously received; and now that the once young and beautiful Serafina was nothing but a great-grandmother in marble, with generations of descendants, a thousand times would he recall the melting black eyes of the alcayde's daughter, who, doubtless, like himself, was still flourishing in fresh juvenility, and breathe a secret wish that he was seated by her side.

He would at once have set on foot another expedition, at his own expense, to cruise in search of the sainted island, but his means were exhausted. He endeavored to rouse others to the enterprise, setting forth the certainty of profitable results, of which his own experience furnished such unquestionable proof. Alas! no one would give faith to his tale, but looked upon it as the feverish dream of a shipwrecked man. He persisted in his efforts, holding forth in all places and in all companies, until he became an object and jeer to the light-minded, who mistook his earnest enthusiasm for a proof of insanity; and the very children in the streets bantered him with the title of "The Adalantado of the Seven Cities."

Finding all efforts in vain, in his native city of Lisbon, he took shipping for the Canaries, as being nearer the latitude of his former cruise, and inhabited by people given to nautical adventure. Here he found ready listeners to his story, for the old pilots and mariners of those parts were devout island-hunters, and devout believers in all the wonders of the seas. Indeed, one and all treated his adventure as a common occurrence, and turning to each other, with a sagacious nod of the head, observed: "He has been at the Island of St. Brandan."

They then went on to inform him of that great marvel and enigma of the ocean, of its repeated appearance to the inhabitants of their island, and of the many but ineffectual expeditions that had been made in search of it. They took him to a promontory of the island

31

of Palma, whence the shadowy St. Brandan had oftenest been descried, and they pointed out the very tract in the west where its mountains had been seen.

Don Fernando listened with rapt attention. He had no longer a doubt that this mysterious and fugacious island must be the same with that of the Seven Cities, and that some supernatural influence connected with it had operated upon himself, and made the events of a night occupy the space of a century.

He endeavored, but in vain, to rouse the islanders to another attempt at discovery; they had given up the phantom island as indeed inaccessible. Fernando, however, was not to be discouraged. The idea wore itself deeper and deeper in his mind, until it became the engrossing subject of his thoughts and object of his being. Every morning he would repair to the promontory of Palma, and sit there throughout the livelong day, in hopes of seeing the fairy mountains of St. Brandan peeping above the horizon; every evening he returned to his home a disappointed man, but ready to resume his post on the following morning.

His assiduity was all in vain. He grew gray in his ineffectual attempt, and was at length found dead at his post. His grave is still shown in the island of Palma, and a cross is erected on the spot where he used to sit and look out upon the sea, in hopes of the reappearance of the phantom island.

STUDY NOTES

1. Consult Irving's *Life and Voyages of Christopher Columbus,* Appendix XXV, for legends concerning the imaginary island, St. Brandan, and Appendix XXVI for legends concerning the Island of the Seven Cities.

2. Indicate the setting and the beginning of action (the "exciting force") in the first two paragraphs of "The Adalantado of the Seven Cities."

3. How do you account for the hero's not being introduced until the sixth paragraph?

4. List the characters and forces that are obstacles to Don Fernando in his nautical expedition, his romance, and his desire to make a second search for St. Brandan.

5. By what methods does Irving delineate the characters of Don Fernando, Don Ramiro, Serafina, the alcayde's daughter, and the old clerk in the office of the Minister of Marine?

6. Comment on the dialogue—its naturalness or unnaturalness and its purpose (whether only to entertain or to portray character or to further the action).

7. Plot the rising action of this story.

8. How does Irving foreshadow the inconstancy of Don Fernando and Serafina and what evidences of inconstancy does he later supply?

9. How do you account for the absence of a dramatic climax?

10. Show that the narrative is more leisurely and combined with larger amounts of description than would be permissible under Poe's theory of short-story structure.

11. What use of the supernatural does this story make and why?

12. Show that this story is predominantly romantic rather than realistic.

THE HORSE OF HURRICANE REEF [1]
(1922)
CHARLES TENNEY JACKSON

"THE mares are for whoever is man enough to take them," retorted Jean Abadie from the bow of the barge which the towing launch was shoving into the mud shoal on the bay side of Île Dautrive. "Rojas has given them up. The white stallion has killed his son, Emile, four years ago. No man of the camps around here will land on this reef; he has a name, that wild white devil!"

"You see, M'sieu Lalande, it is not stealing," added Pierre as he stopped the motor and looked at the stranger in the stern seat.

"It is stealing," grunted Joe Lalande, "else why do we come under cover of a storm to rope the colts and mares? Well, no matter. Once we get them aboard and up the Mississippi plantations, I will show you something, you shrimp-seine Cajans. Throwing a rope, eh? Over westward they never yet showed me a horse I could not break."

The two seine-haulers from Sanchez's platform looked at him doubtfully. "Over westward," to the men of Barataria Bay, began at the dim marsh shore and stretched to infinity. A native never ventured so far; out there anything might be possible. But no man had faced the exiled king of Dautrive reef. Pierre muttered again how they would get the young mares—they would first shoot the white stallion. It was the hurricane month; they knew well enough that an obliterating sea would come this week over the dunes and marshes. Old Rojas, living with his grandchildren, orphaned by the white brute's savagery, on the far west point of the island, would never know what happened to the five mares and colts. More than once the gale off the Gulf had left the shell-beached *chenaies* far up the bay strewn with the dead cattle of the people of the reefs.

The big Lalande laughed as he followed through the salt grass to the first low dunes. "Shoot him! You'll shoot no horse with me! You say he's so bad; show him to me! I'll rope and load him, too, my friends, or he will finish me. If we lift Rojas's animals we take 'em all."

---

[1] First published in *Short Stories* magazine (September 10, 1922). Reprinted by special permission of Charles Tenney Jackson.

The Cajans laughed in nervous disbelief. Lalande, a native also, who had returned this season to haul seine in Sanchez's company, might have been a great man with the pitching broncos he told of, but Rojas's great white stallion—well, this boaster would see! The brute would allow no seine-crew to land on the Île Dautrive; they told of his charging upon the fishing-skiffs clear out to the surf line. Sanchez, the boss, had shot him once as he fled to his lugger, leaving the bleeding stallion to rend and trample an abandoned seine.

Grandpère Rojas, in his camp across the shoal depression that cut through the reef, had never tried to reclaim the wild mares and the colts of the white stud's breed. The generations of them lived on the coarse reef grass and the rain pools; an oysterman had no use for horses, anyhow. His son, Emile, had tried this foolish experiment of raising horses on the reef, and given his life under the stallion's hoofs. *Grandpère* had shrugged and let the breed go wild; yet, as Lalande muttered when Jean and Pierre proposed to use his skill in lifting the younger animals, the horses were his to the scrawniest colt. But Lalande had come. He would show the shrimpers; and even if they only roped and dragged the least unruly to the barge, Lalande could break them and Pierre sell them on the plantations. Yet it was horse stealing. Lalande would not gloss that over, but something else had drawn him here—the stories the islanders told of the white stallion's savagery.

"Old Rojas's son, I will be the avenger," he grunted, sullenly, and came on the day Pierre had chosen for the secret raid.

Abadie had stopped on the sandy trail broken through the mangroves to the top of the sand ridge. "Bon Dieu!" he whispered, pointing. "His track, Lalande! Big as a bucket! *Eh bien!* I'd rather face a hurricane than this white tiger!"

Lalande had stepped out in the open sand patch. From here the dunes fell away to the Gulf beach. Already the sea was rising. Between Dautrive and the outer bar curious, oily currents were twisting in unwonted directions, and beyond them the surf broke in white, serried teeth gleaming against the black southeast. The sky was ribboned in black lines streaming northerly; the wind came in fitful smashes against the mangrove thickets and then seemed sucked up to howl in the writhing clouds.

"There'll have to be quick work," muttered Pierre. "I tell you this is bad, this sea. We waited too long, M'sieu Lalande. We better be back across the bay, and try for the colts another time."

Lalande's gray eyes narrowed surlily. He straightened his powerful figure above the wind-slanting bushes. The two other raiders had crept back through the brush. It was disconcerting to find the animals crossing their trail behind. "If he smells a man he will never let up on us, Lalande," muttered Jean. "Kill him, then!"

The white leader had crossed the trail of the raiders. He turned, broke through the brush, and gained the ridge forty yards from them. Lalande could see him now against the black skyline very plainly. A tremendous brute towering above the others, his shaggy mane flowing backward in the wind, his muzzle outstretched, his neck tensed until the powerful muscles bulged the satin skin. He was suspicious; he stood there a challenging figure to the storm, but his eyes were roving watchfully into the thickets as a tiger scenting prey.

Lalande glanced back. His comrades had slunk below the mangroves. They were brave, hardy men of the hurricane coast, but the evil name of the sea horse of Île Dautrive seemed to hold them nerveless. The horse was coming on along the top of the ridge slowly crashing through the brush with alert glances right and left. His pink nostrils quivered, his iron-gray tail raised and swept in the wind puffs.

"They will shoot," muttered Lalande. "If he trails them the cowards will shoot." And he stepped more in the open, and then shouted, "Come, thieves, let the colts go! I will need you on the throw-line to check and choke this brute!" Breast-high in the wind-swept thickets he was laughing and coiling his rope. This was a foe for a strong man who boasted!

The great horse suddenly upreared with a neigh that was like the roar of a lion. No man had so much as ever put finger on him; he had beaten the brains from one, broken the leg of another; and smashed two seine skiffs in the shallows for invaders. He had been the lord of the reef. Now he reared again and again as he plunged through the mangroves watching for the fugitives as a cat would a mouse under a flimsy cover of straw.

His satiny flanks were toward Lalande; apparently he had not yet discovered the man behind him in this hunt for the others. And then, out of pure panic as the white stallion broke near him, Jean Abadie fired. Lalande cursed and sprang down the slope of dunes after them. He knew he would need their help when he roped this horse; it was no starveling cayuse of the Texas range. But he saw now that the two islanders were skulking for the boat in the last fringe of the mangroves. They would never make it; out in the open the white stallion would crush them both ere they covered half the marsh grass, unless, indeed, they killed him.

The brute saw them now; he swerved in a tremendous rush below the man on the higher sand. Lalande was whirling his rope, and when he heard the hiss of it through the air he laughed, for he knew the throw was true.

"*Eh, bien,* devil! You and me!" He went down sprawling, seeking a root of the tough mangroves to snub the line. He caught one, then it was jerked out; and he went trundling and rolling over and over through the sands hanging to the lariat. He might as well have roped a torpedo. The horse was in the open now rearing and bucking, but with his savage eyes still on the fugitives. They were floundering through the water. Jean was jerking the mooring-lines from the barge, and Pierre poling the launch back from the swamp grass. The stallion was surging on with the line cutting deep in his neck, but they could not see this in the welter of spray he threw in his charge.

Joe Lalande was on his back in the high grass, bruised and dizzy from his ride on the throw-rope. It was lying out taut through the grass; and for a time the man did not stir. The stallion was plunging somewhere out there, still implacable with fury to get at the shrimpers. Then Lalande heard the first throb of the motor. They were getting away, leaving him, then? They must think him killed —a good end for a braggart who would rather fight the stud than steal the mares!

He lay in the grass listening, without even resentment. The wide reach of the bay northward was flecked with white surges rising between those curious oily bulges of water, the first stir of the creeping tides which come upon the Gulf shores before the hurricane winds. Lalande remembered enough of his boyhood among the island folk to know that. Pierre was right; they had waited too long for this week of storm to raid Rojas's wild horses.

He crept around on the jerking line. Above the grass billows he saw the brute. He was whirling madly in the shallows fighting this strange, choking clutch on his neck. Then he charged back up the dunes, and Lalande barely had time to lie out on the end ere he was dragged again. But when the stallion was plunged into the thickets, no human strength could hold. He felt his fingers breaking in the tangle of rope and roots, his face ground into the sand and pounded by showers of sand from the brute's hoofs.

Lalande staggered to his feet presently, cleared his eyes, and followed a crashing trail over the sand ridge. Northward he saw the launch rocking its way across the pass with whiplike streamers of wind hitting the water beyond. Everywhere the coast folk would be debating whether to quit their platform camps and take to the luggers or trust to the oaks of the *chenaies* and their moorings. The hurricane month, and a sea coming up past Cuba! Île Derniere had vanished under the waves; La Caminada gone with six hundred souls; these were traditions of the coast, but the natives knew what a hurricane tide meant on the low, loose sand islands that fringed the Louisiana swamps.

Lalande paused on the highest ridge. There was that sullen glisten of the sea, cut through with patches of white, and the green-back horizon gaping to east and west and blotting out with gray squalls. The great wind had not come yet beyond these first squadrons. The big man shrugged as he regarded it. The hurricane tide was shoving frothy fingers out over the shoals. Across the sandy stretch westward he could just see the shack camp of *Grandpère* Rojas on the highest ridge of Dautrive. A few ragged oaks showed white against the sky. The old man ought to be leaving with his orphaned grandchildren, taking his stout oyster lugger and making for the solid land fourteen miles north across the bay.

"It is no place for little ones," muttered Lalande in the Cajan patois. These people never will leave quick enough before the storms. I can see the old man's lugger still riding behind the point. He is a fool, Old Rojas, afraid to put foot on this end of the reef because of the white stud, but stubborn against the sea which comes like a million white horses."

He went warily on the crushed trail. That throw-rope would foul somewhere in the mangroves; that stallion would choke himself to a stupor, for not all the strength in the world can avail against lungs bursting for air. Then he saw the mares. They were huddled in a hollow of the dunes, the colts about them as if confused, uncertain, their shaggy coats ruffled in the wind. That wind was moaning now, high and far; not so bad here on the reef, but striking in slants on the sea as if the sky had opened to let an arrow loose. A hundred miles away as yet, that Gulf hurricane wind, but mounting; sixty, eighty, a hundred miles an hour—a hundred and twenty-five in the bursts that presently drove the sand dunes into smoke.

The rim of wet sand beyond the dry, hummocky space was covered with sheets of black water racing from the surf line, breaking on the shoals.

And here Lalande saw what he had sought. There was the white mound in the ripples. With a cry he dashed for it. The horse was down. He had not thought it would come so soon. But the end of the trailing rope had fouled a great driftheap, and the brute had kept on charging and fighting until he choked and fell in the first wash of the sea. The slip-noose was bound to cut him down if he kept on hurling his weight against it, Lalande knew.

He wished he had seen the last magnificent fight against it on the sands; but now he walked quickly around the fallen brute, and knelt to touch his distended, quivering nostrils. The eyes were shut but bulging under a film. The great sides were heaving, a rumbling groan found escape somehow; it was as if the mighty heart was breaking with a last throb against this mysterious power choking its strength away.

"Eh, soldier!" whispered Lalande, and felt high on the horse's neck.

A sudden apprehension took him. Perhaps the thong had killed the renegade? He did not mean that; he was filled with a great exultant joy in this savage. He had stalked and subdued him alone! He stood above this outstretched, trembling body in the first sea ripples, laughing.

"Come, boy! The fight's not done yet! Not the end yet." He twisted his fingers into the taut rope, forced on the dragging driftwood, and eased the tension bit by hit. The rope was buried in the white skin; he worked hurriedly, fearing it was too late.

"Come, come; this will not do—" he was whispering into the stallion's tense ear, fighting at the rope. Then came a fierce, convulsive blow, an explosive sigh, a struggle, and the stallion lay quiet again. He was breathing in great, resurging sighs. His filmed eyes opened slowly. Lalande kept on patting his muzzle while he hitched the noose into a knot that would not choke again. He did not know why he did this, only it seemed fair. He was looking close into the brute's eyes which were beginning to glow with sense again; and to withdraw the choking hitch seemed only justice.

Lalande stood up and looked down at the white stallion. The water was roaring out there now. The skyline was blown white as feathers. The mangroves were slanting; and he suddenly realized that the wind was hard as a plank against his cheek. Not bursting, but steadily lying against the land. There was no rain, yet the air was full of water streaming in white lines through a growing darkness.

"Get up!" he shouted. "The sea is coming. This is no place to be! Comrade, on your feet!"

And the great horse did so. First plunging up, but with his haunches squatted in the water as he looked slowly about. Then to all fours and standing with his tail whipped about on his heaving flanks. He seemed watching that wall of blow water from the Gulf. Watching steadily, undaunted. The sands under the racing froth seemed trembling; one could hardly see the mangrove dunes not a hundred yards away.

Lalande swiftly turned his eyes from the ridge at a sound. It had seemed a shriek above the tumult. Then he leaped, and the wind appeared to lift him above the shaking earth.

For the great stud was on him. Upreared above him, a shaggy hoof coming not an inch's breadth from his skull.

Just a glimpse of those red, savage eyes; and the impact of those huge feet almost upon his own. Then Lalande ran. The hurricane wind flung him onward, but he could hear the rush of the white stallion. The entangled rope checked the charge only enough to allow the man to hurl himself into the first mangroves, crawl under them in a whirlwind of rising sands, and keep on crawling. When he stopped he knew the horse was crashing in the thickets hunting him. He saw him as a wraith against the sky, plunging his head low to ferret out his enemy, blowing explosively and hurling the tough mangrove clumps aside.

Lalande kept on his stealthy crawl. He lay, finally, in a water-riven dusk under the lee of the dunes, listening. *"Dieu!"* he panted. "I said, a soldier! The hurricane could not stop that hate of men!"

For half an hour he did not move. The brute had lost his trail. And when Lalande crawled to the top of the dunes he could not stand. All over the weather side the sea had risen. It was white. White, that was all he could say. And the wind? It did not seem a wind, merely a crushing of one's skull and lungs. When he tried to turn away it threw him headlong, but he got to his feet on the northerly, lee side of the sand ridge and fought on.

The sand was dissolving under his feet, and now he saw the water of the bay streaming by him. The inner marshes were gone; the hurricane tide was on, and sixty miles inland it would rush to batter on the cypress forests and the black levees of the plantation lands. Lalande had no illusions about Île Dautrive—he had been a lad on this coast—but he kept on, for the highest ridge was at the western point. Across the sand shoal, beyond this point, was still higher land, a clay fragment in which grew a few stout oaks. By these Old Rojas's camp had stood. It did not stand there now, thought Lalande. Nothing built by man on the reef would stand. *Grandpère* and the children of the man whom the white stallion had killed must certainly have taken to the lugger—escaped before the hurricane tide rushed upon the flimsy shack. Surely, yes. Rojas was no fool!

Lalande kept on, clinging to the thickets when the worst clutch of the wind was on him. The roaring of it all was so steady that actually he seemed in a great silence, as if a new element had enveloped him—a normal thing, this shock and unceasing tenseness of feeling and of sound. Through it he strode steadily himself, a strong man with neither fear nor curiosity—a mere dull plunge on to the last foothold of that reef which was churning to gruel behind his steps. He could not miss the point; there was no other spot to reach, and the hurricane was guide as well as captor.

And his mind was upon the lord of Dautrive Island. "He will go. Perhaps he is gone now. And the mares and colts, all off the reef by now." And a grim satisfaction came that the white stud had turned on him at the last. It was fine to think of. The savage had not cringed. "I do not want anything that can be stolen," he murmured, and spat the sea spray from his sore lips. "His mares and colts, he fights for them—that devil."

41

And he began shouting profane, fond challenges and adulations to his conqueror somewhere in this white chaos of a night. A whipping wisp of scud was that charging shape above the torn thickets; any single shriek of the storm, his trumpeted challenge in return. Lalande boasted to his soul that he was seeking his foe; if it was the last stroke of his hand he wished it raised to taunt the white, oncoming devil.

Even the storm glimmer had faded when he felt the water shoaling from his armpits to his waist. This was the west point, the highest, and here, with hands locked to the stoutest of the mangroves, he would have to let the sea boil over him as long as a strong man could—then go.

On the western high point at last, and nothing to see, nothing to feel but the submerged bushes and the earth dissolving so that he had to keep his feet moving to avoid each becoming the center of a whirlpool.

"It is a storm," Lalande grunted. "Two white devils on this reef." He remembered seeing spaces of mirrored calm, peaceful coves over which they told him orange trees had bloomed in cottage yards of the reef dwellers. The sea had devoured the islands in a night, dug the hole, and lain down in it like a fed tiger. Lalande, crowded closer to the stouter thickets, put out his hand in the dark. He touched a wet, warm surface, heaving slightly.

The skin of a brute. He smoothed the hair in the rushing water, felt along. A wall of steely flesh broadside to the tidal wave. Lalande softly slipped his hand over the huge round flank. The water was swirling about them both to the man's armpits now. Lalande knew. They were on the highest point, but ahead lay the shoal pass. The sea was eating away this point; what was left was sinking, flicked off into the meeting currents around Dautrive and swept inland. The island would be silt on some cane planter's back fields forty miles up the Mississippi delta within the week.

But for the last of his domain the lord of Dautrive was fighting with his last foothold. The white devil of the sea was doing what man could not do. Lalande laughed in the blackness. The stallion could not feel his soft touch in all that beating welter of sand and debris churning around him. He rested his arm across the unseen back—the brute would think it was a driftwood branch. The man stepped forward. There was no other foothold now, it seemed. He reached his hand to the shoulder, up to feel the stiff, wet mane. He laughed and patted the bulged muscles.

"We go, you and I," he grumbled. The mangroves were slatted out on the tiderush, tearing loose, reeling past them. "Eh, friend? The last—"

And then he knew that the horse had whirled, upreared in the blackness with a scream of fury. Lalande sprang to the left, into deep, moiling water.

He felt the plunge of his foe just missing him once more. But another body struck him and then was whirled off in the meeting tides. He collided with a colt in the dark; and now he guessed that the white stallion's breed had been gathered on the refuge shielded to the last by his huge bulk against the inexorable seas.

They were gone now. There was no more foothold on Dautrive either for the exiles or the man who had come to subdue them. Lalande knew he must not go with the tidal wave. It was death anywhere out there. The water would rush fifty miles inland over the battered reefs. So he fought powerfully back to get a handhold on the mangrove thickets through a whirlpool of dissolving sand.

But the man could not breast those surges through the dark; he felt himself driven farther back in a tangle of foam and debris, and suddenly came a whiplike tightening about his legs. He was dragged under and out across the current until he fought down to reach this thing that had him.

It was his throw-rope, the new and heavy line that he had brought to conquer the white stud that the island men feared. Lalande plunged up and along it. The rope was tight and surging athwart the drift. When he got his head above water he knew he was clear of the disintegrating sand point, overwhelmed by the rollers in the pass and stung by the spray, but moving.

An unseen guide, a mighty power was drawing aslant the inshore tide. Lalande hauled along until he felt the rhythmic beat of the stallion's stroke; along until he touched his flank. When he could put his hand to his long mane Lalande laughed. He hung there, and felt the brute plunge higher at this contact. Once, twice, and then the stud settled to his fight.

The lord of Dautrive could not shake him off nor rend him with teeth or hoof. He was being ridden through the blackness and the sea.

Lalande began shouting. He could not resist the impulse of defiance; the great horse had been merciless to him on the island, so now he howled at him whenever he could keep the salt water from his teeth.

"*Eh, bien!* Big fellow, you see I am here! If you go, I go! Lalande is with you—devil! Fight! Fight on; a man is on your back at last. A last ride, too, white devil!"

For he had no hope of anything except to be battered to a pulp by the driftlogs and wreckage in the pass or drowned over the flooded marshes. But the stallion would not give to the northward tide, always he kept fighting to windward and westerly. When he plunged on these tacks Lalande swung out straight over his back, but clinging lightly and calling his taunting courage to the brute.

"The west ridge," muttered the rider. "He knows that, the oaks and the clay soil. If anything hangs together in this sea it will be that." So he clung in the dark. Nothing but the incessant battles of the horse's broadside in the hurricane tide kept that feeling in Lalande's heart that the swimmer was trying to cross the pass to Rojas's oak grove. The white devil was blind in the white sea, but he remembered that. Lalande could feel the leg strokes steady and true even when the waves lifted or buried them, or when they were half drowned in the whipped foam among patches of reef wreckage. The man was fighting at this debris to keep it from the sailor's neck when he felt something else streaming along his flanks. It appeared to be submerged bushes or thick, long grass twisting about beneath them. And there was a changed note to the hurricane's tumult.

Lalande swung up on the stallion's back, listening. The swells of the pass were slower here, huge and strangling, but not with the fierce rush they had battled. The horse was swimming more to seaward, almost head on now, and once he arose as if his forefeet had struck the earth.

"He has found the marsh," muttered Lalande. "Night of wonders; nothing else!"

Still that powerful, steady stroke under the man's clinging limbs.

44

The brute was seeking whatever land might be above the water. Then Lalande began to think, as again he felt the forefeet touch bottom.

"Then we fight again, eh, tiger?" Shake me off and come at me! Make the oaks and we'll see!"

The horse plunged past a torn oak stump which smashed him in the side. He was in water to his withers, but Lalande knew he was climbing. He got a foothold, leaned against the tide rushing through the oak grove, and kept on. Against the man and horse there crushed another trunk, denuded of leaves, swinging by its roots, staggering them with its blows. The sea was over this also, Lalande knew. If it came higher there was no hope here.

Then the stallion stopped. He stood belly deep in the lee of another oak trunk which Lalande could feel in the utter dark. And the man sat silent astride the white king of Dautrive who had lost his domain and his subjects. He moved his legs across the heaving flanks—a sort of stealthy challenge. He wanted the white stud to know that he, Joe Lalande, was there astride him. He laughed and leaned to pat the unseen arch of the neck.

And then again came that furious, uprearing plunge of the great brute. His head came about in a side blow, his teeth tearing at Lalande's face as the rider swerved out under this twisting, maddened attack. He heard that trumpet cry again of the wild horse seeking him as he dragged himself about the oak tree in the water. He stood clutching the rope, trying to make out the brute's form.

Then he knew that the swells riding through the twisted oaks were slowed; the yelling of the winds more fitful, higher; and a sort of check came to the clutch on his body against the tree. Lalande seemed to stand in a frothy eddy as if the sea had stopped running and was foaming to an apex about him. And he knew what it meant, the moment that always comes in the Gulf hurricanes. The wind was dying off and changing. The sea could do no more. It had piled its flood as far inland and as high as even its strength could hold. Its whirling center was now over the coast, the wind whipping fitfully, now southwest, westerly, northward, and beginning to rise again. But there came one moment when it was almost a calm, silence except for that roaring in the sky.

"La revanche," [2] muttered the man. "Now comes the worst—
the rush of the tide back to sea. The good God help them all, these
Cajans who have not found refuge up the bay. *La revanche*—that
is when they die!"

He felt about his oak trunk, wondering if it were still rooted
firmly. The white stallion must be just about the torn branches,
for Lalande still had the trailing line. And then came something
that numbed him with uncanny fear. A voice out in the dark, a
child's cry among the oaks.

"La revanche! Grandpère, it is coming! Get the lines the other
way, *Grandpère—"*

Lalande went plunging toward the spot. *"Nom de Dieu!* It is
not possible? Rojas!" He shouted, and stumbled among wreckage
of trees and timbers around his waist. "Rojas, you are in the grove?"

A dim light glowed behind a blanket. He saw a boy had
snatched this moment of the falling wind to try the lantern. When
Lalande waded to the spot an old man straightened up on the other
side of a sunken raft. Upon it, under the blankets, were lashed
the forms of Rojas's children, the orphans of Emile, who had once
sought to tame the white horse of Île Dautrive. Old Rojas held
the lantern close to his white beard. He seemed as frightened as
was the small boy by the stranger's coming.

Old Rojas had been trying to spike a cross-piece to his shattered
raft. His lugger had been smashed in the first reach of the hurricane, and he had torn up the planks of his camp floor to build
this refuge anchored to the biggest oaks of the grove. They knew
what to do, these Cajans of the reefs, when they were caught by
the hurricane tide. Cut the mast from the lugger and drift inland,
seize an anchorage before the dreaded *revanche* took them seaward;
or if not that, hang to one's oak stumps!

Lalande did not waste the precious moments with a single question.

"A brave fight, old man. I see you made a brave fight! Give me
your raft-lines. The other way around now, and to the stoutest trees.
This sea, it is like a mad tiger when it has to go back defeated!

---

[2] Literally, "the revenge" or "the return"; the second part of the storm in
which winds carry a violent tide of water outward from the land and the bays
into the Gulf.

Come." He took the mooring-line and plunged off in the waist-deep froth.

"Day of wonders!" mumbled old Rojas. "A man on the reef—living! A big man, strong after the hurricane! It is impossible!" He went hammering his raft as it surged and plunged by his shoulders, ordering the youngster to make himself fast once more in the life ropes which held them all to the shaking planks. There was no whimper from the four children. They raised big dark eyes staring from *Grandpère* to the strange man who was battling back in the first seaward rush of the waters to make them fast against *la revanche*. The wind was smiting again. It appeared to fall out of the blackness to the north, blast after blast, rising swifter, smiting the piled-up waters, hurling them over the reef islands with thrice the speed they had come in.

The dim lantern went out. The fugitives tied themselves on again. If the worn lines held and the raft kept together they might live. "Name of Names!" grumbled old Rojas. "A man coming to us out of the sea? He said he would make fast for us. If not, my children—well, we must trust him."

Lalande had struggled off into the new rush of the wind with the raft-lines. They were frayed and ragged. He made them fast to his own new throw-rope. He would get this rope off the stallion somehow, and make it fast to the big oak. If not—he shrugged, well, then, nothing! Every wreck of a lugger, plank of a camp, driftlog, tree, that was loose would be miles in the open Gulf to-morrow to eddy endlessly in *la revanche*.

The old man's mooring-lines would not reach tthe big oak. Lalande had thought that, combined, they might last the night out, but the sea and wind were whipping fast on him in the dark. He had to plunge out shoulder deep to the tree, feeling of his line.

"The white devil is there and quiet," he grumbled. "If he would let me slip the rope from his shoulders and tie it to the tree!" He breasted the brimming tides over the submerged isle past the oak, his hand cautiously out to the dark, "Devil!" he called softly. "This is for Emile Roja's young ones. The rope, devil! We've fought, you and I, but now let me have it."

The line was tight past the oak stump. The weight of the raft was already coming strongly on it as the tide began to seethe through

47

the shattered grove. Lalande could hardly keep his feet, or his eyes open against the bitter spray. Then he was off his feet; he was hanging to the line, fighting out on it, calling to his foe, reaching for him. The brute must be swimming now, for the footing had gone from under them both.

Lalande felt a plunging on the line. It was too late now to hope to get the rope to the oak. The fighting horse was on it, and it began to give slowly past the man's hands. *La revanche* was bearing them on, the raft, the man, and the white devil who was its sole anchor, now. Lalande clung with one arm to the oak and drew in on the line. The dead weight of the raft had its way. The bucking, plunging brute, now touching the ground, now surging in the tide, was being drawn to him. Lalande began to call again. He had a great sense of pity for the stud. There were things that could not be withstood even by his lion heart; yet even the sea might not conquer except for this choking drag of the raft that held Rojas's grandchildren.

Lalande touched the stallion's muzzle now, coming on fighting with the obstinate ferocity of a white shark. He crouched in the crotch of the oak and held out his arms to the stallion's neck. When finally the brute crashed upon the sunken oak, Lalande reached his fingers to the cleft where the throw-rope cut into his neck. He dragged on the line, vainly trying to ease that tension. Once he thought of his knife; he might cut that choking grip from the white stud's throat. Then Lalande lay back in the crotch above the plunging hoofs and eased the great head above his own shoulder. Dragging on the line with all his power he kept up his whispering as the hurricane tide rushed under them, swinging the oak on its roots, twisting it seaward, and sucking the earth away in whirls where Rojas's house had stood.

"I tell you we are still here, you and I," called Lalande after a while. "You and I, devil! You and I—smashed up together, my face against your own! *Eh, bien!* Be quiet, Emile Rojas may be watching his children, and you in this storm! Remember that, white devil, you have returned for them!" He laughed and shouted in the dark, his arm about the neck of the horse working his fingers under the rope, trying to take some of the strain upon his own flesh and bone. And presently he grumbled, "And remember, also, I am not a thief. Not a thief, eh?"

They clung that way five hours, until the crest of *La revanche* was passed. The sun even got through the huge rifts of black clouds streaming south by the time old Rojas stirred about from his creaking raft in the scrub oaks. Everywhere a brown, dirty, sullen sea setting out, flecked with drift and wreckage, and of all Île Dautrive nothing showed but these few battered, branchless trees.

The stout old man waded waist-deep from his raft where now Emile's young ones sat up stiff and drowsy from the sea's nightlong flailing. He followed his mooring-line out to where it sogged under water by the big oak. The eldest boy had stood up looking after him.

"*Grandpère!*" screamed the lad suddenly. "Look! The white horse has come! By the tree, with the man!"

Old Rojas waded and struggled there, too astounded to speak. The sight was a queer one, indeed. The white horse was drawn against the oak-crotch, pinned in there, in fact; and the rope from his neck also crushed the strange man against his shoulder. Joe Lalande appeared to be crucified against the satin coat of the stallion. But he lifted his free arm faintly when the old man floundered near them.

"M'sieu?" gasped Rojas. "You here?" He had to touch Lalande's drenched body ere he could believe that the man lived. Then he fell to loosening the slacked rope so that Lalande lurched down from the horse's neck into the water where he could hardly stand but clung to the tree trunk watching the animal. The rope had cut through Lalande's arm and shoulder until it made a long red-scarred mark from neck to elbow. He could not speak for a time from his salt-swollen lips.

"Yes, I am here," he whispered at last, and staggered weakly.

"Name of God, the white horse!" cried the old man. He put his hand out to touch the smooth side, but as if fearing him even now. Lalande was trying to discover whether or not the heart of the white stallion still beat; and then he turned away, his eyes closing wearily. He seemed to be shaken by a sob, a grief that the islander could not comprehend.

"What's the matter, M'sieu? We are safe; the boats will find us.

49

Le bon Dieu! that was a storm! I have never seen a greater on this reef!"

Then he looked curiously at the still form of his old enemy. *"Eh, bien!* It took a white sea to kill this white devil, my friend!"

"It was not the sea," grumbled Lalande. "The touch of a rope on his neck, M'sieu. I saw his heart break last night, but it was for the children of Emile. A rope and the touch of my hand upon his neck, they were not to be endured, M'sieu." Then Lalande turned away, as if speaking to the lord of Dautrive against the tree: "At least you must know this, white devil, the hand on you was not the hand of a thief."

STUDY NOTES

1. Consult George Bancroft, *The History of the United States,* Volume IV, Chapter VIII, and Hawthorne's *American Note-Books* for accounts of the exiling of the French Acadians (the Cajuns).

2. Show that the dialogue and the speech tags in the opening part of "The Horse of Hurricane Reef" serve at least two purposes—that they help to present Joe Lalande's character and that they reveal the action in which he and his companions on the barge were engaged.

3. Show that Lalande's character is also revealed by the subjective method, that is, by the author's comments.

4. Show that Lalande's character also expresses itself in his speeches to and actions toward the horse.

5. Whom did the two Cajuns accompanying Lalande consider had claim to the stallion, the mares, and the colts (or at least had once owned them) and why did they think him less likely to press that claim than formerly?

6. Why did Lalande's two companions regard the stallion as unconquerable—in what evil or tragic actions had the horse participated?

7. Distinguish between Lalande's motive for making the raid and that of Jean and Pierre.

8. What disposition is made of Jean and Pierre—how do they drop out of the story?

9. What fate befell the mares and the colts?

10. Summarize the part of the plot dealing with the stallion's fight against Lalande's life.

11. By what measures did Lalande conquer the horse, causing the animal to serve the useful purpose of saving both Lalande and the Rojas family from destruction by the hurricane?

12. Repeat the essence of the descriptions of the hurricane, during the northward blow, the brief lull, and the return toward the Gulf.

COMPARISON EXERCISES

1. Which story, "The Adalantado of the Seven Cities" or "The Horse of Hurricane Reef," moves faster with action?

2. Which rises to a sharper and more dramatic climax?

3. Which deals more with supernatural action or effect?

4. Which has the larger amount of extravagant fancy?

5. Which shows the greater interest in nature?

WRITING SUGGESTION

Create a story dominated by plot, making each main incident, after the first, more exciting than the one preceding.

CHARACTER

Introduction to Stories Dominated by Characterization

PLOT and characterization have sometimes been regarded as the two most important elements of short stories, and characterization has sometimes been rated as an even higher art than plot construction. Character portrayal appears in all stories and in some stories predominates.

Every story must have characters—a minimum of two,[1] a protagonist and an antagonist. Characters are necessary that conflict and plot may exist and they add to the interest of a story by making possible a contrast between leading and subordinate personages. The characters whose personalities are individualized must be few— perhaps the hero and one helper and the villain and one associate— because of the limited space available to the short story. Strong characters need weaker characters as foils. The weak characters help the stronger to appear doubly impressive. Contrast relieves monotony.

Adequate motivation is essential to the lifelikeness of a character. Every character very important to the story should be presented early that the reader may be expecting action from the character at intervals not too far apart and will not be surprised by perhaps only one appearance possibly in the climax. The characters should be vivid and realistic; they should seem like flesh-and-blood people rather than author-dominated puppets.

The characters should usually be normal rather than freakish or pathological. They should have real worth. It is better to leave morbid characters to the study of psychological laboratories. Each

---

[1] The editor of *Life* in 1919 said that a short story must have at least two characters. See Fred Lewis Pattee, *The Development of the American Short Story*, New York: Harper & Brothers, 1923, p. 372.

character should represent a class; he should also be individualized, largely in terms of a dominant trait, such as coyness or egotism or other striking characteristic.

For making characters lifelike both the subjective method and the objective techniques may be used. The main objective methods are personal description, dialogue, and action, all involving the person whom the author wishes to portray. The most successful methods for picturing characters vividly are objective.

Subjective characterization through the author's direct statement, through his reporting of a character's thoughts or emotions or moods, though permissible, should not stand unsupported. This method, when used, should be combined with one or more objective techniques.

Similarly, though concrete facts in the description of physical appearance may help reveal character, they are not alone sufficient to establish individuality. Whatever description of physical appearance may be employed should be sifted in among the narrative details. The features most worth describing are those which tend to individualize the person. The physical description must be supplemented by other characterization methods such as the presentation of actions and the use of dialogue.

The actions which spring from a character should both classify and individualize him. They should place him in a class and show how he differs from other members of that class. They should indicate the influence of environment and of other personalities upon him. Environmental forces that notably develop or reveal character are the obstacle that causes a struggle, religion, economic necessity, or the powerful intellect or emotion of a fellow being. The actions through which a person reveals his character need to be described and the manner in which they are performed should be indicated. Sometimes that manner gives clear and immediate insight. If lips curl, shoulders shrug, or teeth grate together, the very nature of the curl, the shrug, or the grating noise indexes character.

Dialogue is another principal method of revealing one's personality. This revelation may be made chiefly through the character's own utterances or partly, even mainly, through the speeches of other persons concerning him. A prime requisite of dialogue is that the speeches must be in character. Reprobates, racing enthusiasts, ranters, half-wits, and other types of individual should use the quality of diction that each type would naturally employ.

Characterization and plot should advance simultaneously. Incident that is interesting not only as action but also as character portrayal contributes to the compactness of the story. The personalities of the characters help to determine plot. It is from characters that situations arise and from situations that crises develop. Toward the climax most stories move, and without the attractive climax those stories would be failures. One of the main instruments for giving a story dramatic power is characterization.

THE REVOLT OF "MOTHER" [1]
(1890)

MARY E. WILKINS FREEMAN

"Father!"

"What is it?"

"What are them men diggin' over there in the field for?"

There was a sudden dropping and enlarging of the lower part of the old man's face, as if some heavy weight had settled therein; he shut his mouth tight and went on harnessing the great bay mare. He hustled the collar on to her neck with a jerk.

"Father!"

The old man slapped the saddle upon the mare's back.

"Look here, father, I want to know what them men are diggin' over in the field for, an' I'm goin' to know."

"I wish you'd go into the house, mother, an' 'tend to your own affairs," the old man said then. He ran his words together, and his speech was almost as inarticulate as a growl.

But the woman understood; it was her most native tongue. "I ain't goin' into the house till you tell me what them men are doin' over there in the field," said she.

Then she stood waiting. She was a small woman, short and straightwaisted like a child in her brown cotton gown. Her forehead was mild and benevolent between the smooth curves of gray hair; there were meek downward lines about her nose and mouth; but her eyes, fixed upon the old man, looked as if the meekness had been the result of her own will, never of the will of another.

They were in the barn, standing before the wide open doors. The spring air, full of the smell of growing grass and unseen blossoms, came in their faces. The deep yard in front was littered with farm wagons and piles of wood; on the edges, close to the fence and the house, the grass was a vivid green, and there were some dandelions.

The old man glanced doggedly at his wife as he tightened the last buckles on the harness. She looked as immovable to him as one of the rocks in his pasture-land, bound to the earth with gen-

---

[1] First published in *Harper's Magazine* (September, 1890) and republished in *A New England Nun and Other Stories* (1891).

erations of blackberry vines. He slapped the reins over the horse
and started forth from the barn.

"*Father!*" said she.

The old man pulled up. "What is it?"

"I want to know what them men are diggin' over there in that
field for."

"They're diggin' a cellar, I s'pose, if you've got to know."

"A cellar for what?"

"A barn."

"A barn? You ain't goin' to build a barn over there where we
was goin' to have a house, father?"

The old man said not another word. He hurried the horse into
the farm wagon and clattered out of the yard, jouncing as sturdily
on his seat as a boy.

The woman stood a moment looking after him, then she went
out of the barn across a corner of the yard to the house. The house,
standing at right angles with the great barn and a long reach of
sheds and outbuildings, was infinitesimal compared with them. It
was scarcely as commodious for people as the little boxes under the
barn eaves were for doves.

A pretty girl's face, pink and delicate as a flower, was looking
out of one of the windows. She was watching three men who were
digging over in the field which bounded the yard near the road
line. She turned quietly when the woman entered.

"What are they digging for, mother?" said she. "Did he tell
you?"

"They're diggin' for—a cellar for a new barn."

"Oh, mother, he ain't going to build another barn?"

"That's what he says."

A boy stood before the kitchen glass combing his hair. He
combed slowly and painstakingly, arranging his brown hair in a
smooth hillock over his forehead. He did not seem to pay any
attention to the conversation.

"Sammy, did you know father was going to build a new barn?"
asked the girl.

The boy combed assiduously.

"Sammy!"

He turned and showed a face like his father's under his smooth
crest of hair. "Yes, I s'pose I did," he said, reluctantly.

57

"How long have you known it?" asked his mother.

"'Bout three months, I guess."

"Why didn't you tell of it?"

"Didn't think 'twould do no good."

"I don't see what father wants another barn for," said the girl, in her sweet, slow voice. She turned again to the window and stared out at the digging men in the field. Her tender, sweet face was full of a gentle distress. Her forehead was as bald and innocent as a baby's, with the light hair strained back from it in a row of curl-papers. She was quite large, but her soft curves did not look as if they covered muscles.

Her mother looked sternly at the boy. "Is he goin' to buy more cows?" said she.

The boy did not reply; he was tying his shoes.

"Sammy, I want you to tell me if he's goin' to buy more cows."

"I s'pose he is."

"How many?"

"Four, I guess."

His mother said nothing more. She went into the pantry, and there was a clatter of dishes. The boy got his cap from a nail behind the door, took an old arithmetic from the shelf, and started for school. He was lightly built, but clumsy. He went out of the yard with a curious spring in the hips that made his loose homemade jacket tilt up in the rear.

The girl went to the sink and began to wash the dishes that were piled up there. Her mother came promptly out of the pantry and shoved her aside. "You wipe 'em," said she; "I'll wash. There's a good many this mornin'."

The mother plunged her hands vigorously into the water, the girl wiped the plates slowly and dreamily. "Mother," said she, "don't you think it's too bad father's going to build that new barn, much as we need a decent house to live in?"

Her mother scrubbed a dish fiercely. "You ain't found out yet we're women-folks, Nanny Penn," said she. "You ain't seen enough of men-folks yet to. One of these days you'll find it out, an' then you'll know that we know only what men-folks think we do, so far as any use of it goes, an' how we'd ought to reckon

58

men-folks in with Providence, an' not complain of what they do any more than we do of the weather."

"I don't care; I don't believe George is anything like that, anyhow," said Nanny. Her delicate face flushed pink, her lips pouted softly, as if she were going to cry.

"You wait an' see. I guess George Eastman ain't no better than other men. You hadn't ought to judge father, though. He can't help it, 'cause he don't look at things jest the way we do. An' we've been pretty comfortable here, after all. The roof don't leak— ain't never but once—that's one thing. Father's kept it shingled right up."

"I do wish we had a parlor."

"I guess it won't hurt George Eastman any to come to see you in a nice clean kitchen. I guess a good many girls don't have as good a place as this. Nobody's ever heard me complain."

"I ain't complained either, mother."

"Well, I don't think you'd better, a good father an' a good home as you've got. S'pose your father made you go out an' work for your livin'? Lots of girls have to that ain't no stronger an' better able to than you be."

Sarah Penn washed the frying-pan with a conclusive air. She scrubbed the outside of it as faithfully as the inside. She was a masterly keeper of her box of a house. Her one living room never seemed to have in it any of the dust which the friction of life with inanimate matter produces. She swept, and there seemed to be no dirt to go before the broom; she cleaned, and one could see no difference. She was like an artist: so perfect that he has apparently no art. Today she got out a mixing bowl and a board, and rolled some pies, and there was no more flour upon her than upon her daughter who was doing finer work. Nanny was to be married in the fall, and she was sewing on some white cambric and embroidery. She sewed industriously while her mother cooked; her soft, milk-white hands and wrists showed whiter than her delicate work.

"We must have the stove moved out in the shed before long," said Mrs. Penn. "Talk about not havin' things, it's been a real blessin' to be able to put a stove up in that shed in hot weather. Father did one good thing when he fixed that stove-pipe out there."

MANNER

Sarah Penn's face as she rolled her pies had that expression of meek vigor which might have characterized one of the New Testament saints. She was making mince-pies. Her husband, Adoniram Penn, liked them better than any other kind. She baked twice a week. Adoniram often liked a piece of pie between meals. She hurried this morning. It had been later than usual when she began, and she wanted to have a pie baked for dinner. However deep a resentment she might be forced to hold against her husband, she would never fail in sedulous attention to his wants.

Nobility of character manifests itself at loopholes when it is not provided with large doors. Sarah Penn's showed itself today in flaky dishes of pastry. So she made the pies faithfully, while across the table she could see, when she glanced up from her work, the sight that rankled in her patient and steadfast soul—the digging of the cellar of the new barn in the place where Adoniram forty years ago had promised her their new house should stand.

The pies were done for dinner. Adoniram and Sammy were home a few minutes after twelve o'clock. The dinner was eaten with serious haste. There was never much conversation at the table in the Penn family. Adoniram asked a blessing, and they ate promptly, then rose up and went about their work.

Sammy went back to school, taking soft sly lopes out of the yard like a rabbit. He wanted a game of marbles before school and feared his father would give him some chores to do. Adoniram hastened to the door and called after him, but he was out of sight.

"I don't see what you let him go for, mother," said he. "I wanted him to help me unload that wood."

Adoniram went to work out in the yard, unloading wood from the wagon. Sarah put away the dinner dishes, while Nanny took down her curl-papers and changed her dress. She was going down to the store to buy some more embroidery and thread.

When Nanny was gone, Mrs. Penn went to the door. "Father!" she called.

"Well, what is it!"

"I want to see you jest a minute, father."

"I can't leave this wood nohow. I've got to git it unloaded an' go for a load of gravel afore two o'clock. Sammy had ought to help me. You hadn't ought to let him go to school so early."

"I want to see you jest a minute."

"I tell ye I can't, nohow, mother."

"Father, you come here," Sarah Penn stood in the door like a queen; she held her head as if it bore a crown; there was that patience which makes authority royal in her voice. Adoniram went.

Mrs. Penn led the way into the kitchen and pointed to a chair. "Sit down, father," said she; "I've got somethin' I want to say to you."

He sat down heavily; his face was quite stolid, but he looked at her with restive eyes. "Well, what is it, mother?"

"I want to know what you're buildin' that new barn for, father?"

"I ain't got nothin' to say about it."

"It can't be you think you need another barn?"

"I tell ye I ain't got nothin' to say about it, mother; an' I ain't goin' to say nothin'."

"Be you goin' to buy more cows?"

Adoniram did not reply; he shut his mouth tight.

"I know you be, as well as I want to. Now, father, look here"— Sarah Penn had not sat down; she stood before her husband in the humble fashion of a Scripture woman—"I'm goin' to talk real plain to you; I never have since I married you, but I'm goin' to now. I ain't never complained, an' I ain't goin' to complain now, but I'm goin' to talk plain. You see this room here, father; you look at it well. You see there ain't no carpet on the floor, an' you see the paper is all dirty, an' droppin' off the walls. We ain't had no new paper on it for ten year, an' then I put it on myself, an' it didn't cost but ninepence a roll. You see this room, father; it's all the one I've had to work in an' eat in an' sit in sence we was married. There ain't another woman in the whole town whose husband ain't got half the means you have but what's got better. It's all the room Nanny's got to have her company in; an' there ain't one of her mates but what's got better, an' their fathers not so able as hers is. It's all the room she'll have to be married in. What would you have thought, father, if we had had our weddin' in a room no better than this? I was married in my mother's parlor, with a carpet on the floor, an' stuffed furniture, an' a mahogany card-table. An' this is all the room my daughter will have to be married in. Look here, father!"

Sarah Penn went across the room as though it were a tragic

stage. She flung open a door and disclosed a tiny bedroom, only large enough for a bed and bureau, with a path between. "There, father," said she—"there's all the room I've had to sleep in forty year. All my children were born there—the two that died an' the two that's livin'. I was sick with a fever there."

She stepped to another door and opened it. It led into the small, ill-lighted pantry. "Here," said she, "is all the buttery I've got— every place I've got for my dishes, to set away my victuals in, an' to keep my milk-pans in. Father, I've been takin' care of the milk of six cows in this place, an' now you're goin' to build a new barn, an' keep more cows, an' give me more to do in it."

She threw open another door. A narrow crooked flight of stairs wound upward from it. "There, father," said she, "I want you to look at the stairs that go up to them two unfinished chambers that are all the places our son an' daughter have had to sleep in all their lives. There ain't a prettier girl in town nor a more ladylike one than Nanny, an' that's the place she has to sleep in. It ain't so good as your horse's stall; it ain't so warm an' tight."

Sarah Penn went back and stood before her husband. "Now, father," said she, "I want to know if you think you're doin' right an' accordin' to what you profess. Here, when we was married, forty year ago, you promised me faithful that we should have a new house built in that lot over in the field before the year was out. You said you had money enough, an' you wouldn't ask me to live in no such place as this. It is forty year now, an' you've been makin' more money, an' I've been savin' of it for you ever since, an' you ain't built no house yet. You've built sheds an' cowhouses an' one new barn, an' now you're goin' to build another. Father, I want to know if you think it's right. You're lodgin' your dumb beasts better than you are your own flesh an' blood. I want to know if you think it's right."

"I ain't got nothin' to say."

"You can't say nothin' without ownin' it ain't right, father. An' there's another thing—I ain't complained; I've got along forty year, an' I s'pose I should forty more, if it wa'n't for that—if we don't have another house. Nanny, she can't live with us after she's married. She'll have to go somewhere else to live away from us, an' it don't seem as if I could have it so, noways, father. She wa'n't ever strong. She's got considerable color, but there wa'n't never any backbone to her. I've always took the heft of everything off her, an' she ain't fit to keep house an' do everything herself. She'll be all worn out inside of a year. Think of her doin' all the washin' an' ironin' an' bakin' with them soft white hands an' arms, an' sweepin'! I can't have it so, noways, father."

Mrs. Penn's face was burning; her mild eyes gleamed. She had pleaded her little cause like a Webster; she had ranged from severity to pathos; but her opponent employed that obstinate silence which makes eloquence futile with mocking echoes. Adoniram arose clumsily.

"Father, ain't you got nothin' to say?" said Mrs. Penn.

"I've got to go off after that load of gravel. I can't stan' here talkin' all day."

"Father, won't you think it over, an' have a house built there instead of a barn?"

"I ain't got nothin' to say."

Adoniram shuffled out. Mrs. Penn went into her bedroom. When she came out, her eyes were red. She had a roll of unbleached cotton cloth. She spread it out on the kitchen table and began cutting out some shirts for her husband. The men over in the field had a team to help them this afternoon; she could hear their halloos. She had a scanty pattern for the shirts; she had to plan and piece the sleeves.

Nanny came home with her embroidery and sat down with her needlework. She had taken down her curl-papers, and there was a soft roll of fair hair like an aureole over her forehead, her face was as delicately fine and clear as porcelain. Suddenly she looked up, and the tender red flamed all over her face and neck. "Mother," said she.

"What say?"

"I've been thinking—I don't see how we're goin' to have any— wedding in this room. I'd be ashamed to have his folks come if we didn't have anybody else."

"Mebbe we can have some new paper before then; I can put it on. I guess you won't have no call to be ashamed of your belongin's."

"We might have the wedding in the new barn," said Nanny,

with gentle pettishness. "Why, mother, what makes you look so?"

Mrs. Penn had started and was staring at her with a curious expression. She turned again to her work and spread out a pattern carefully on the cloth. "Nothin'," said she.

Presently Adoniram clattered out of the yard in his two-wheeled dump cart, standing as proudly upright as a Roman charioteer. Mrs. Penn opened the door and stood there a minute looking out; the halloos of the men sounded louder.

It seemed to her all through the spring months that she heard nothing but the halloos and the noises of saws and hammers. The new barn grew fast. It was a fine edifice for this little village. Men came on pleasant Sundays, in their meeting suits and clean shirt bosoms, and stood around it admiringly. Mrs. Penn did not speak of it, and Adoniram did not mention it to her, although sometimes, upon a return from inspecting it, he bore himself with injured dignity.

"It's a strange thing how your mother feels about the new barn," he said, confidentially, to Sammy one day.

Sammy only grunted after an odd fashion for a boy; he had learned it from his father.

The barn was all completed ready for use by the third week in July. Adoniram had planned to move his stock in on Wednesday, on Tuesday he received a letter which changed his plans. He came in with it early in the morning. "Sammy's been to the post office," said he, "an' I've got a letter from Hiram." Hiram was Mrs. Penn's brother, who lived in Vermont.

"Well," said Mrs. Penn, "what does he say about the folks?"

"I guess they're all right. He says he thinks if I come up country right off there's a chance to buy jest the kind of a horse I want." He stared reflectively out of the window at the new barn.

Mrs. Penn was making pies. She went on clapping the rolling pin into the crust, although she was very pale, and her heart beat loudly.

"I dun' know but what I'd better go," said Adoniram. "I hate to go off jest now, right in the midst of hayin', but the ten-acre lot's cut, an' I guess Rufus an' the others can git along without me three or four days. I can't get a horse round here to suit me, nohow, an' I've got to have another for all that wood-haulin' in the fall. I told Hiram to watch out, an' if he got wind of a good horse to let me know. I guess I'd better go."

"I'll get out your clean shirt an' collar," said Mrs. Penn calmly.

She laid out Adoniram's Sunday suit and his clean clothes on the bed in the little bedroom. She got his shaving-water and razor ready. At last she buttoned on his collar and fastened his black cravat.

Adoniram never wore his collar and cravat except on extra occasions. He held his head high, with a rasped dignity. When he was all ready, with his coat and hat brushed, and a lunch of pie and cheese in a paper bag, he hesitated on the threshold of the door. He looked at his wife, and his manner was defiantly apologetic. "If them cows come today, Sammy can drive 'em into the new barn," said he; "an' when they bring the hay up, they can pitch it in there."

"Well," replied Mrs. Penn.

Adoniram set his shaven face ahead and started. When he had cleared the doorstep, he turned and looked back with a kind of nervous solemnity. "I shall be back by Saturday if nothin' happens," said he.

"Do be careful, father," returned his wife.

She stood in the door with Nanny at her elbow and watched him out of sight. Her eyes had a strange, doubtful expression in them; her peaceful forehead was contracted. She went in, and about her baking again. Nanny sat sewing. Her wedding-day was drawing nearer, and she was getting pale and thin with her steady sewing. Her mother kept glancing at her.

"Have you got that pain in your side this mornin'?" she asked.

"A little."

Mrs. Penn's face, as she worked, changed, her perplexed forehead smoothed, her eyes were steady, her lips firmly set. She formed a maxim for herself, although incoherently with her unlettered thoughts. "Unsolicited opportunities are the guide-posts of the Lord to the new roads of life," she repeated in effect, and she made up her mind to her course of action.

"S'posin' I *had* wrote to Hiram," she muttered once, when she was in the pantry—"s'posin' I had wrote, an' asked him if he knew of any horse? But I didn't, an' father's goin' wa'n't none

65

of my doin'. It looks like a providence." Her voice rang out quite loud at the last.

"What you talkin' about, mother?" called Nanny.

"Nothin'."

Mrs. Penn hurried her baking; at eleven o'clock it was all done. The load of hay from the west field came slowly down the cart track and drew up at the new barn. Mrs. Penn ran out. "Stop!" she screamed—"stop!"

The men stopped and looked; Sammy upreared from the top of the load and stared at his mother.

"Stop!" she cried out again. "Don't you put the hay in that barn; put it in the old one."

"Why, he said to put it in here," returned one of the haymakers, wonderingly. He was a young man, a neighbor's son, whom Adoniram hired by the year to help on the farm.

"Don't you put the hay in the new barn; there's room enough in the old one, ain't there?" said Mrs. Penn.

"Room enough," returned the hired man, in his thick, rustic tones. "Didn't need the new barn, nohow, far as room's concerned. Well, I s'pose he changed his mind." He took hold of the horses' bridles.

Mrs. Penn went back to the house. Soon the kitchen windows were darkened, and a fragrance like warm honey came into the room.

Nanny laid down her work. "I thought father wanted them to put the hay into the new barn?" she said, wonderingly.

"It's all right," replied her mother.

Sammy slid down from the load of hay and came in to see if dinner was ready.

"I ain't goin' to get a regular dinner today, as long as father's gone," said his mother. "I've let the fire go out. You can have some bread an' milk an' pie. I thought we could get along." She set out some bowls of milk, some bread, and a pie on the kitchen table. "You'd better eat your dinner now," said she. "You might jest as well get though with it. I want you to help me afterward."

Nanny and Sammy stared at each other. There was something strange in their mother's manner. Mrs. Penn did not eat anything herself. She went into the pantry, and they heard her moving dishes while they ate. Presently she came out with a pile of plates. She got the clothes-basket out of the shed and packed them in it. Nanny and Sammy watched. She brought out cups and saucers and put them in with the plates.

"What you goin' to do, mother?" inquired Nanny, in a timid voice. A sense of something unusual made her tremble, as if it were a ghost. Sammy rolled his eyes over his pie.

"You'll see what I'm goin' to do," replied Mrs. Penn. "If you're through, Nanny, I want you to go upstairs an' pack up your things; an' I want you, Sammy, to help me take down the bed in the bedroom."

"Oh, mother, what for?" gasped Nanny.

"You'll see."

During the next few hours a feat was performed by this simple, pious New England mother which was equal in its way to Wolfe's storming of the Heights of Abraham. It took no more genius and audacity of bravery for Wolfe to cheer his wondering soldiers up those steep precipices, under the sleeping eyes of the enemy, than for Sarah Penn, at the head of her children, to move all their little household goods into the new barn while her husband was away.

Nanny and Sammy followed their mother's instructions without a murmur; indeed, they were overawed. There is a certain uncanny and superhuman quality about all such purely original undertakings as their mother's was to them. Nanny went back and forth with her light loads, and Sammy tugged with sober energy.

At five o'clock in the afternoon the little house in which the Penns had lived for forty years had emptied itself into the new barn.

Every builder builds somewhat for unknown purposes and is in a measure a prophet. The architect of Adoniram Penn's barn, while he designed it for the comfort of four-footed animals, had planned better than he knew for the comfort of humans. Sarah Penn saw at a glance its possibilities. Those great box-stalls, with quilts hung before them, would make better bedrooms than the one she had occupied for forty years, and there was a tight carriage-room. The harness-room, with its chimney and shelves, would make a kitchen of her dreams. The great middle space would make a parlor, by-and-by, fit for a palace. Upstairs there was as much room as down. With partitions and windows, what a house would there be! Sarah looked at the row of stanchions before the allotted space for cows and reflected that she would have her front entry there.

At six o'clock the stove was up in the harness-room, the kettle was boiling, and the table set for tea. It looked almost as home-like as the abandoned house across the yard had ever done. The young hired man milked, and Sarah directed him calmly to bring the milk to the new barn. He came gaping, dropping little blots of foam from the brimming pails on the grass. Before the next morning he had spread all over the little village the story of Adoniram Penn's wife moving into the new barn. Men assembled in the store and talked it over, women with shawls over their heads scuttled into each other's houses before their work was done. Any deviation from the ordinary course of life in this quiet town was enough to stop all progress in it. Everybody paused to look at the staid, independent figure on the side track. There was a difference of opinion with regard to her. Some held her to be insane; some, of a lawless and rebellious spirit.

Friday the minister went to see her. It was in the forenoon, and she was at the barn door shelling peas for dinner. She looked up and returned his salutation with dignity; then she went on with her work. She did not invite him in. The saintly expression of her face remained fixed, but there was an angry flush over it.

The minister stood awkwardly before her and talked. She handled the peas as if they were bullets. At last she looked up, and her eyes showed the spirit that her meek front had covered for a lifetime.

"There ain't no use talkin' Mr. Hersey," said she. "I've thought it all over an' over, an' I believe I'm doin' what's right. I've made it the subject of prayer, an' it's betwixt me an' the Lord an' Adoniram. There ain't no call for nobody else to worry about it."

"Well, of course, if you have brought it to the Lord in prayer and feel satisfied that you are doing right, Mrs. Penn," said the minister, helplessly. His thin, gray-bearded face was pathetic. He was a sickly man; his youthful confidence had cooled; he had to scourge himself up to some of his pastoral duties as relentlessly as a Catholic ascetic, and then he was prostrated by the smart.

"I think it's right jest as much as I think it was right for our forefathers to come over from the old country 'cause they didn't have what belonged to 'em," said Mrs. Penn. She arose. The barn threshold might have been Plymouth Rock from her bearing. "I don't doubt you mean well, Mr. Hersey," said she, "but there are things people hadn't ought to interfere with. I've been a member of the church for over forty year. I've got my own mind an' my own feet, an' I'm goin' to think my own thoughts an' go my own ways, an' nobody but the Lord is goin' to dictate to me unless I've a mind to have him. Won't you come in an' set down? How is Mis' Hersey?"

"She is well, I thank you," replied the minister. He added some more perplexed apologetic remarks; then he retreated.

He could expound the intricacies of every character study in the Scriptures; he was competent to grasp the Pilgrim Fathers and all historical innovators; but Sarah Penn was beyond him. He could deal with primal cases, but parallel ones worsted him. But, after all, although it was aside from his province, he wondered more how Adoniram Penn would deal with his wife than how the Lord would. Everybody shared the wonder. When Adoniram's four new cows arrived, Sarah ordered three to be put in the old barn, the other in the house shed where the cooking-stove had stood. That added to the excitement. It was whispered that all four cows were domiciled in the house.

Towards sunset on Saturday, when Adoniram was expected home, there was a knot of men in the road near the new barn. The hired man had milked, but he still hung around the premises. Sarah Penn had supper all ready. There were brown-bread and baked beans and a custard pie; it was the supper that Adoniram loved on a Saturday night. She had on a clean calico, and she bore herself imperturbably. Nanny and Sammy kept close at her heels. Their eyes were large, and Nanny was full of nervous tremors. Still, there was to them more pleasant excitement than anything else. An inborn confidence in their mother over their father asserted itself.

Sammy looked out of the harness-room window. "There he is," he announced, in an awed whisper. He and Nanny peeped around the casing. Mrs. Penn kept on about her work. The children watched Adoniram leave the new horse standing in the drive while he went to the house door. It was fastened. Then he went around to the shed. That door was seldom locked, even when the family was away. The thought how her father would be confronted by the cow flashed upon Nanny. There was a hysterical sob in her throat. Adoniram emerged from the shed and stood looking about in a dazed fashion. His lips moved; he was saying something, but they could not hear what it was. The hired man was peeping around a corner of the old barn, but nobody saw him.

Adoniram took the new horse by the bridle and led him across the yard to the new barn. Nanny and Sammy slunk close to their mother. The barn doors rolled back, and there stood Adoniram, with the long milk face of the great Canadian farm horse looking over his shoulder.

Nanny kept behind her mother, but Sammy stepped suddenly forward and stood in front of her.

Adoniram stared at the group. "What on airth you all down here for?" said he. "What's the matter over to the house?"

"We've come here to live, father,' said Sammy. His shrill voice quavered out bravely.

"What"—Adoniram sniffed—"what is it smells like cookin'?" said he. He stepped forward and looked in the open door of the harness-room. Then he turned to his wife. His old bristling face was pale and frightened. "What on airth does this mean, mother?" he gasped.

"You come in here, father," said Sarah. She led the way into the harness-room and shut the door. "Now, father," said she, "you needn't be scared. I ain't crazy. There ain't nothin' to be upset over. But we've come here to live, an' we're goin' to live here. We've got jest as good a right here as new horses an' cows. The house wa'n't fit for us to live in any longer, an' I made up my mind I wa'n't goin' to stay there. I've done my duty by you for forty year, an' I'm goin' to do it now; but I'm goin' to live here. You've got to put in some windows and partitions; an' you'll have to buy some furniture."

"Why, mother!" the old man gasped.

"You'd better take your coat off an' get washed—there's the wash-basin—an' then we'll have supper."

"Why, mother!"

Sammy went past the window, leading the new horse to the

old barn. The old man saw him and shook his head speechlessly. He tried to take off his coat, but his arms seemed to lack the power. His wife helped him. She poured some water into the tin basin and put in a piece of soap. She got the comb and brush and smoothed his thin gray hair after he had washed. Then she put the beans, hot bread, and tea on the table. Sammy came in and the family drew up. Adoniram sat looking dazedly at his plate, and they waited.

"Ain't you goin' to ask a blessin', father?" said Sarah.

And the old man bent his head and mumbled.

All through the meal he stopped eating at intervals and stared furtively at his wife; but he ate well. The home food tasted good to him, and his old frame was too sturdily healthy to be effected by his mind. But after supper he went out and sat down on the step of the smaller door at the right of the barn, through which he had meant his Jerseys to pass in stately file, but which Sarah designed for her front house door, and he leaned his head on his hands.

After the supper dishes were cleared away and the milk-pans washed, Sarah went out to him. The twilight was deepening. There was a clear green glow in the sky. Before them stretched the smooth level of field; in the distance was a cluster of haystacks like the huts of a village; the air was very cool and calm and sweet. The landscape might have been an ideal one of peace.

Sarah bent over and touched her husband on one of his thin, sinewy shoulders. "Father!"

The old man's shoulders heaved; he was weeping.

"Why, don't do so, father." said Sarah.

"I'll—put up the—partitions, an'—everything you—want, mother."

Sarah put her apron up to her face; she was overcome by her own triumph.

Adoniram was like a fortress whose walls had no active resistance and went down the instant the right besieging tools were used.

"Why, mother," he said hoarsely, "I hadn't no idee you was so set on't as all this comes to."

STUDY NOTES

1. Outline the plot of "The Revolt of 'Mother,'" pointing out the exciting force and the climax as well as the intervening incidents.

2. How early in the story does the first action occur?

3. What light do Adoniram Penn's reticence under his wife's questioning and his impetuous actions when harnessing the mare throw upon his character?

4. What other facets of his character does the story reveal and by what devices?

5. Cite evidences of Sarah Penn's meekness and of her vigor and will power.

6. Characterize her as a housekeeper, a wife, and a mother.

7. By what methods does the author portray Sarah's character?

8. How does the story create the impression that Sarah deserved a more spacious and more tastefully furnished home than her husband had provided?

9. Why is the length of time that the Penns had been married stressed?

10. Interpret the maxim, "Unsolicited opportunities are the guide-posts of the Lord to the new roads of life," with application to Mrs. Penn.

JUDGE[1]
(1935)

WALTER DUMAUX EDMONDS

W HEN Charley Haskell died in the spring, he left a widow
with nine children, a four-room house, a rickety barn, and a
dollar owing from the Judge for the sale of a calf. The widow
was a plain, honest, and fairly easy-going woman. She worked
hard enough in the house to keep it and the children's clothes
clean, but for outside things she had depended on her husband.
For a few weeks after his death she apparently put her trust in God.
Then she had a talk with John.

John was the oldest boy. The next oldest was only seven, and
in between were girls. She told him, therefore, that it was up to him
to take his father's place toward his brothers and sisters. They
looked to him for their support, and she depended on him. She
kissed him a little tearfully, and took up her existence again exactly where she had left it off when Charley died—as if by a few
words, she had settled it in the accustomed grooves for an indefinite time.

The sight of her unexpected tears, however, had sobered John,
so that he hung up his fishing pole and went out to look at the corn
patch. He found it full of weeds. It was an unusual thing for him
to get the hoe without being told to, but he did, and after he had
cleaned the first row, he found that it looked much better when you
could see the corn.

When he came in that night to supper, he had a quarter of the
field hoed. He called his mother and sisters out to see what he had
done and listened with pride as they said that it looked nice. It
was while his mother was looking at the corn that she remembered
that they had never collected the dollar from the Judge for the
calf. She told John that he had better get it that evening.

John was frightened at the idea of going to the Judge's house.
In 1830, the settlement at High Falls was a poor place of small
houses, which made the Judge's stone house seem like a palace. John,
for one, had never seen the inside of it, but he had seen the curtains

---

[1] Copyright, 1935, by the Curtis Publishing Company. Reprinted by permission
of Harold Ober.

through the windows, and the oil lamps, when he went by at night, two or even three in the same room. For Judge Doane was the great man of the district. He owned a vast amount of land and held mortgages on most of the rest and had been representative of the county.

John's mother had brushed his coat for him, but even so, it looked very shabby and frayed and outgrown as he knocked on the front door and asked the hired girl if he could see the Judge. He had the feeling that it was an impertinence to ask a person like the Judge to pay a dollar, even when he owned it to you. He thought that probably the Judge would throw him out of the house. But his mother said they needed the dollar for flour, and at least he had to try to get it.

The maid came back for him and led him to the Judge's office, opened the door, and closed it behind him. John stood with his back to the door and his hat in both hands, a lanky, overgrown boy, with a thin, rather pale face, and brown frightened eyes. Compared to the Judge, he looked like someone made of splinters.

"Hello, John," said the Judge. "What do you want with me?"

He sounded unfriendly, so John managed, after a couple of attempts, to say that he had come for the dollar for the calf.

"Oh, yes," said the Judge. "I'd forgotten about that. I'm sorry."

He got up from his leather armchair and went to his writing desk and took one end of his gold watch chain from the pocket of his well-filled, speckled waistcoat and unlocked a drawer. While his back was turned, John was able to see the room, with the impressive lace on the curtains of the windows, the silver plate hung on the chimney piece, and the fire on the hearth where the Judge burned wood just for the sake of seeing it burn.

The Judge relocked the drawer, replaced the key in his pocket, and handed John a dollar bill. He resumed his seat and told John to sit down for a minute. John did so, on the edge of the nearest chair.

"How are you making out?" asked the Judge.

"All right, I guess," said John. "I wouldn't have bothered you for this, only we had to have flour."

"That's all right," said the Judge slowly. "I should have remembered it. I didn't think of it because your father owed me money anyway."

74

"I didn't know that," said John. He couldn't think of anything to say. He only looked at the Judge and wondered how his father had had the nerve to borrow money from a man like him.

The Judge made an impressive figure before his fire. He was a massive man with a red face, strong white hair, and uncompromising light blue eyes. He was staring at John, too, rather curiously.

He nodded, after a while, and said, "He owed me forty dollars."

That was what John had wanted to know, but he was shocked at the amount of it. All he could think of to say was, "I didn't know that, sir."

"No," said the Judge, "probably not. He was a kind of cousin of my wife's, but we neither of us said much about it. And after Mrs. Doane died he didn't come around much." His brows drew bushily together and he stared into the fire. "How old are you, son?" he asked.

John replied that he was sixteen.

The Judge went on to ask about the family, the age of each child, and what Charley Haskell had got planted that spring. John answered him everything, and as he did he felt a little more confidence. It seemed odd that anyone living in High Falls settlement could know so little about anyone else. Why, he knew a lot more about the Judge than the Judge did about him. He told how high the corn stood. He said, "It stands as high as any I've seen around here, excepting yours, Judge. And now I've started looking out for it, maybe it will catch up.

The Judge said, "Hoeing is the best garden fertilizer in the world. And sweat is the next best thing to money."

"Yes, sir." said John. It made him feel proud that he had hoed so much of his corn that day. Tomorrow he'd really get after the piece.

"You can't live on potatoes and corn though," said the Judge. "What are you going to do?"

John was awed to be talking so familiarly to a man half the town was scared of; a man, it was said, who had even talked out in legislature down in Albany. But his face wrinkled and he managed to grin.

"Work, I guess, sir."

The Judge grunted then and stood up and dripped his quid into the sandbox.

75

"You do that and you'll take care of your family all right. Maybe you'll even pay the forty dollars your father owed me." He held out his hand, which John hardly dared to take. "When do you suppose that'll be?"

John got white. "I don't know, sir."

The Judge smiled.

"I like that a lot better than easy promises, John."

He walked beside John into the hall, his meaty hand on John's shoulder.

"Good luck to you," he said from the front door.

During the summer John managed to get work from time to time, hiring out for as much as forty cents a day, sometimes as often as three days a week. At first he didn't have much luck getting jobs, for though he was a good deal stronger than he appeared to be and worked hard, people remembered his father and preferred getting other help when they could. Besides, in the 30's, there weren't many people in High Falls who could afford to hire help, even at forty cents a day; so, by working in the evenings and on Sundays also, John had ample time to take care of their corn and potatoes and the garden truck he had planted late himself.

He used to wonder how his father had ever been able to take life so easily. He wondered often how it was that he never had time to go fishing that summer. And the one or two times he did have the time, he thought of the forty dollars he owed Judge Doane, and he went out and looked for work. He even found occasional jobs at Greig, five miles up the river, and walked back and forth every morning and evening. Little by little, the forty dollars became an obsession with him, and though at first he had given all his earnings to his mother to spend, he now began to save out a few pennies here and there. When, at the end of August, he had saved out his first complete dollar and held it all at once in his hand, he realized that some day he might pay off the debt; and from there his mind went further, and he began to see that it was even possible that some day he would be able to build a decent house for his mother, perhaps even get married; perhaps, when the settlement became a town, as they said it would, get elected to the town board.

By the middle of October, John had saved up enough money to see the family through the winter, as he calculated it, for besides his secret bit, he had persuaded his mother to lay by some of what he gave her. Further, she had been moved by the sight of a decent garden to preserve some beans and also some berries that the girls had gathered, especially since it was the first time in several years that she had felt able to buy sugar ahead of the immediate demand. The potato piece had yielded forty bushels of potatoes; and the corn, which John had sold, had brought in a few dollars more.

The day before he finished cutting the winter wood supply, John counted up his money and decided he would make the first payment on the forty-dollar debt to the Judge that night. It amounted to five dollars, even, but to John that seemed a great deal.

He went up to the big house when he felt sure that the Judge would have finished supper; and he had the same business of knocking and waiting in the hall while the maid took his name in. He found the Judge sitting as he had found him the first time, only the fire was about two logs bigger.

"Sit down, John," said the Judge, "and tell me what I can do for you."

John obviously did not know how to begin his business properly, and after watching him under his brows for a moment, the Judge continued in his gruff voice. "I may as well tell you I've kind of kept my eye on you this summer, John. I like the way you've taken hold. I'm willing to admit, too, that I was kind of surprised. And I'll be glad to help you out."

John flushed right up to his hair.

"I didn't come to ask for anything, Judge." He fished in his pocket and pulled out his coins. His hands were stiffly clumsy. Some of the coins fell to the floor and one rolled musically all the way under the desk. As he went on his knees to retrieve it, John wished he had had a sense to tie them together instead of jingling them loosely in his pocket all the way up. He couldn't bear to look at the Judge when he handed him the coins. He said, "I wanted to pay something back on that forty dollars, sir. It's only five dollars, even." The Judge had to cup his two hands. "Maybe you'd count it, sir." But it didn't look like so much in the Judge's hands.

The Judge, however, said, "Quite right, John," and counted up the money. Then he went to his desk, put the money in a drawer, and wrote out a receipt which he gave to John.

"Yes, sir," said John, wondering what it was.

The Judge looked grave.

"That's a receipt, John. It says you've paid me back five dollars." John wondered.

"Why," he said, "it's kind of like money, ain't it?"

"In a way," said the Judge, shaking hands. "What are you going to do this winter, John?"

"I don't know, sir. I tried to get a job from Brown at the hotel, splitting firewood, but he's hired Ance instead. Mr. Freel's got all the help he needs at the tannery."

Those were about the only winter jobs in High Falls a man could hope to find. The Judge nodded and said, "I'd offer you something if it didn't mean getting rid of someone else, John. I couldn't rightly do that."

"No, sir," John said, and started home.

But somehow, he felt so happy all the way home that when he reached the house and found his mother sitting up in the kitchen, he couldn't help telling her the whole business. He blurted it all out—the way he had saved a little now and then until he had actually got five dollars. And then he showed her the receipt.

His mother didn't say a word as she looked at the receipt, but her head gradually bent farther and farther forward, and all at once she started crying. John could not understand at first. Finally she lifted her face to him.

"Oh, John, why did you do that?"

"I wanted to pay off that debt Pa laid up," he said, uneasily. "Ain't that all right?"

"I guess it is, John. But why didn't you tell me first?"

"I kind of wanted to surprise you," he mumbled. "I didn't mean for to make you feel bad, Ma."

"It ain't that, John."

"But ain't I give you enough?"

"Oh, yes. You've done fine, John. But the way you've been working has made me kind of different. I got to thinking people talked to us different now. I never thought about that before."

As he thought it over during the next two or three days, John felt all torn up in his chest. He began to see that by starting to be respectable, he had done more than just work for himself. He had done something to his mother, too. And now, by going through with it, he had put her back where she used to be. It did not seem logical, but that was how it was.

Perhaps he would have fallen back then and there to his old ways of letting the world slide, if he hadn't met Seth one evening at the blacksmith's, where he had gone to get the big cook kettle mended. Seth was there, too, having Jorgen do some work on a few of his beaver traps.

Seth was an Indian. In summer he worked in the sawmills when it occurred to him to do so, but in winter he went into the north woods. People distrusted Seth. They did not like the way he smelled. Even in the forge you could smell him, greasy sweat, through his thick tobacco smoke.

He said he was planning to go north in about two weeks. He was late, but the winter looked slow. He thought the furs would be coming up pretty quick though. Better than last year. Last year he had cleared only two hundred dollars.

"Two hundred dollars," thought John. He wondered how a man like Seth could spend all that. All he knew was that the Indian took it to Utica every spring. He supposed there were places in such a big town that an Indian could go to. Two hundred dollars.

He turned shyly to the Indian.

"How much does a man need to get traps and food for the winter?" he asked.

The Indian turned his brown face. He wasn't amused, or he did not show it if he was.

"Sev'nty-five dollar, maybe. You got a gun?"

John nodded.

"Seventy-five dollars," he thought. He knew only one person who could stake him that much.

The Indian asked, "You going?"

"Maybe," said John.

"You come wit' me. Good range over mine. Plenty room us both. I help you make a cabin."

"I'll see."

It was almost 10:30 at night when he got to the Judge's. He

had made up his mind he would ask the Judge, if there was a downstairs light still on when he got there. If not, he wouldn't.

The house was dark on the town side, but when John went round to the office window, his heart contracted to see that the Judge was still up. He tapped on the window. The Judge did not start. He got slowly up and came to the window and opened it to the frosty night. When he saw the boy's white face and large eyes, he said harshly, "What do you want?"

"Please, Judge," said John, "could I talk to you?"

"It's damned late," said the Judge, staring with his cold blue eyes for a while. Then he shut the window, and presently opened the front door. He was looking a little less threatening by then, but he wasn't looking friendly.

"Be as quick as you can," he said, when they were back in the office.

John was as white as a person could be. His tongue stuttered.

"I wanted to ask you something, Judge. But if you don't like it, say so plain. It's about me and getting to trap this winter, on account of that five dollars I paid you." He couldn't think decently straight.

The Judge barked at him.

"Talk plain, boy! Begin at the beginning. What's the five dollars got to do with it?"

John began to talk. He repeated what had happened with his mother, how she felt, how odd it seemed to him, but there it was. The Judge began to sit less stiffly. He even nodded. "Women are the devil," he observed. "You want to take back that money?"

"No, no, I don't," John said desperately. "But people don't like giving me work yet, and I want Ma to feel respectable. I thought if you could make a stake to go trapping."

"How much?"

"Seth said seventy-five dollars," he almost whispered. "But I guess I could get along with fifty. I'd get the traps and some powder and ball, and I could go light on the food. I don't eat a great lot and I'm a handy shot, Judge."

"Seventy-five dollars, said the Judge. "You're asking me to lend that much to a sixteen-year-old boy, just like that?"

His red face was particularly heavy-looking.

"I'd make it on fifty," said John, "but it was just an idea. If you don't think it's all right, I won't bother you any more."

"Then you want the five back, too, I suppose—makes it eighty. And forty is a hundred and twenty.'

"It would be ninety-five, wouldn't it, if you give me fifty?"

"Shut up," barked the Judge. "If I'm going to stake you I'll do it so I'll have a chance of getting my money back. It won't pay me to send you in with so little you'll starve to death before spring, will it?"

John could only gape.

"How about this Seth?" asked the Judge. "He's a drunken brute. Can you trust him?"

"I've met him in the woods," said John. "He's always been nice to me."

The Judge grumbled. He got up and took five dollars from his desk and gave it to John.

"You bring me back that receipt tomorrow night," was all he said.

When John gave the money to his mother, it made her so happy that he felt wicked to feel so miserable himself. It seemed as if all his summer's work had been burned with one spark. And he was frightened to go next night to the Judge's house. But he went.

The Judge only kept him a moment.

He took the receipt and gave John another paper.

"Put a cross in the right-hand bottom corner," he directed; and when John had done so, "That is a receipt for seventy-five dollars. Here's the money. Don't lose it going home."

He walked John to the door and shook hands.

"Good luck. Come here next spring as soon as you get back."

"Thanks," was all John could say.

The Judge made a harsh noise in his throat and fished a chew from his pocket.

"Good-by," he said.

John got Seth to help select his outfit. The Indian enjoyed doing that. And John felt so proud over his new traps, his powder flask and bullet pouch, and his big basket of provisions, and he felt so grateful to the Indian that he offered to buy him a drink out of the two-shilling bit he had left.

"No drink," said the Indian. "Next spring, oh, yes."

He shared his canoe with John up the Moose River, and they spent two weeks getting in to Seth's range. They dumped his stuff in the little log cabin and moved over the range together to the one Seth had selected for John. There they laid up a small cabin just like the Indian's, and built a chimney. They had trouble finding clay to seal the cracks, for by then the frost was hard and snow coming regularly each afternoon.

Then the Indian took John with him while he laid out his own lines, and, after two days, went with John, showing him what to start on. After that the Indian spent all his spare time making John snowshoes. He finished them just in time for the first heavy snow.

John learned a great deal from Seth that fall. First of all he learned that an Indian in the woods is a much different person from the Indian imitating white men. He had always liked Seth, but he had never suspected his generosity and good humor. Even when the snow got heavy, the Indian paid him a weekly visit and asked him back to his cabin in return.

He learned how to make pens for beaver under water and ice, and sink fresh twigs, and when the younger beaver swam in, to drop the closing pole and let them drown. He never got as good as Seth had, as a still-hunting fisher. But Seth said, either you could do that or you could not; there was no shame in not being able.

But John did well. Early in March his bale of furs had mounted up so well that he had Seth come over and appraise them. The Indian said he had more than two hundred dollars' worth. It would depend on the market. By the end of the month he might have two hundred and fifty dollars' worth.

The snow went down quickly, but the ice held. John began to be eager to leave. He wanted to show his furs. He would be able to pay off the Judge, not only the stake but the share, and also the debt, and he would have a few dollars to start the summer on. Next winter he would make a clear profit. He would put money in the bank.

He went over to Seth's and told him he would start next week. He could not bear to wait, and if he went early he could get across the Moose River on the ice somewhere. The Indian said, "Yes," but he begged John to wait. There was still two weeks for the fur to hold up well, and he had sometimes made some lucky catches in March.

But John's heart was set on going. He couldn't put his mind on trapping any more. He had done so well already. So finally Seth agreed to come over and help him pack his furs and traps. They had a big feed on about the last of John's grub.

In the morning he set out and the Indian walked with him to the end of his own south line, and shook hands.

"You one damn good boy, John," he said unexpectedly. "You come again next year."

"I will sure," said John. "Thanks for all you've done for me, Seth. Without you I wouldn't have done this." He hitched the heavy pack up on his shoulder. "I guess next to the Judge, you're about the best friend I ever had."

The Indian's brown face wrinkled all over beneath his battered hat. He made a big gesture with his hand.

"Oh, sure," he said. "Big country. Nice company. Plenty furs us both."

He held John's hand.

He said, "Now listen to Seth. If creeks open, you cut two logs crossing. You mind Seth. You cut two logs. One log roll. Two logs safe crossing water."

"Yes, sure," said John. He wanted to get away. The sun was well up by now.

" 'By," said Seth.

John walked hard. He felt strong that morning. He felt like a grown man. The weight of the pack, galling his shoulders, was a pleasure to carry.

Every time he eased it one way or another, he thought about what it was going to mean. He thought about coming home and telling his mother. He would buy her a new dress. He would make a purchase of some calico for his sisters. "Make a purchase," he thought, was quite a mouthful. He'd never even thought of it before.

He would see the Judge. He imagined himself walking into the Judge's office and dropping the pack on the floor, and looking the Judge in the eye. He realized that that meant more to him than doing things for his family.

He remembered the way he had started the winter. He had got Seth to estimate the worth of each first pelt. When they had figured up to forty dollars, he had made a bundle of them. They were still packed together in the bottom of the pack. It seemed to him that getting that first forty dollars' worth was twice as much a job as all the rest for him to have done.

The snow was a little slushy here and there, but it held up well in the big woods and he made pretty good time. Nights, he set himself up a lean-to of cedar and balsam branches, and sitting before his small fire, he would think ahead a few years. He could see himself some day, pretty near like the Judge. He even figured on teaching himself to read and write—write his own name, anyway. No matter how you looked at it, you couldn't make a cross seem like "John Haskell" wrote out in full, with big and little letters in it.

Mornings, he started with the first gray light, when the mist was like a twilight on the water and the deer moused along the runways and eyed him, curious as chipmunks. He walked south down the slopes of the hills across the shadows of the sunrise, when the snow became full of color and the hills ahead wore a bloody purple shadow on their northern faces.

Now and then he heard the first stirring of a small brook under the snow in a sunny place, and he found breath holes under falls wide open.

He had grown taller during the winter, and he seemed even lankier, but his eyes were still the brown, boy's eyes of a year ago.

He crossed the Moose River on the ice about where McKeever now is, just at dusk. He had not made as good time that day. The snow had been a good deal softer and his legs ached and the pack weighed down a bit harder than usual. But though the ice had been treacherous close to shore, he had found a place easily enough.

That night, however, as he lay in his lean-to, he heard the river ice begin to work. It went out in the morning with a grinding roar and built a jam half a mile below his camp.

He saw it with a gay heart as he set out after breakfast. It seemed to him as if it were the most providential thing he ever had heard of. If he had waited another day before starting, he would never have found the river open and he would have had to go back to Seth's cabin and wait till the Indian was ready to come out. But as it was, now, he would have only brooks to cross.

There were a good many of them, and most of them were opening. But he found places to cross them, and he had no trouble till afternoon, when he found some running full. They were high with black snow water, some of them so high that he had to go upstream almost a mile to find a place where he could fell a bridge across.

Each time he dropped two logs and went over easily enough. But each time the delay chafed him a little more. By late afternoon, when he was only five miles from High Falls and began to recognize his landmarks, he came to what he knew was the last creek.

It was a strong stream, with a great force of water, and it was boiling full. Where John happened on it, it began a slide down the steep bank for the river, with one bend and then a straight chute. But it was narrow there, and beside where he stood grew a straight hemlock long enough to reach across.

Hardly stopping to unload his pack, John set to work with his ax. The tree fell nicely, just above the water. There was no other tree close by, but John thought about that only for a moment. It was the last creek, he was almost home, and his heart was set on getting there that night. Besides, he had had no trouble on the other crossings. He was sure-footed, and in every case he had run across one log.

He gave the tree a kick, but it lay steady, and suddenly he made up his mind to forget what Seth had said. He could get over easy enough and see the Judge that evening.

With his furs on his back, his ax in one hand and his gun in the other, he stepped out on the log. It felt solid as stone under his feet and he went along at a steady pace. The race of water just under the bark meant nothing to John. His head was quite clear and his eyes were on the other side already, and he thought, in his time, he had crossed a lot of logs more rickety than this one.

It was just when he was halfway over that the log rolled without any warning and pitched John into the creek.

The water took hold of him and lugged him straight down and rolled him over and over like a dead pig. He had no chance even to yell. He dropped his gun and ax at the first roll and instinctively tugged at the traps which weighted him so. As he struggled to the top, he felt the fur pack slip off. He made a desperate grab at them, but they went away. When he finally washed up on the bend and crawled out on the snow, he hadn't a thing left but his life.

That seemed worthless to him, lying on the snow. He could not even cry about it.

He lay there for perhaps half an hour while the dusk came in on the river. Finally he got his feet and searched downstream poking with a stick along the bottom. But he was hopeless. The creek ran like a millrace down the slope for the river and the chances were a hundred to one that the traps as well as the furs had been taken by the strength of water and the slide all the way down to the river.

But he continued his search till nearly dark before he gave up.

By the time he reached High Falls, he had managed to get back just enough of his courage to go straight to the Judge. It was very late, but the office light was still burning, and John knocked and went in. He stood on the hearth, shivering and dripping, but fairly erect, and told the Judge exactly what had happened, even to Seth's parting admonition, in a flat, low voice.

The Judge said never a word till the boy was done. He merely sat studying him from under his bushy white brows. Then he got up and fetched him a glass of whisky.

Though the drink seemed to bring back a little life, it only made John more miserable. He waited like a wavering ghost for the Judge to have his say.

But the Judge only said in his heavy voice, "You'd better go on home. You'd better start hunting work tomorrow." His voice became gruffer: "Everybody has to learn things. It's been bad luck for us both that you had to learn it like this."

John went home. All he could remember was that the Judge had said it was bad luck for them both. It seemed to him that that was a very kind thing for the Judge to say.

John did not see anything of the Judge that summer. He worked hard, planting corn and potatoes and the garden, and later he managed to find work. He seemed to get work more easily that summer. But his family seemed to need more money. Now and then people visited a little, and that meant extra money for food and tea. By working hard though, John found himself in the fall about where he had been on the preceding year.

He had put in a bid with the tannery for winter work and had had the job promised to him. Two days before he would have started, however, the Judge sent word for him to come to the big house.

The Judge made him sit down.

"John," he said, "you've kept your courage up when it must have been mighty hard. I've been thinking about you and me. I think the best thing for us both, the best way I can get my money back, is to give you another stake, if you're willing to go."

John felt that he was much nearer crying than he had been when he lost his furs. He hardly found the voice to say that he would go.

Seth, for no good reason, had decided to move west in the state, so John had to go into the woods alone. But he had good luck that winter, better even than he had had the year before. He stayed right through to the end of the season, and his pack was so heavy he had to leave his traps behind.

The river was open when he reached it, so he had to ferry himself over on a raft. It took a day to build. And from that point on he took plenty of time when he came to the creeks, and dropped two logs over them, and made a trial trip over and back without his fur pack. It took him three extra days coming out, but he brought his furs with him.

The Judge saw to it that he got good prices; and when the dealer was done with the buying, John was able to pay the Judge for both stakes and for the forty dollars as well. The year after that he made a clear profit.

John did well in the world. He found time to learn to read and write and handle figures. From time to time he visited the Judge, and he found that the Judge was not a person anyone needed to be afraid of. When the Judge died in John's thirtieth year, John was owner of Freel's tannery and one of the leading men of High Falls.

It is a simple story, this of John Haskell's, but it is not quite done. When the Judge died and the will was read, it was found that he had left to John Haskell the big house and a share of his money. There was also a sealed letter for John.

That night in his house, John opened the letter. It was dated the same day as the one on which John had received the money for his first pack of furs. It was just a few lines long and it contained forty dollars in bills.

Dear John: *Here is the forty dollars, and I am making you a confession with it. I liked your looks when you came to me that first time. I thought you had stuff in you. It was a dirty thing to do, in a way, but I wanted to make sure of you. I never liked your father and I would never lend him a cent. I invented that debt. Good luck. John.*

STUDY NOTES

1. Which element do the introductory paragraphs of "Judge" deal with mainly—setting, characterization, or action?

2. Find proof that upper New York State, which serves as the background of much of Edmonds's writing, is the setting of this story.

3. Defend your choice as to whether "Judge" or "John Haskell" is the more appropriate title for the story.

4. Show that the dialogue advances the plot and delineates character.

5. How is Judge Doane individualized—distinguished from other judges?

6. Give examples from the story showing the various methods used in characterizing John Haskell, the judge, Charley Haskell, John's mother, Seth.

7. Point the contrast between Charley and John.

8. Compare this story with Edmonds's *Two Logs Crossing,* a revised form of "Judge" adapted to young readers.

COMPARISON EXERCISES

1. Which story, "The Revolt of 'Mother' " or "Judge," makes the more effective use of dialogue for delineating character?

2. Compare the naturalness of the dialogue in the two stories as shown by such devices as rapid repartee, the use of contractions and colloquialisms, and the revealment or concealment of motives.

3. Which story makes the larger use of dialogue to further the plot?

4. Which story employs the greater amount of conversation by others for revealing a referred-to character's personality?

5. Compare the two stories for their use of the following techniques of characterization:
   a. The author's statements about a person's character
   b. Description of the personal appearance
   c. The character's behavior
   d. The effect of other persons' behavior upon a particular character.

WRITING SUGGESTION

Write a story dominated by its characters but still interesting for its plot, employing natural dialogue and motive-revealing actions and any other characterization devices that may seem helpful and making each character as realistic as possible (perhaps by placing within each traits drawn from real people, one quality from one real-life person, and a second from another, and so on for as many traits as may be attributed to the character).

SETTING

Introduction to Stories That Emphasize Setting

IN SOME stories the setting is relatively unimportant, merely a backdrop to the incidents, something to prevent drama from occurring in a vacuum. In other stories the environment looms large, becoming as important as a principal character. Stories dominated by setting are comparatively rare, though Poe and several other American writers have sometimes created narratives of this type. For a story to be successful with almost no setting is exceptional.

Setting is either the physical or the spiritual environment or both (what the French people call the *milieu*) in which the action of the story occurs. Setting usually includes the objective details of time and place and may also include the spirit of the people who perform the action, their unique ideas, their customs, their moods, their idiosyncrasies.

The chief purpose or value of setting is to create an impression of realism. The concrete details descriptive of scene help to produce the illusion of reality and to cause the reader to think that the action passing before his mind belongs to life, has "a local habitation," and fits a particular time. A secondary function that the background sometimes serves is to emphasize some action by contrast—the action and the setting being opposite in tone, as if, for example, a horrible crime were to be committed in a scene that had suggested nothing but peace. Usually, however, settings and deeds harmonize and the function of the former is to give the realistic impression.

The time setting should be brief, perhaps only a few moments or at most a short period, because of the brevity of the short story form and action. The place setting should usually be only one locale and at the most a very few places because of the demand for compactness. Limiting the number of scenes can help the story to be unified.

Environment is important for its effect upon character. What a person does depends largely upon where he is and upon the influences that are brought to bear upon him. One can hardly escape completely the effect of his environment; in fact, some people are overwhelmed by their surroundings. A person's character is partly the product of the physical and social and economic circumstances that surround him. A larger and more tastefully furnished office in which to work, a change in the moral standards of his associates, an increase in salary might make a noticeable imprint on his disposition and demeanor.

Setting is also important for its contribution to atmosphere, the emotional effect of locale upon the reader. Though atmosphere may be produced by several techniques other than setting, vivid description of environment is unmistakably one method for creating atmosphere. The background may be either described or suggested or both. The suggestions may appear in dialogue (are especially effective in dialect), characterization, and connotative, emotion-producing diction. Either method, direct description or suggestion, may contribute to the atmosphere.

The description of setting should be interspersed unobtrusively in the story, not presented in one bulk at the beginning or elsewhere. The setting should not be conceived of as something entirely or almost distinct from the forward movement of the narrative but should be interwoven with the dialogue and integrated with the action. Character portrayal and plot movement and setting should be interlocked. A character's demeanor should harmonize with his personality and his environment.

A beginning short story writer should depict settings with which he is familiar, avoiding trite words and phrases. If he chooses to delineate an unfamiliar background, he will face the danger of becoming preoccupied with the setting to the neglect of such other important story elements as characterization and plot. He may run the further risk of inaccurate or inadequate depiction. Only by intensive study would he have a fair chance of presenting a foreign setting adequately. If he will describe places that he has seen firsthand rather than those about which he has read and if he will put into those descriptions details that represent his own selection and interpretation and original phrasing, he may create a work of art.

THE OUTCASTS OF POKER FLAT [1]
(1869)
BRET HARTE

A S MR. JOHN OAKHURST, gambler, stepped into the main
street of Poker Flat on the morning of the 23rd of November,
1850, he was conscious of a change in its moral atmosphere since
the preceding night. Two or three men, conversing earnestly together, ceased as he approached, and exchanged significant glances.
There was a Sabbath lull in the air, which, in a settlement unused
to Sabbath influences, looked ominous.

Mr. Oakhurst's calm, handsome face betrayed small concern in
these indications. Whether he was conscious of any predisposing
cause was another question. "I reckon they're after somebody," he
reflected; "likely it's me." He returned to his pocket the handkerchief with which he had been whipping away the red dust of
Poker Flat from his neat boots, and quietly discharged his mind
of any further conjecture.

In point of fact, Poker Flat was "after somebody." It had lately
suffered the loss of several thousand dollars, two valuable horses,
and a prominent citizen. It was experiencing a spasm of virtuous
reaction, quite as lawless and ungovernable as any of the acts that
had provoked it. A secret committee had determined to rid the
town of all improper persons. This was done permanently in regard of two men who were then hanging from the boughs of a
sycamore in the gulch, and temporarily in the banishment of certain objectionable characters. I regret to say that some of these
were ladies. It is but due to the sex, however, to state that their
impropriety was professional, and it was only in such easily established standards of evil that Poker Flat ventured to sit in judgment.

Mr. Oakhurst was right in supposing that he was included in this
category. A few of the committee had urged hanging him as a
possible example and a sure method of reimbursing themselves from
his pockets the large sums he had won from them. "It's agin
justice," said Jim Wheeler, "to let this yer young man from Roaring Camp—an entire stranger—carry away our money." But a

---

[1] First published in *The Overland Monthly* (January, 1869).

crude sentiment of equity residing in the breasts of those who had been fortunate enough to win from Mr. Oakhurst overruled this narrowed local prejudice.

Mr. Oakhurst received his sentence with philosophic calmness, none the less coolly that he was aware of the hesitation of his judges. He was too much of a gambler not to accept fate. With him life was at best an uncertain game, and he recognized the usual percentage in favor of the dealer.

A body of armed men accompanied the deported wickedness of Poker Flat to the outskirts of the settlement. Besides Mr. Oakhurst, who was known to be a coolly desperate man, and for whose intimidation the armed escort was intended, the expatriated party consisted of a young woman familiarly known as "The Duchess"; another who had won the title of "Mother Shipton"; and "Uncle Billy," a suspected sluice-robber and confirmed drunkard. The cavalcade provoked no comments from the spectators, nor was any word uttered by the escort. Only when the gulch which marked the uttermost limit of Poker Flat was reached, the leader spoke briefly and to the point. The exiles were forbidden to return at the peril of their lives.

As the escort disappeared, their pent-up feelings found vent in a few hysterical tears from the Duchess, some bad language from Mother Shipton, and a Parthian volley[2] of expletives from Uncle Billy. The philosophic Oakhurst alone remained silent. He listened calmly to Mother Shipton's desire to cut somebody's heart out, to the repeated statements of the Duchess that she would die in the road, and to the alarming oaths that seemed to be bumped out of Uncle Billy as he rode forward. With the easy good humor characteristic of his class, he insisted upon exchanging his own riding-horse, "Five-Spot," for the sorry mule which the Duchess rode. But even this act did not draw the party into any closer sympathy. The young woman readjusted her somewhat draggled plumes with a feeble, faded coquetry; Mother Shipton eyed the possessor of "Five-Spot" with malevolence, and Uncle Billy included the whole party in one sweeping anathema.

The road to Sandy Bar—a camp that, not having as yet ex-

---

[2] Parting shot; called "a Parthian volley" because the Parthians were noted for shooting arrows when retreating.

perienced the regenerating influences of Poker Flat, consequently seemed to offer some invitation to the emigrants—lay over a steep mountain range. It was distant a day's severe travel. In that advanced season the party soon passed out of the moist, temperate regions of the foothills into the dry, cold, bracing air of the Sierras. The trail was narrow and difficult. At noon the Duchess, rolling out of her saddle upon the ground, declared her intention of going no farther, and the party halted.

The spot was singularly wild and impressive. A wooded amphi-theater, surrounded on three sides by precipitous cliffs of naked granite, sloped gently toward the crest of another precipice that overlooked the valley. It was, undoubtedly, the most suitable spot for a camp, had camping been advisable. But Mr. Oakhurst knew that scarcely half the journey to Sandy Bar was accomplished, and the party were not equipped or provisioned for delay. This fact he pointed out to his companions curtly, with a philosophic com-mentary on the folly of "throwing up their hand before the game was played out." But they were furnished with liquor, which in this emergency stood them in place of food, fuel, rest and pre-science. In spite of his remonstrances, it was not long before they were more or less under its influence. Uncle Billy passed rapidly from a bellicose state into one of stupor, the Duchess became maud-lin, and Mother Shipton snored. Mr. Oakhurst alone remained erect, leaning against a rock, calmly surveying them.

Mr. Oakhurst did not drink. It interfered with a profession which required coolness, impassiveness, and presence of mind, and, in his own language, he "couldn't afford it." As he gazed at his recumbent fellow exiles, the loneliness begotten of his pariah trade, his habits of life, his very vices, for the first time seriously oppressed him. He bestirred himself in dusting his black clothes, washing his hands and face, and other acts characteristic of his studiously neat habits, and for a moment forgot his annoyance. The thought of deserting his weaker and more pitiable companions never perhaps occurred to him. Yet he could not help feeling the want of that excitement which, singularly enough, was most conducive to that calm equanimity for which he was notorious. He looked at the gloomy walls that rose a thousand feet sheer above the circling pines around him, at the sky ominously clouded, at the valley below, already deepening into shadow; and, doing so, suddenly he heard his own name called.

A horseman slowly ascended the trail. In the fresh open face of the newcomer Mr. Oakhurst recognized Tom Simson, otherwise known as "The Innocent," of Sandy Bar. He had met him some months before over a "little game," and had, with perfect equanimity, won the entire fortune—amounting to some forty dollars—of that guileless youth. After the game was finished, Mr. Oakhurst drew the youthful speculator behind the door and thus addressed him: "Tommy, you're a good little man, but you can't gamble worth a cent. Don't try it over again." He then handed him his money back, pushed him gently from the room, and so made a devoted slave of Tom Simson.

There was a remembrance of this in his boyish and enthusiastic greeting of Mr. Oakhurst. He had started, he said, to go to Poker Flat to seek his fortune. "Alone?" No, not exactly alone; in fact (a giggle), he had run away with Piney Woods. Didn't Mr. Oakhurst remember Piney? She that used to wait on the table at the Temperance House? They had been engaged a long time, but old Jake Woods had objected, and so they had run away, and were going to Poker Flat to be married, and here they were. And they were tired out, and how lucky it was they had found a place to camp, and company. All this the Innocent delivered rapidly, while Piney, a stout, comely damsel of fifteen, emerged from behind the pine-tree, where she had been blushing unseen, and rode to the side of her lover.

Mr. Oakhurst seldom troubled himself with sentiment, still less with propriety; but he had a vague idea that the situation was not fortunate. He retained, however, his presence of mind sufficiently to kick Uncle Billy, who was about to say something, and Uncle Billy was sober enough to recognize in Mr. Oakhurst's kick a superior power that would not bear trifling. He then endeavored to dissuade Tom Simson from delaying further, but in vain. He even pointed out the fact that there was no provision, nor means of making a camp. But, unluckily, the Innocent met this objection by assuring the party that he was provided with an extra mule loaded with provisions, and by the discovery of a rude attempt at a log house near the trail. "Piney can stay with Mrs. Oakhurst," said the Innocent, pointing to the Duchess, "and I can shift for myself."

Nothing but Mr. Oakhurst's admonishing foot saved Uncle Billy from bursting into a roar of laughter. As it was, he felt constrained to retire up the cañon until he could recover his gravity. There he confided the joke to the tall pine-trees, with many slaps of his leg, contortions of his face, and the usual profanity. But when he returned to the party, he found them seated by a fire—for the air had grown strangely chill and the sky overcast—in apparently amicable conversation. Piney was actually talking in an impulsive girlish fashion to the Duchess, who was listening with an interest and animation she had not shown for many days. The Innocent was holding forth, apparently with equal effect, to Mr. Oakhurst, and Mother Shipton, who was actually relaxing into amiability. "Is this yer a d—d picnic?" said Uncle Billy, with inward scorn, as he surveyed the sylvan group, the glancing firelight, and the tethered animals in the foreground. Suddenly an idea mingled with the alcoholic fumes that disturbed his brain. It was apparently of a jocular nature, for he felt impelled to slap his leg again and cram his fist into his mouth.

As the shadows crept slowly up the mountain, a slight breeze rocked the tops of the pine-trees and moaned through their long and gloomy aisles. The ruined cabin, patched and covered with pine boughs, was set apart for the ladies. As the lovers parted, they unaffectedly exchanged a kiss, so honest and sincere that it might have been heard above the swaying pines. The frail Duchess and the malevolent Mother Shipton were probably too stunned to remark upon this last evidence of simplicity, and so turned without a word to the hut. The fire was replenished, the men lay down before the door, and in a few minutes were asleep.

Mr. Oakhurst was a light sleeper. Toward morning he awoke benumbed and cold. As he stirred the dying fire, the wind, which was now blowing strongly, brought to his cheek that which caused the blood to leave it,—snow!

He started to his feet with the intention of awakening the sleepers, for there was no time to lose. But turning to where Uncle Billy had been lying, he found him gone. A suspicion leaped to his brain, and a curse to his lips. He ran to the spot where the

97

mules had been tethered—they were no longer there. The tracks were already rapidly disappearing in the snow.

The momentary excitement brought Mr. Oakhurst back to the fire with his usual calm. He did not waken the sleepers. The Innocent slumbered peacefully, with a smile on his good-humored, freckled face; the virgin Piney slept beside her frailer sisters as sweetly as though attended by celestial guardians; and Mr. Oakhurst, drawing his blanket over his shoulders, stroked his mustaches and waited for the dawn. It came slowly in a whirling mist of snowflakes that dazzled and confused the eye. What could be seen of the landscape appeared magically changed. He looked over the valley, and summed up the present and future in two words, "Snowed in!"

A careful inventory of the provisions, which, fortunately for the party, had been stored within the hut, and so escaped the felonious fingers of Uncle Billy, disclosed the fact that with care and prudence they might last ten days longer. "That is," said Mr. Oakhurst, *sotto voce* to the Innocent, "If you're willing to board us. If you ain't—and perhaps you'd better not—you can wait till Uncle Billy gets back with provisions." For some occult reason, Mr. Oakhurst could not bring himself to disclose Uncle Billy's rascality, and so offered the hypothesis that he had wandered from the camp and had accidentally stampeded the animals. He dropped a warning to the Duchess and Mother Shipton, who of course knew the facts of their associate's defection. "They'll find out the truth about us *all* when they find out anything," he added significantly, "and there's no good frightening them now."

Tom Simson not only put all his worldly store at the disposal of Mr. Oakhurst, but seemed to enjoy the prospect of their enforced seclusion. "We'll have a good camp for a week, and then the snow'll melt, and we'll all go back together." The cheerful gaiety of the young man and Mr. Oakhurst's calm infected the others. The Innocent, with the aid of pine boughs, extemporized a thatch for the roofless cabin, and the Duchess directed Piney in the rearrangement of the interior with a taste and tact that opened the blue eyes of that provincial maiden to their fullest extent. "I reckon now you're used to fine things at Poker Flat," said Piney. The Duchess turned away sharply to conceal something that reddened her cheeks through their professional tint, and Mother Shipton requested Piney not to "chatter." But when Mr. Oakhurst returned from a weary search for the trail, he heard the sound of happy laughter echoed from the rocks. He stopped in some alarm, and his thoughts first naturally reverted to the whiskey, which he had prudently *cached*. "And yet it don't somehow sound like whiskey," said the gambler. It was not until he caught sight of the blazing fire through the still blinding storm, and the group around it, that he settled to the conviction that it was "square fun."

Whether Mr. Oakhurst had *cached* his cards with the whiskey as something debarred the free access of the community, I cannot say. It was certain that, in Mother Shipton's words, he "didn't say 'cards' once" during that evening. Haply the time was beguiled by an accordian, produced somewhat ostentatiously by Tom Simson from his pack. Notwithstanding some difficulties attending the manipulation of this instrument, Piney Woods managed to pluck several reluctant melodies from its keys, to an accompaniment by the Innocent on a pair of bone castanets. But the crowning festivity of the evening was reached in a rude camp-meeting hymn, which the lovers, joining hands, sang with great earnestness and vociferation. I fear that a certain defiant tone and Convenanter's [3] swing to its chorus, rather than any devotional quality, caused it speedily to infect the others, who at last joined in the refrain:—

> "I'm proud to live in the service of the Lord,
> And I'm bound to die in His army."

The pines rocked, the storm eddied and whirled above the miserable group, and the flames of their altar leaped heaven-ward, as if in token of the vow.

At midnight the storm abated, the rolling clouds parted, and the stars glittered keenly above the sleeping camp. Mr. Oakhurst, whose professional habits had enabled him to live on the smallest possible amount of sleep, in dividing the watch with Tom Simson somehow managed to take upon himself the greater part of that duty. He

---

[3] The Scotch Presbyterians had struggled for the privilege of worshiping in the way they chose. They became known as Covenanters, because in 1638 they formed a "Solemn League and Covenant for the Reformation and Defense of Religion." Their hymns were rather vigorous, as had been their defiance of Charles I in forming the covenant.

excused himself to the Innocent by saying that he had "often been a week without sleep." "Doing what?" asked Tom. "Poker!" replied Oakhurst sentenciously. "When a man gets a streak of luck,—nigger-luck,—he don't get tired. The luck gives in first. Luck," continued the gambler reflectively, "is a mighty queer thing. All you know about it for certain is that it's bound to change. And it's finding out when it's going to change that makes you. We've had a streak of bad luck since we left Poker Flat,—you come along, and slap you got into it, too. If you can hold your cards right along you're all right. For," added the gambler, with cheerful irrelevance—

" 'I'm proud to live in the service of the Lord,
And I'm bound to die in His army.' "

The third day came, and the sun, looking through the white-curtained valley, saw the outcasts divide their slowly decreasing store of provisions for the morning meal. It was one of the peculiarities of that mountain climate that its rays diffused a kindly warmth over the wintry landscape, as if in regretful commiseration of the past. But it revealed drift on drift of snow piled high around the hut,—a hopeless, uncharted, trackless sea of white lying below the rocky shores to which the castaways still clung. Through the marvelously clear air the smoke of the pastoral village of Poker Flat rose miles away. Mother Shipton saw it, and from a remote pinacle of her rocky fastness hurled in that direction a final malediction. It was her last vituperative attempt, and perhaps for that reason was invested with a certain degree of sublimity. It did her good, she privately informed the Duchess. "Just you go out there and cuss, and see." She then set herself to the task of amusing "the child," as she and the Duchess were pleased to call Piney. Piney was no chicken, but it was a soothing and original theory of the pair thus to account for the fact that she didn't swear and wasn't improper.

When night crept up again through the gorges, the reedy notes of the accordian rose and fell in fitful spasms and long-drawn gasps by the flickering camp-fire. But music failed to fill entirely the aching void left by insufficient food, and a new diversion was proposed by Piney,—story-telling. Neither Mr. Oakhurst nor his female companions caring to relate their personal experiences, this plan would have failed too, but for the Innocent. Some months before he had chanced upon a stray copy of Mr. Pope's ingenious translation of the Iliad. He now proposed to narrate the principal incidents of that poem—having thoroughly mastered the argument and fairly forgotten the words—in the current vernacular of Sandy Bar. And so for the rest of that night the Homeric demigods again walked the earth. Trojan bully and wily Greek wrestled in the winds, and the great pines in the cañon seemed to bow to the wrath of the son of Peleus. Mr. Oakhurst listened with quiet satisfaction. Most especially was he interested in the fate of "Ashheels," as the Innocent persisted in denominating the "swift-footed Achilles."

So, with small food and much of Homer and the accordion, a week passed over the heads of the outcasts. The sun again forsook them, and again from leaden skies the snowflakes were sifted over the land. Day by day closer around them drew the snowy circle, until at last they looked from their prison over drifted walls of dazzling white, that towered twenty feet above their heads. It became more and more difficult to replenish their fires, even from the fallen trees beside them, now half hidden in the drifts. And yet no one complained. The lovers turned from the dreary prospect and looked into each other's eyes, and were happy. Mr. Oakhurst settled himself coolly to the losing game before him. The Duchess, more cheerful than she had been, assumed the care of Piney. Only Mother Shipton—once the strongest of the party—seemed to sicken and fade. At midnight on the tenth day she called Oakhurst to her side. "I'm going," she said, in a voice of querulous weakness, "but don't say anything about it. Don't waken the kids. Take the bundle from under my head, and open it." Mr. Oakhurst did so. It contained Mother Shipton's rations for the last week, untouched. "Give 'em to the child," she said, pointing to the sleeping Piney. "You've starved yourself," said the gambler. "That's what they call it," said the woman querulously, as she lay down again, and, turning her face to the wall, passed quietly away.

The accordion and the bones were put aside that day, and Homer was forgotten. When the body of Mother Shipton had been committed to the snow, Mr. Oakhurst took the Innocent aside, and showed him a pair of snowshoes, which he had fashioned from the old pack-saddle. "There's one chance in a hundred to save her yet," he said, pointing to Piney; "but it's there," he added, pointing to-

101

ward Poker Flat. "If you can reach there in two days she's safe." "And you?" asked Tom Simson. "I'll stay here," was the curt reply.

The lovers parted with a long embrace. "You are not going, too?" said the Duchess, as she saw Mr. Oakhurst apparently waiting to accompany him. "As far as the cañon," he replied. He turned suddenly and kissed the Duchess, leaving her pallid face aflame, and her trembling limbs rigid with amazement.

Night came, but not Mr. Oakhurst. It brought the storm again and the whirling snow. Then the Duchess, feeding the fire, found that some one had quietly piled beside the hut enough fuel to last a few days longer. The tears rose to her eyes, but she hid them from Piney.

The women slept but little. In the morning, looking up into each other's faces, they read their fate. Neither spoke, but Piney, accepting the position of the stronger, drew near and placed her arm around the Duchess's waist. They kept this attitude for the rest of the day. That night the storm reached its greatest fury, and, rending asunder the protecting vines, invaded the very hut.

Toward morning they found themselves unable to feed the fire, which gradually died away. As the embers slowly blackened, the Duchess crept closer to Piney, and broke the silence of many hours: "Piney, can you pray?" "No, dear," said Piney simply. The Duchess, without knowing exactly why, felt relieved, and, putting her head upon Piney's shoulder, spoke no more. And so reclining, the younger and purer pillowing the head of her soiled sister upon her virgin breast, they fell asleep.

The wind lulled as if it feared to waken them. Feathery drifts of snow, shaken from the long pine boughs, flew like white winged birds, and settled about them as they slept. The moon through the rifted clouds looked down upon what had been the camp. But all human stain, all trace of earthly travail, was hidden beneath the spotless mantle mercifully flung from above.

They slept all day that day and the next, nor did they waken when voices and footsteps broke the silence of the camp. And when pitying fingers brushed the snow from their wan faces, you could scarcely have told from the equal peace that dwelt upon them which was she that had sinned. Even the law of Poker Flat recognized this, and turned away, leaving them still locked in each other's arms.

But at the head of the gulch, on one of the largest pine-trees, they found the deuce of clubs pinned to the bark with a bowie-knife. It bore the following, written in pencil in a firm hand:—

BENEATH THIS TREE

LIES THE BODY

OF

JOHN OAKHURST,

WHO STRUCK A STREAK OF BAD LUCK

ON THE 23D OF NOVEMBER 1850,

AND

HANDED IN HIS CHECKS[4]

ON THE 7TH DECEMBER, 1850.

And pulseless and cold, with a Derringer by his side and a bullet in his heart, though still calm as in life, beneath the snow lay he who was at once the strongest and yet the weakest of the outcasts of Poker Flat.

STUDY NOTES

1. By indicating the total time covered and by mentioning the scene or scenes of the action, show that "The Outcasts of Poker Flat" observes at least two of the dramatic unities—those of time and place.

2. Who is the dominant character and how early is he introduced?

3. Does the action begin soon enough and move fast enough to conform to Poe's theory that the whole story—every sentence—should contribute to a preconceived effect and that the movement should not be blocked or diverted by needless description and explanation?

4. If, as has been alleged, Harte in this story combines humor and pathos somewhat in the manner of his master, Dickens, what is the single emotional effect that the narrative produces?

5. Show the effect of the wildness of the camp site in the Sierras, and of the danger in which the campers found themselves, upon the outcasts (at least, indicate the harmony of their actions with the setting).

6. State the philosophy that underlies this story, the conception of human nature that the author here communicates.

---

[4] He died. Checks were the counters, or money tokens, in a gambling card game.

MANNER

7. By what methods does Harte present Mr. Oakhurst, the Duchess, Mother Shipton, Uncle Billy, Tom Simson, and Piney Woods as somewhat realistic and individualized characters?

8. Show the influence of the young couple in bringing forth the better natures of the outcasts—causing hitherto dormant virtues to find expression.

9. Prove that the passages descriptive of setting are distributed within the plot—here a word, there a phrase or clause, and elsewhere a sentence.

10. Show that Bret Harte used impressionism in portraying the characters of this story—that the persons are types rather than three-dimensional beings, that they result from emphasis upon some peculiarity or extreme quality.

11. State whether the climax is serious, as Harte's climaxes usually are, or sentimental, as they occasionally are, and justify your position.

12. If, as Pattee has stated, the dominant impression that Harte's stories make is local color, explain why this is true.

A MUNICIPAL REPORT [1]
(1909)
O. HENRY

Fancy a novel about Chicago or Buffalo, let us say, or Nashville, Tennessee! There are just three big cities in the United States that are "story cities"—New York, of course, New Orleans, and, best of the lot, San Francisco.[2]—FRANK NORRIS

EAST IS EAST, and West is San Francisco, according to Californians. Californians are a race of people; they are not merely inhabitants of a State. They are the Southerners of the West. Now, Chicagoans are no less loyal to their city; but when you ask them why, they stammer and speak of lake fish and the new Odd Fellows' Building. But Californians go into detail.

Of course they have, in the climate, an argument that is good for half an hour while you are thinking of your coal bills and heavy underwear. But as soon as they come to mistake your silence for conviction, madness comes upon them, and they picture the city of the Golden Gate as the Bagdad of the New World. So far, as a matter of opinion, no refutation is necessary. But, dear cousins all (from Adam and Eve descended), it is a rash one who will lay his finger on the map and say: "In this town there can be no romance—what could happen here?" Yes, it is a bold and rash deed to challenge in one sentence history, romance, and Rand and McNally.

> NASHVILLE.—A city, port of delivery, and the capital of the State of Tennessee, is on the Cumberland River and on the N. C. & St. L. and the L. & N. railroads. This city is regarded as the most important educational center in the South.

I stepped off the train at 8 P. M. Having searched the thesaurus in vain for adjectives, I must, as a substitution, hie me to comparison in the form of a recipe.

Take of London fog 30 parts; malaria 10 parts; gas leaks 20 parts; dewdrops gathered in a brickyard at sunrise, 25 parts; odor of honeysuckle 15 parts. Mix.

[1] From *Strictly Business* by O. Henry, Copyright, 1910, by Doubleday & Company, Inc. By permission of the publisher.
[2] From Norris's story, "The House with the Blinds."

105

The mixture will give you an approximate conception of a Nashville drizzle. It is not so fragrant as a moth-ball nor as thick as pea-soup; but 'tis enough—'twill serve.

I went to a hotel in a tumbril. It required strong self-suppression for me to keep from climbing to the top of it and giving an imitation of Sidney Carton. The vehicle was drawn by beasts of a bygone era and driven by something dark and emancipated.

I was sleepy and tired, so when I got to the hotel I hurriedly paid it the fifty cents it demanded (with approximate lagniappe, I assure you). I knew its habits; and I did not want to hear it prate about its old "marster" or anything that happened "befo' de wah."

The hotel was one of the kind described as "renovated." That means twenty thousand dollars' worth of new marble pillars, tiling, electric lights and brass cuspidors in the lobby, and a new L. & N. time-table and a lithograph of Lookout Mountain in each one of the great rooms above. The management was without reproach, the attention full of exquisite Southern courtesy, the service as slow as the progress of a snail and as good-humored as Rip Van Winkle. The food was worth traveling a thousand miles for. There is no other hotel in the world where you can get such chicken livers *en brochette*.

At dinner I asked a negro waiter if there was anything doing in town. He pondered gravely for a minute, and then replied: "Well, boss, I don't really reckon there's anything at all doin' after sundown."

Sundown had been accomplished; it had been drowned in the drizzle long before. So that spectacle was denied me. But I went forth upon the streets in the drizzle to see what might be there.

> It is built on undulating grounds; and the streets are lighted by electricity at a cost of $32,470 per annum.

As I left the hotel there was a race riot. Down upon me charged a company of freedmen, or Arabs, or Zulus, armed with— no, I saw with relief that they were not rifles, but whips. And I saw dimly a caravan of black, clumsy vehicles; and at the reassuring shouts, "Kyar you anywhere in the town, boss, fuh fifty cents," I reasoned that I was merely a "fare" instead of a victim.

I walked through long streets, all leading uphill. I wondered how those streets ever came down again. Perhaps they didn't until they were "graded." On a few of the "main streets" I saw lights in stores here and there; saw street-cars go by conveying worthy burghers hither and yon; saw people pass engaged in the art of conversation; and heard a burst of semi-lively laughter issuing from a soda-water and ice-cream parlor. The streets other than "main" seemed to have enticed upon their borders houses consecrated to peace and domesticity. In many of them lights shone behind discreetly drawn window shades; in a few, pianos tinkled orderly and irreproachable music. There was, indeed, little "doing." I wished I had come before sundown. So I returned to my hotel.

In November, 1864, the Confederate General Hood advanced against Nashville, where he shut up a National force under General Thomas. The latter then sallied forth and defeated the Confederates in a terrible conflict.

All my life I have heard of, admired, and witnessed the fine marksmanship of the South in its peaceful conflicts in the tobacco chewing regions. But in my hotel a surprise awaited me. There were twelve bright, new, imposing, capacious brass cuspidors in the great lobby, tall enough to be called urns and so wide-mouthed that the crack pitcher of a lady baseball team should have been able to throw a ball into each one of them at five paces distant. But, although a terrible battle had raged and was still raging, the enemy had not suffered. Bright, new, imposing, capacious, untouched, they stood. But, shades of Jefferson Brick! the tile floor— the beautiful tile floor! I could not avoid thinking of the battle of Nashville, and trying to draw, as is my foolish habit, some deductions about hereditary marksmanship.

Here I first saw Major (by misplaced courtesy) Wentworth Caswell. I knew him for a type the moment my eyes suffered from the sight of him. A rat has no geographical habitat. My old friend, A. Tennyson, said, as he so well said almost everything:

> "Prophet, curse me the blabbing lip,
> And curse me the British vermin, the rat." [3]

---

[3] From *Maud*, Part II, 11. 295-6. Tennyson was O. Henry's favorite poet.

MANNER

Let us regard the word "British" as interchangeable *ad lib*. A rat is a rat.

This man was hunting about the hotel lobby like a starved dog that had forgotten where he had buried a bone. He had a face of great acreage, red, pulpy, and with a kind of sleepy massiveness like that of Buddha. He possessed one single virtue—he was smoothly shaven. The mark of the beast is not indelible upon a man until he goes about with a stubble. I think that if he had not used his razor that day I would have repulsed his advances, and the criminal calendar of the world would have been spared the addition of one murder.

I happened to be standing within five feet of a cuspidor when Major Caswell opened fire upon it. I had been observant enough to perceive that the attacking force was using Gatlings instead of squirrel rifles; so I side-stepped so promptly that the Major seized the opportunity to apologize to a non-combatant. He had the blabbing lip. In four minutes he had become my friend and had dragged me to the bar.

I desire to interpolate here that I am a Southerner. But I am not one by profession or trade. I eschew the string tie, the slouch hat, the Prince Albert, the number of bales of cotton destroyed by Sherman, and plug chewing. When the orchestra plays "Dixie" I do not cheer. I slide a little lower on the leather-cornered seat and—well—order another Würzburger and wish that Longstreet had—but what's the use?

Major Caswell banged the bar with his fist, and the first gun at Fort Sumter reëchoed. When he fired the last one at Appomattox I began to hope. But then he began on family trees, and demonstrated that Adam was only a third cousin of a collateral branch of the Caswell family. Genealogy disposed of, he took up, to my distaste, his private family matters. He spoke of his wife, traced her descent back to Eve, and profanely denied any possible rumor that she may have had relations in the land of Nod.

By this time I began to suspect that he was trying to obscure by the noise the fact that he had ordered the drinks, on the chance that I would be bewildered into paying for them. But when they were down he crashed a silver dollar loudly upon the bar. Then, of course, another serving was obligatory. And when I had paid for that I took leave of him brusquely; for I wanted no more of him. But before I had obtained my release he had prated loudly of an income that his wife received, and showed a handful of silver money.

When I got my key at the desk the clerk said to me courteously: "If that man Caswell has annoyed you, and if you would like to make a complaint, we will have him ejected. He is a nuisance, a loafer, and without any known means of support, although he seems to have money most of the time. But we don't seem to be able to hit upon any means of throwing him out legally."

"Why, no," said I, after some reflection; "I don't see my way clear to make a complaint. But I would like to place myself on record as asserting that I do not care for his company. Your town," I continued, "seems to be a quiet one. What manner of entertainment, adventure, or excitement have you to offer to the stranger within your gates?"

"Well, sir," said the clerk, "there will be a show here next Thursday. It is—I'll look it up and have the announcement sent up to your room with the ice water. Good-night."

After I went up to my room I looked out of the window. It was only about ten o'clock, but I looked upon a silent town. The drizzle continued, spangled with dim lights, as far apart as currants in a cake sold at the Ladies' Exchange.

"A quiet place," I said to myself, as my first shoe struck the ceiling of the occupant of the room beneath mine. "Nothing of the life here that gives color and variety to the cities in the East and West. Just a good, ordinary, humdrum, business town."

> Nashville occupies a foremost place among the manufacturing centers of the country. It is the fifth boot and shoe market in the United States, the largest candy and cracker manufacturing city in the South, and does an enormous wholesale dry-goods, grocery, and drug business.

I must tell you how I came to be in Nashville, and I assure you the digression brings as much tedium to me as it does to you. I was traveling elsewhere on my own business, but I had a commission from a Northern literary magazine to stop over there and establish a connection between the publication and one of its personal contributors, Azalea Adair.

109

MANNER

Adair (there was no clue to the personality except the hand-writing) had sent in some essays (lost art!) and poems that had made the editors swear approvingly over their one-o'clock luncheon. So they had commissioned me to round up said Adair and corner by contract his or her output at two cents a word before some other publisher offered her ten or twenty.

At nine o'clock the next morning, after my chicken livers *en brochette* (try them if you find that hotel), I strayed out into the drizzle, which was still on for an unlimited run. At the first corner, I came upon Uncle Caesar. He was a stalwart negro older than the pyramids, with gray wool and a face that reminded me of Brutus, and a second afterwards of the late King Cetewayo.[4] He wore the most remarkable coat that I ever had seen or expect to see. It reached to his ankles and had once been a Confederate gray in color. But rain and sun and age had so variegated it that Joseph's coat, beside it, would have faded to a pale monochrome. I must linger with that coat, for it has to do with the story—the story that is so long in coming, because you can hardly expect anything to happen in Nashville.

Once it must have been the military coat of an officer. The cape of it had vanished, but all adown its front it had been frogged and tasseled magnificently. But now the frogs and tassels were gone. In their stead had been patiently stitched (I surmise by some surviving "black mammy") new frogs made of cunningly twisted common hempen twine. This twine was frayed and disheveled. It must have been added to the coat as a substitute for vanished splendors, with tasteless but painstaking devotion, for it followed faithfully the curves of the long-missing frogs. And, to complete the comedy and pathos of the garment, all its buttons were gone save one. The second button from the top alone remained. The coat was fastened by other twine strings tied through the buttonholes and other holes rudely pierced on the opposite side. There was never such a weird garment so fantastically bedecked and of so many mottled hues. The lone button was the size of a half-dollar, made of yellow horn and sewed on with coarse twine.

This negro stood by a carriage so old that Ham himself might have started a hack-line after he left the ark with the two animals

---

[4] The Zulu chief who rebelled against the British government in 1868.

110

hitched to it. As I approached he threw open the door, drew out a feather duster, waved it without using it, and said in deep, rumbling tones:

"Step right in, suh; ain't a speck of dust in it—jus' got back from a funeral, suh."

I inferred that on such gala occasions carriages were given an extra cleaning. I looked up and down the street and perceived that there was little choice among the vehicles for hire that lined the curb. I looked in my memorandum book for the address of Azalea Adair.

"I want to go to 861 Jessamine Street," I said, and was about to step into the hack.

But for an instant the thick, gorilla-like arm of the old negro barred me. On his massive and saturnine face a look of sudden suspicion and enmity flashed for a moment. Then, with quickly returning conviction, he asked blandishingly: "What are you gwine there for, boss?"

"What is that to you?" I asked a little sharply.

"Nothin', suh, jus' nothin'. Only it's a lonesome kind of part of town and few folks ever has business there. Step right in. The seats is clean—jes' got back from a funeral, suh."

A mile and a half it must have been to our journey's end. I could hear nothing but the fearful rattle of the ancient hack over the uneven brick paving; I could smell nothing but the drizzle, now further flavored with coal smoke and something like a mixture of tar and oleander blossoms. All I could see through the streaming windows were two rows of dim houses.

> The city has an area of 10 square miles; 181 miles of streets of which 137 miles are paved; a system of waterworks that cost $2,000,000, with 77 miles of mains.

Eight-sixty-one Jessamine Street was a decayed mansion. Thirty yards back from the street it stood, outmerged in a splendid grove of trees and untrimmed shrubbery. A row of box bushes overflowed and almost hid the paling fence from sight; the gate was kept closed by a rope noose that encircled the gate-post and the first paling of the gate. But when you got inside you saw that eight-sixty-one was a shell, a shadow, a ghost of former grandeur and excellence. But in the story, I have not yet got inside.

111

When the hack had ceased from rattling and the weary quadrupeds came to a rest, I handed my Jehu his fifty cents with an additional quarter, feeling a glow of conscious generosity as I did so. He refused it.

"It's two dollars, suh," he said.

"How's that?" I asked. "I plainly heard you call out at the hotel: 'Fifty cents to any part of the town.'"

"It's two dollars, suh," he repeated obstinately. "It's a long ways from the hotel."

"It is within the city limits and well within them," I argued. "Don't think that you have picked up a greenhorn Yankee. Do you see those hills over there?" I went on, pointing toward the east (I could not see them, myself, for the drizzle); "well, I was born and raised on their other side. You old fool nigger, can't you tell people from other people when you see 'em?"

The grim face of King Cetewayo softened. "Is you from the South, suh? I reckon it was them shoes of yourn fooled me. They is somethin' sharp in the toes for a Southern gen'l'man to wear."

"Then the charge is fifty cents, I suppose?" said I inexorably.

His former expression, a mingling of cupidity and hostility, returned, remained ten seconds, and vanished.

"Boss," he said, "fifty cents is right; but I *needs* two dollars, suh; I'm *obleeged* to have two dollars. I ain't *demandin'* it now, suh, after I knows whar you's from; I'm jus' sayin' that I *has* to have two dollars to-night, and business is mighty po'."

Peace and confidence settled upon his heavy features. He had been luckier than he had hoped. Instead of having picked up a greenhorn, ignorant of rates, he had come upon an inheritance.

"You confounded old rascal," I said, reaching down to my pocket, "you ought to be turned over to the police."

For the first time I saw him smile. He knew; he *knew;* HE KNEW.

I gave him two one-dollar bills. As I handed them over I noticed that one of them had seen parlous times. Its upper right-hand corner was missing, and it had been torn through the middle, but joined again. A strip of blue tissue paper, pasted over the split, preserved its negotiability.

Enough of the African bandit for the present: I left him happy, lifted the rope, and opened the creaky gate.

The house, as I said, was a shell. A paint-brush had not touched it in twenty years. I could not see why a strong wind should not have bowled it over like a house of cards until I looked again at the trees that hugged it close—the trees that saw the battle of Nashville and still drew their protecting branches around it against storm and enemy and cold.

Azalea Adair, fifty years old, white-haired, a descendant of the cavaliers, as thin and frail as the house she lived in, robed in the cheapest and cleanest dress I ever saw, with an air as simple as a queen's, received me.

The reception room seemed a mile square, because there was nothing in it except some rows of books, on unpainted white-pine bookshelves, a cracked marble-top table, a rag rug, a hairless horse-hair sofa, and two or three chairs. Yes, there was a picture on the wall, a colored crayon drawing of a cluster of pansies. I looked around for the portrait of Andrew Jackson and the pinecone hanging basket, but they were not there.

Azalea Adair and I had conversation, a little of which will be repeated to you. She was a product of the old South, gently nurtured in the sheltered life. Her learning was not broad, but was deep and of splendid originality in its somewhat narrow scope. She had been educated at home, and her knowledge of the world was derived from inference and by inspiration. Of such is the precious, small group of essayists made. While she talked to me I kept brushing my fingers, trying, unconsciously, to rid them guiltily of the absent dust from the half-calf backs of Lamb, Chaucer, Hazlitt, Marcus Aurelius, Montaigne, and Hood. She was exquisite, she was a valuable discovery, nearly everybody nowadays knows too much—oh, so much too much—of real life.

I could perceive clearly that Azalea Adair was very poor. A house and a dress she had, not much else, I fancied. So, divided between my duty to the magazine and my loyalty to the poets and essayists who fought Thomas in the valley of the Cumberland, I listened to her voice, which was like a harpsichord's, and found that I could not speak of contracts. In the presence of the nine Muses and the three Graces one hesitated to lower the topic to two cents. There would have to be another colloquy after I had regained my commercialism. But I spoke of my mission, and three o'clock of the next afternoon was set for the discussion of the business proposition.

"Your town," I said, as I began to make ready to depart (which is the time for smooth generalities), "seems to be a quiet, sedate place. A home town, I should say, where few things out of the ordinary ever happen."

It carries an extensive trade in stoves and hollow ware with the West and South, and its flouring mills have a daily capacity of more than two thousand barrels.

Azalea Adair seemed to reflect.

"I have never thought of it that way," she said, with a kind of sincere intensity that seemed to belong to her. "Isn't it in the still, quiet places that things do happen? I fancy that when God began to create the earth on the first Monday morning one could have leaned out one's window and heard the drops of mud splashing from His trowel as He built up the everlasting hills. What did the noisiest project in the world—I mean the building of the tower of Babel—result in finally? A page and a half of Esperanto in the *North American Review.*"

"Of course," I said platitudinously, "human nature is the same everywhere; but there is more color—er—more drama and movement and—er—romance in some cities than in others."

"On the surface," said Azalea Adair. "I have traveled many times round the world in a golden airship wafted on two wings —print and dreams. I have seen (on one of my imaginary tours) the Sultan of Turkey bowstring with his own hands one of his wives who had uncovered her face in public. I have seen a man in Nashville tear up his theater tickets because his wife was going out with her face covered—with rice powder. In San Francisco's Chinatown I saw the slave girl Sing Yee dipped slowly, inch by inch, in boiling almond oil to make her swear she would never see her American lover again. She gave in when the boiling oil had reached three inches above her knee. At a euchre party in East Nashville the other night, I saw Kitty Morgan cut dead by seven of her schoolmates and lifelong friends because she had married a house painter. The boiling oil was sizzling as high as her heart; but I wish you could have seen the fine little smile that

114

she carried from table to table. Oh, yes, it is a humdrum town. Just a few miles of red brick houses and mud stores and lumber yards."

Some one knocked hollowly at the back of the house. Azalea Adair breathed a soft apology and went to investigate the sound. She came back in three minutes with brightened eyes, a faint flush on her cheeks, and ten years lifted from her shoulders.

"You must have a cup of tea before you go," she said, "and a sugar cake."

She reached and shook a little iron bell. In shuffled a small negro girl about twelve, barefoot, not very tidy, glowering at me with thumb in mouth and bulging eyes.

Azalea Adair opened a tiny, worn purse and drew out a dollar bill, with the upper right-hand corner missing, torn in two pieces and pasted together again with a strip of blue tissue paper. It was one of the bills I had given the piratical negro—there was no doubt of it.

"Go up to Mr. Baker's store on the corner, Impy," she said, handing the girl the dollar bill, "and get me a quarter of a pound of tea—the kind he always sends me—and ten cents' worth of sugar cakes. Now, hurry. The supply of tea in the house happens to be exhausted," she explained to me.

Impy left by the back way. Before the scrape of her hard, bare feet had died away on the back porch, a wild shriek—I was sure it was hers—filled the hollow house. Then the deep, gruff tones of an angry man's voice mingled with the girl's further squeals and unintelligible words.

Azalea Adair rose without surprise or emotion and disappeared. For two minutes I heard the hoarse rumble of the man's voice; then something like an oath and a slight scuffle, and she returned calmly to her chair.

"This is a roomy house," she said, "and I have a tenant for part of it. I am sorry to have to rescind my invitation to tea. It was impossible to get the kind I always use at the store. Perhaps to-morrow Mr. Baker will be able to supply me."

I was sure that Impy had not had time to leave the house. I inquired concerning street-car lines and took my leave. After I was well on my way I remembered that I had not learned Azalea Adair's name. But to-morrow would do.

That same day I started in on the course of iniquity that this uneventful city forced upon me. I was in the town only two days, but in that time I managed to lie shamelessly by telegraph, and to be an accomplice—after the fact, if that is the correct legal term—to a murder.

As I rounded the corner nearest my hotel the Afrite coachman of the polychromatic, nonpareil coat seized me, swung open the dungeony door of his peripatetic sarcophagus, flirted his feather duster, and began his ritual: "Step right in, boss. Carriage is clean —jus' got back from a funeral. Fifty cents to any—"

And then he knew me and grinned broadly. " 'Scuse me, boss; you is de gen'l'man what rid out with me dis mawnin'. Thank you kindly, suh."

"I am going out to eight-sixty-one again to-morrow afternoon at three," said I, "and if you will be here, I'll let you drive me. So you know Miss Adair?" I concluded, thinking of my dollar bill.

"I belonged to her father, Judge Adair, suh," he replied.

"I judge that she is pretty poor," I said. "She hasn't much money to speak of, has she?"

For an instant I looked again at the fierce countenance of King Cetewayo, and then he changed back to an extortionate old Negro hack-driver.

"She ain't gwine to starve, suh," he said slowly. "She has reso'ces, suh; she has reso'ces."

"I shall pay you fifty cents for the trip," said I.

"Dat is puffeckly correct, suh," he answered humbly. "I jus' *had* to have dat two dollars dis mawnin', boss."

I went to the hotel and lied by electricity. I wired the magazine: "A. Adair holds out for eight cents a word."

The answer that came back was: "Give it to her quick, you duffer."

Just before dinner "Major" Wentworth Caswell bore down upon me with the greetings of a long-lost friend. I have seen few men whom I have so instantaneously hated, and of whom it was so difficult to be rid. I was standing at the bar when he invaded me; therefore I could not wave the white ribbon in his face. I would have paid gladly for the drinks, hoping, thereby, to escape another; but he was one of those despicable, roaring, advertising bibbers who must have brass bands and fireworks attend upon every cent that they waste in their follies.

With an air of producing millions he drew two one-dollar bills from a pocket and dashed one of them upon the bar. I looked once more at the dollar bill with the upper right-hand corner missing, torn through the middle, and patched with a strip of blue tissue paper. It was my dollar bill again. It could have been no other.

I went up to my room. The drizzle and the monotony of a dreary, eventless Southern town had made me tired and listless. I remember that just before I went to bed I mentally disposed of the mysterious dollar bill (which might have formed the clue to a tremendously fine detective story of San Francisco) by saying to myself sleepily: "Seems as if a lot of people here own stock in the Hack-Driver's Trust. Pays dividends promptly, too. Wonder if—" Then I fell asleep.

King Cetewayo was at his post the next day, and rattled my bones over the stones out to eight-sixty-one. He was to wait and rattle me back again when I was ready.

Azalea Adair looked paler and cleaner and frailer than she had looked on the day before. After she had signed the contract at eight cents per word, she grew still paler and began to slip out of her chair. Without much trouble I managed to get her up on the antediluvian horse-hair sofa and then I ran out to the sidewalk and yelled to the coffee-coloured pirate to bring a doctor. With a wisdom that I had not suspected in him, he abandoned his team and struck off up the street afoot, realizing the value of speed. In ten minutes he returned with a grave, gray-haired, and capable man of medicine. In a few words (worth much less than eight cents each) I explained to him my presence in the hollow house of mystery. He bowed with stately understanding and turned to the old negro.

"Uncle Caesar," he said calmly, "run up to my house and ask Miss Lucy to give you a cream pitcher full of fresh milk and half a tumbler of port wine. And hurry back. Don't drive—run. I want you to get back sometime this week."

It occurred to me that Dr. Merriman also felt a distrust as to the speeding powers of the land-pirate's steeds. After Uncle Caesar was gone, lumberingly, but swiftly, up the street, the doctor looked me over with great politeness and as much careful calculation until he had decided that I might do.

"It is only a case of insufficient nutrition," he said. "In other words, the result of poverty, pride, and starvation. Mrs. Caswell has many devoted friends who would be glad to aid her, but she will accept nothing except from that old negro, Uncle Caesar, who was once owned by her family."

"Mrs. Caswell!" said I, in surprise. And then I looked at the contract and saw that she had signed it "Azalea Adair Caswell."

"I thought she was Miss Adair," said I.

"Married to a drunken, worthless loafer, sir," said the doctor. "It is said that he robs her even of the small sums that her old servant contributes toward her support."

When the milk and wine had been brought, the doctor soon revived Azalea Adair. She sat up and talked of the beauty of the autumn leaves that were in season, and their height of color. She referred lightly to her fainting seizure as the outcome of an old palpitation of the heart. Impy fanned her as she lay on the sofa. The doctor was due elsewhere, and I followed him to the door. I told him that it was within my power and intentions to make a reasonable advance of money to Azalea Adair on future contributions to the magazine, and he seemed pleased.

"By the way," he said, "perhaps you would like to know that you have had royalty for a coachman. Old Caesar's grandfather was a king in Congo. Caesar himself has royal ways, as you may have observed."

As the doctor was moving off I heard Uncle Caesar's voice inside: "Did he git bofe of dem two dollars from you, Mis' Zalea?"

"Yes, Caesar," I heard Azalea Adair answer weakly.

And then I went in and concluded business negotiations with our contributor. I assumed the responsibility of advancing fifty dollars, putting it as a necessary formality in binding our bargain. And then Uncle Caesar drove me back to the hotel.

Here ends all of my story as far as I can testify as a witness. The rest must be only bare statements of facts.

At about six o'clock I went out for a stroll. Uncle Caesar was at his corner. He threw open the door of his carriage, flourished his duster, and began his depressing formula: "Step right in, suh. Fifty cents to anywhere in the city—hack's puffickly clean, suh—jus' got back from a funeral—"

And then he recognized me. I think his eyesight was getting bad. His coat had taken on a few more faded shades of color, the twine strings were more frayed and ragged, the last remaining button— the button of yellow horn—was gone. A motley descendant of kings was Uncle Caesar!

About two hours later I saw an excited crowd besieging the front door of the drug-store. In a desert where nothing happens this was manna; so I edged my way inside. On an extemporized couch of empty boxes and chairs was stretched the mortal corporeality of Major Wentworth Caswell. A doctor was testing him for the immortal ingredient. His decision was that it was conspicuous by its absence.

The erstwhile Major had been found dead on a dark street and brought by curious and ennuied citizens to the drug-store. The late human being had been engaged in terrific battle—the details showed that. Loafer and reprobate though he had been he had been also a warrior. But he had lost. His hands were yet clinched so tightly that his fingers would not be opened. The gentle citizens who had known him stood about and searched their vocabularies to find some good words, if it were possible, to speak of him. One kind-looking man said, after much thought: "When 'Cas' was about fo'teen he was one of the best spellers in school."

While I stood there the fingers of the right hand of "the man that was," which hung down the side of a white-pine box, relaxed, and dropped something at my feet. I covered it with one foot quickly, and a little later on I picked it up and pocketed it. I reasoned that in his last struggle his hand must have seized that object unwittingly and held it in a death grip.

At the hotel that night the main topic of conversation, with the possible exception of politics and prohibition, was the demise of Major Caswell. I heard one man say to a group of listeners:

"In my opinion, gentlemen, Caswell was murdered by some of those no-account niggers for his money. He had fifty dollars this afternoon which he showed to several gentlemen in the hotel. When he was found the money was not on his person." ·

I left the city the next morning at nine, and as the train was crossing the bridge over the Cumberland River, I took out of my pocket a yellow horn overcoat button the size of a fifty-cent piece, with frayed ends of coarse twine hanging from it, and cast it out of the window into the slow, muddy waters below.

I wonder what's doing in Buffalo!

STUDY NOTES

1. Show that in "A Municipal Report" O. Henry mingles humor and pathos but finally leaves one main effect, pathetic tragedy.
2. Name the exciting force—the action that initiates the chain of incidents that culminate in the tragic climax.
3. State the dominating theme—an idea somewhat the opposite of that in the quotation from Norris prefixed to the story.
4. Summarize the impressions of important activities going on in Nashville made by the quotations from an atlas.
5. Cite instances of the dramatic foreshadowing of murder.
6. By what methods does O. Henry endow Major Wentworth Caswell, Azalea Adair, and Uncle Caesar with such personalities, true-to-life or otherwise, as these characters possess?
7. Why does the action move much more slowly in the first third of the story than in most of O. Henry's plots—what is his purpose in being so deliberate?
8. Cite the examples of satire that you find in this story.
9. Give reasons why you consider this narrative as treating seriously an important problem of life or as being merely a harlequin performance, according to your point of view.
10. List the methods by which O. Henry represents Nashville as a romantic city.

COMPARISON EXERCISES

1. Contrast the Poker-Flat-and-environs setting with that of Nashville at the time dealt with in "A Municipal Report."
2. List the devices used in "The Outcasts of Poker Flat" and those in "A Municipal Report" for describing landscape.
3. Which story gives the truer picture of human nature?
4. Which shows the stronger tendency toward melodrama?
5. In which is the relationship of the background to the action the more obvious and intimate?

WRITING SUGGESTION

Compose a short short story, laying the scene in some region in which you have lived and making the environment have a clearly perceivable and logical effect upon the action.

THEME

Introduction to Stories That Present a Theme

MANY stories are far from being deliberately didactic, but a story may have a theme without trying to preach a moral or a religious precept. In the broad sense usually attached to *theme* in critical discussions, the sense of significant meaning or purpose, every worth-while story does possess a theme. Most brief fictions (one must admit there are exceptions) attempt to do more than narrate action for the sake of entertainment. They intend to communicate truth, at least by implication.

A story's theme is its central or controlling thought, its underlying meaning, its universal significance, or a fundamental law of life, or an important truth that directly concerns some aspect of man's conduct. A theme is "the extractable meaning or paraphrase" of the total meaning of a story. [1] A theme may be the presentation of a problem or of a principle of behavior, the explanation of a motive, or the interpretation of a significant phase of human experience. A theme may be based on some law of nature, some aspect of human nature, an elemental human passion, or any truth concerning human life. A theme may be, but is not always, a moral. It is simply the main idea, the leading impression, that the author seeks to establish. The really great themes deal with heroic struggle prompted and guided by a fundamentally strong motive, by elemental and universal human emotion.

Certain themes have long been used in stories, for example: The sanctity of home should be preserved even at great sacrifice; Religion

---

[1] Ray B. West, Jr., and Robert Wooster Stallman, *The Art of Modern Fiction*, New York: Rinehart & Company, 1949, p. 652.

121

can give consolation when all other influences fail; and Most old people have a valuable stock of accumulated knowledge and wisdom. Any traditional theme may be used to advantage in a short story, and may increase the sales of the story, if the theme is handled somewhat originally, stated in a variant form, provided with a new setting and new characters, and given emotional appeal. Modern central ideas—themes which deliberately contradict others that are much older and that have received wide usage in narratives—are also employed with telling effect by such writers as Aiken, Sherwood Anderson, Caldwell, and Faulkner. A successful theme may be either ancient or modern.

The theme may be either stated or implied, more likely the latter. Sometimes it is specifically and emphatically expressed in a one-sentence paragraph. It may be hinted at in one or two sentences. It may be interwoven with the construction of plot or the delineation of character or the depiction of setting or atmosphere. In some stories the theme is effectively repeated several times, the repetitions varying somewhat from any previous statement. Sometimes titles hint at themes.

In a thematic story, the plot should illustrate and grow out of the theme. Plot is obviously one of the most important methods available to a writer for communicating any guiding idea that he may wish to make—any impression that he may have concerning human experience. All the incidents should harmonize with the main revelation that the author is seeking to convey. The theme may make the plot really unified and significant. Indeed a theme once found may help to create plot.

Likewise, the individuality of the main character should illustrate the theme. Characterization, like plot, is a useful tool for communicating a lesson or a moral or a philosophic idea—one main impression of life. Furthermore, the theme may help to create characters and their personalities. Though a fundamental truth may be highly important in its effect on characterization, the delineation of character, particularly of the chief personage, is likely to be remembered longer than the treatment of theme. Characterization, if skilful, is more likely to make a story great than is the presentation of an underlying principle of social conduct or any kind of central thought. If, however, the theme contributes to the character portrayal, the finding and handling of the theme will deserve some credit for the greatness of the characterization.

The setting should also illustrate or grow out of and harmonize with the theme. Any story that has a main intention must have setting (whether physical or spiritual or both) suitable to that impulse or the disharmony will violate the unity of effect which Poe and Brander Matthews have declared essential. Setting and theme should be integrated.

Moreover, the theme may help to produce atmosphere and atmosphere in turn may reveal the theme. The atmosphere and the theme must be appropriate to each other. In a good many stories, the atmosphere (the *Dictionary of World Literature* has defined the term thus: "the particular world in which the events of a story . . . occur: time, place, conditions, and the attendant mood") [2] helps make the reader aware of the theme. For example, the atmosphere of mystery which Hawthorne creates in "Rappaccini's Daughter" prepares the reader to receive the double theme that solitariness is abnormal and that science may be too coldly objective, irresponsible, and fiendish.

Any writer who wishes to create a theme story that will hold the reader's interest must not let the truth conveyed be too axiomatic, too self-evident. A controlling idea that will make possible a story not obviously didactic and not terribly boring after a few sentences should probably have two dominant opposing concepts, for example, law versus criminal tendency, or something versus something else. A satisfactory theme must contain the essence of plot possibility. And this theme is more likely to hold the reader's attention if implied rather than expressed, if interwoven with the plot and characterization and setting and atmosphere so as to need to be extracted from the whole story.

---

[2] Joseph T. Shipley (ed.), *Dictionary of World Literature,* New York: The Philosophical Library, Inc., 1943, p. 59.

THE GREAT STONE FACE [1]
(1850)
NATHANIEL HAWTHORNE

ONE afternoon, when the sun was going down, a mother and her little boy say at the door of their cottage, talking about the Great Stone Face.[2] They had but to lift their eyes, and there it was plainly to be seen, though miles away, with the sunshine brightening all its features.

And what was the Great Stone Face?

Embosomed amongst a family of lofty mountains, there was a valley so spacious that it contained many thousand inhabitants. Some of these good people dwelt in log-huts, with the black forest all around them, on the steep and difficult hillsides. Others had their homes in comfortable farmhouses and cultivated the rich soil on the gentle slopes or level surfaces of the valley. Others, again, were congregated into populous villages, where some wild, highland rivulet, tumbling down from its birthplace in the upper mountain region, had been caught and tamed by human cunning and compelled to turn the machinery of cotton-factories. The inhabitants of this valley, in short, were numerous and of many modes of life. But all of them, grown people and children, had a kind of familarity with the Great Stone Face, although some possessed the gift of distinguishing this grand natural phenomenon more perfectly than many of their neighbors.

The Great Stone Face, then, was the work of Nature in her mood of majestic playfulness, formed on the perpendicular side of a mountain by some immense rocks, which had been thrown together in such a position as, when viewed at a proper distance, precisely to resemble the features of the human countenance. It seemed as if an enormous giant, or a Titan, had sculptured his own likeness on the precipice. There was the broad arch of the forehead, a hundred feet in height; the nose, with its long bridge; and the vast lips, which, if they could have spoken, would have rolled their thunder accents from one end of the valley to the other. True it is, that if the spectator approached too near, he lost the outline of the gigantic

---

[1] First published in the *National Era* (January, 1850).

[2] The Old Man of the Mountain. A huge rock formation on the Profile Mountain, in the Franconia Range, New Hampshire.

visage and could discern only a heap of ponderous and gigantic rocks, piled in chaotic ruin one upon another. Retracing his steps, however, the wondrous features would again be seen; and the farther he withdrew from them, the more like a human face, with all its original divinity intact, did they appear; until, as it grew dim in the distance, with the clouds and glorified vapor of the mountain clustering about it, the Great Stone Face seemed positively to be alive.

It was a happy lot for children to grow up to manhood or womanhood with the Great Stone Face before their eyes, for all the features were noble, and the expression was at once grand and sweet, as if it were the glow of a vast, warm heart, that embraced all mankind in its affections and had room for more. It was an education only to look at it. According to the belief of many people, the valley owed much of its fertility to this benign aspect that was continually beaming over it, illuminating the clouds and infusing its tenderness into the sunshine.

As we began with saying, a mother and her little boy sat at their cottage-door, gazing at the Great Stone Face and talking about it. The child's name was Ernest.[3]

"Mother," said he, while the Titanic visage smiled on him, "I wish that it could speak, for it looks so very kindly that its voice must needs be pleasant. If I were to see a man with such a face, I should love him dearly."

"If an old prophecy should come to pass," answered his mother, "we may see a man, some time or other, with exactly such a face as that."

"What prophecy do you mean, dear mother?" eagerly inquired Ernest. "Pray tell me all about it!"

So his mother told him a story that her own mother had told to her, when she herself was younger than little Ernest; a story, not of things that were past, but of what was yet to come; a story, nevertheless, so very old that even the Indians, who formerly inhabited this valley, had heard it from their forefathers, to whom, as they affirmed, it had been murmured by the mountain streams and whispered by the wind among the tree-tops. The purport was that, at

---

[3] The original of this character may have been Ralph Waldo Emerson. Vernon Loggins, in his *Visual Outline of American Literature*, New York: Longmans, Green and Company, 1933, p. 56, refers to Hawthorne's story, "The Great Stone Face," as a "tribute to Emerson."

some future day, a child should be born hereabouts, who was destined to become the greatest and noblest personage of his time and whose countenance, in manhood, should bear an exact resemblance to the Great Stone Face. Not a few old-fashioned people, and young ones likewise, in the ardor of their hopes, still cherished an enduring faith in this old prophecy. But others, who had seen more of the world, had watched and waited till they were weary, and had beheld no man with such a face nor any man that proved to be much greater or nobler than his neighbors, concluded it to be nothing but an idle tale. At all events, the great man of the prophecy had not yet appeared.

"O mother, dear mother!" cried Ernest, clapping his hands above his head, "I do hope that I shall live to see him!"

His mother was an affectionate and thoughtful woman and felt that it was wisest not to discourage the generous hopes of her little boy. So she only said to him, "Perhaps you may."

And Ernest never forgot the story that his mother told him. It was always in his mind, whenever he looked upon the Great Stone Face. He spent his childhood in the log-cottage where he was born, and was dutiful to his mother and helpful to her in many things, assisting her much with his little hands and more with his loving heart. In this manner, from a happy yet often pensive child, he grew up to be a mild, quiet, unobtrusive boy, and sun-browned with labor in the fields, but with more intelligence brightening his aspect than is seen in many lads who have been taught at famous schools. Yet Ernest had had no teacher, save only that the Great Stone Face became one to him. When the toil of the day was over, he would gaze at it for hours, until he began to imagine that those vast features recognized him and gave him a smile of kindness and encouragement, responsive to his own look of veneration. We must not take upon us to affirm that this was a mistake, although the Face may have looked no more kindly at Ernest than at all the world besides. But the secret was that the boy's tender and confiding simplicity discerned what other people could not see; and thus the love, which was meant for all, became his peculiar portion.

About this time there went a rumor throughout the valley that the great man, foretold from ages long ago, who was to bear a resemblance to the Great Stone Face, had appeared at last. It seems that, many years before, a young man had migrated from the valley and settled at a distant seaport, where, after getting together a little money, he had set up as a shopkeeper. His name—but I could never learn whether it was his real one or a nickname that had grown out of his habits and success in life—was Gathergold. Being shrewd and active, and endowed by Providence with that inscrutable faculty which develops itself in what the world calls luck, he became an exceedingly rich merchant and owner of a whole fleet of bulky-bottomed ships. All the countries of the globe appeared to join hands for the mere purpose of adding heap after heap to the mountainous accumulation of this one man's wealth. The cold regions of the North, almost within the gloom and shadow of the Arctic Circle, sent him their tribute in the shape of furs; hot Africa sifted for him the golden sands of her rivers and gathered up the ivory tusks of her great elephants out of the forests; the East came bringing him the rich shawls, and spices, and teas, and the effulgence of diamonds, and the gleaming purity of large pearls. The ocean, not to be behindhand with the earth, yielded up her mighty whales, that Mr. Gathergold might sell their oil and make a profit on it. Be the original commodity what it might, it was gold within his grasp. It might be said of him, as of Midas, in the fable, that whatever he touched with his finger immediately glistened and grew yellow and was changed at once into sterling metal or, which suited him still better, into piles of coin. And, when Mr. Gathergold had become so very rich that it would have taken him a hundred years only to count his wealth, he bethought himself of his native valley and resolved to go back thither and end his days where he was born. With this purpose in view, he sent a skilful architect to build him such a palace as should be fit for a man of his vast wealth to live in.

As I have said above, it had already been rumored in the valley that Mr. Gathergold had turned out to be the prophetic personage so long and vainly looked for, and that his visage was the perfect and undeniable similitude of the Great Stone Face. People were the more ready to believe that this must needs be the fact, when they beheld the splendid edifice that rose, as if by enchantment, on the site of his father's old weather-beaten farmhouse. The exterior was of marble, so dazzlingly white that it seemed as though the whole structure might melt away in the sunshine, like those humbler ones which Mr. Gathergold, in his young play-days, before his fingers were gifted with the touch of transmutation, had been accustomed to build of snow. It had a richly ornamented portico, supported by tall pillars, beneath which was a lofty door, studded with silver knobs and made of a kind of variegated wood that had been brought from beyond the sea. The windows, from the floor to the ceiling of each stately apartment, were composed, respectively, of but one enormous pane of glass, so transparently pure that it was said to be a finer medium than even the vacant atmosphere. Hardly anybody had been permitted to see the interior of this palace; but it was reported, and with good semblance of truth, to be far more gorgeous than the outside, insomuch that whatever was iron or brass in other houses was silver or gold in this; and Mr. Gathergold's bedchamber, especially, made such a glittering appearance that no ordinary man would have been able to close his eyes there. But, on the other hand, Mr. Gathergold was now so inured to wealth that perhaps he could not have closed his eyes unless where the gleam of it was certain to find its way beneath his eyelids.

In due time, the mansion was finished; next came the upholsterers, with magnificent furniture; then, a whole troop of black and white servants, the harbingers of Mr. Gathergold, who, in his own majestic person, was expected to arrive at sunset. Our friend Ernest, meanwhile, had been deeply stirred by the idea that the great man, the noble man, the man of prophecy, after so many ages of delay, was at length to be made manifest in his native valley. He knew, boy as he was, that there were a thousand ways in which Mr. Gathergold, with his vast wealth, might transform himself into an angel of beneficence and assume a control over human affairs as wide and benignant as the smile of the Great Stone Face. Full of faith and hope, Ernest doubted not that what the people said was true and that now he was to behold the living likeness of those wondrous features on the mountain-side. While the boy was still gazing up the valley, and fancying, as he always did, that the Great Stone Face returned his gaze and looked kindly at him, the rumbling of wheels was heard, approaching swiftly along the winding road.

"Here he comes!" cried a group of people who were assembled to witness the arrival. "Here comes the great Mr. Gathergold!"

A carriage, drawn by four horses, dashed round the turn of the road. Within it, thrust partly out of the window, appeared the physiognomy of the old man, with a skin as yellow as if his own Midas-hand had transmuted it. He had a low forehead, small, sharp eyes, puckered about with innumerable wrinkles, and very thin lips, which he made still thinner by pressing them forcibly together.

"The very image of the Great Stone Face!" shouted the people. "Sure enough, the old prophecy is true; and here we have the great man come, at last!"

And, what greatly perplexed Ernest, they seemed actually to believe that here was the likeness which they spoke of. By the roadside there chanced to be an old beggar-woman and two little beggar-children, stragglers from some far-off region, who, as the carriage rolled onward, held out their hands and lifted up their doleful voices, most piteously beseeching charity. A yellow claw—the very same that had clawed together so much wealth—poked itself out of the coach-window and dropped some copper coins upon the ground; so that, though the great man's name seems to have been Gathergold, he might just as suitably have been nicknamed Scattercopper. Still, nevertheless, with an earnest shout, and evidently with as much good faith as ever, the people bellowed:

"He is the very image of the Great Stone Face!"

But Ernest turned sadly from the wrinkled shrewdness of that sordid visage and gazed up the valley, where, amid a gathering mist, gilded by the last sunbeams, he could still distinguish those glorious features which had impressed themselves into his soul. Their aspect cheered him. What did the benign lips seem to say?

"He will come! Fear not, Ernest; the man will come!"

The years went on, and Ernest ceased to be a boy. He had grown to be a young man now. He attracted little notice from the other inhabitants of the valley; for they saw nothing remarkable in his way of life, save that, when the labor of the day was over, he still loved to go apart and gaze and meditate upon the Great Stone Face. According to their idea of the matter, it was a folly, indeed, but pardonable, inasmuch as Ernest was industrious, kind, and neighborly, and neglected no duty for the sake of indulging this idle habit. They knew not that the Great Stone Face had become a teacher to him and that the sentiment which was expressed in it would enlarge the young man's heart and fill it with wider and deeper sympathies than other hearts. They knew not that thence would come a better wisdom than could be learned from books and a better life than could be molded on the defaced example of other human lives. Neither did Ernest know that the thoughts and affections which came to him so naturally, in the fields and at the fireside and wherever he communed with himself, were of a higher tone than those which all men shared with him. A simple soul—simple as when his mother first taught him the old prophecy—, he beheld the marvelous features beaming adown the valley and still wondered that their human counterpart was so long in making his appearance.

By this time poor Mr. Gathergold was dead and buried; and the oddest part of the matter was that his wealth, which was the body and spirit of his existence, had disappeared before his death, leaving nothing of him but a living skeleton, covered over with a wrinkled, yellow skin. Since the melting away of his gold, it had been very generally conceded that there was no such striking resemblance, after all, betwixt the ignoble features of the ruined merchant and that majestic face upon the mountain-side. So the people ceased to honor him during his lifetime and quietly consigned him to forgetfulness after his decease. Once in a while, it is true, his memory was brought up in connection with the magnificent palace which he had built and which had long ago been turned into a hotel for the accommodation of strangers, multitudes of whom came, every summer, to visit that famous natural curiosity, the Great Stone Face. Thus, Mr. Gathergold being discredited and thrown into the shade, the man of prophecy was yet to come.

It so happened that a native-born son of the valley, many years before, had enlisted as a soldier, and, after a great deal of fighting had now become an illustrious commander. Whatever he may be called in history, he was known in camps and on the battlefield under the nickname of Old Blood-and-Thunder.[4] This war-worn veteran, being now infirm with age and wounds and weary of the turmoil of a military life and of the roll of the drum and the clangor of the trumpet, that had so long been ringing in his ears, had lately signified a purpose of returning to his native valley, hoping to find repose where he remembered to have left it. The

---

[4] This soldier character may have been based, at least in part, on the famed American general of the War of 1812, Winfield Scott, who was contemporaneous with Hawthorne.

inhabitants, his old neighbors and their grown-up children, were resolved to welcome the renowned warrior with a salute of cannon and a public dinner; and all the more enthusiastically, it being affirmed that now, at last, the likeness of the Great Stone Face had actually appeared. An aid-de-camp of Old Blood-and-Thunder, traveling through the valley, was said to have been struck with the resemblance. Moreover the schoolmates of the general were ready to testify, on oath, that, to the best of their recollection, the aforesaid general had been exceedingly like the majestic image, even when a boy, only that the idea had never occurred to them at that period. Great, therefore, was the excitement throughout the valley; and many people, who had never once thought of glancing at the Great Stone Face for years before, now spent their time in gazing at it, for the sake of knowing exactly how General Blood-and-Thunder looked.

On the day of the great festival, Ernest, with all the other people of the valley, left their work and proceeded to the spot where the sylvan banquet was prepared. As he approached, the loud voice of the Rev. Dr. Battleblast was heard, beseeching a blessing on the good things set before them and on the distinguished friend of peace in whose honor they were assembled. The tables were arranged in a cleared space of the woods, shut in by the surrounding trees, except where a vista opened eastward and afforded a distant view of the Great Stone Face. Over the general's chair, which was a relic from the home of Washington, there was an arch of verdant boughs, with the laurel profusely intermixed, and surmounted by his country's banner, beneath which he had won his victories. Our friend Ernest raised himself on his tiptoes, in hopes to get a glimpse of the celebrated guest; but there was a mighty crowd about the tables anxious to hear the toasts and speeches and to catch any word that might fall from the general in reply; and a volunteer company, doing duty as a guard, pricked ruthlessly with their bayonets at any particularly quiet person among the throng. So Ernest, being of an unobstrusive character, was thrust quite into the background, where he could see no more of Old Blood-and-Thunder's physiognomy than if it had been still blazing on the battlefield. To console himself, he turned towards the Great Stone Face, which, like a faithful and long-remembered friend, looked back and smiled upon him through the vista of the forest. Meantime, however, he could overhear the remarks of various individuals, who were comparing the features of the hero with the face on the distant mountain-side.

" 'Tis the same face, to a hair!" cried one man, cutting a caper for joy.

"Wonderfully like, that's a fact!" responded another.

"Like! why, I call it Old Blood-and-Thunder himself, in a monstrous looking glass!" cried a third.

"And why not? He's the greatest man of this or any other age, beyond a doubt."

And then all three of the speakers gave a great shout, which communicated electricity to the crowd and called forth a roar from a thousand voices, that went reverberating for miles among the mountains, until you might have supposed that the Great Stone Face had poured its thunder-breath into the cry. All these comments, and this vast enthusiasm, served the more to interest our friend; nor did he think of questioning that now, at length, the mountain-visage had found its human counterpart. It is true, Ernest had imagined that this long-looked-for personage would appear in the character of a man of peace, uttering wisdom, and doing good, and making people happy. But, taking an habitual breadth of view, with all his simplicity, he contended that Providence should choose its own method of blessing mankind, and could conceive that this great end might be effected even by a warrior and a bloody sword, should inscrutable wisdom see fit to order matters so.

"The general! the general!" was now the cry. "Hush! silence! Old Blood-and-Thunder's going to make a speech."

Even so; for, the cloth being removed, the general's health had been drunk, amid shouts of applause, and he now stood upon his feet to thank the company. Ernest saw him. There he was, over the shoulders of the crowd, from the two glittering epaulets and embroidered collar upward, beneath the arch of green boughs with intertwined laurel, and the banner drooping as if to shade his brow! And there, too, visible in the same glance, through the vista of the forest, appeared the Great Stone Face! And was there, indeed, such a resemblance as the crowd had testified? Alas, Ernest could not recognize it! He beheld a war-worn and weather-beaten countenance, full of energy, and expressive of an iron will; but the gentle wisdom, the deep, broad, tender sympathies, were altogether wanting in Old Blood-and-Thunder's visage; and even if the Great Stone Face had assumed his look of stern command, the milder traits would still have tempered it.

"This is not the man of prophecy," sighed Ernest to himself, as he made his way out of the throng. "And must the world wait longer yet?"

The mists had congregated about the distant mountain-side, and there were seen the grand and awful features of the Great Stone Face, awful but benignant, as if a mighty angel were sitting among the hills and enrobing himself in a cloud-vesture of gold and purple. As he looked, Ernest could hardly believe but that a smile beamed over, the whole visage, with a radiance still brightening, although without motion of the lips. It was probably the effect of the western sunshine, melting through the thinly diffused vapors that had swept between him and the object that he gazed at. But— as it always did—the aspect of his marvelous friend made Ernest as hopeful as if he had never hoped in vain.

"Fear not, Ernest," said his heart, even as if the Great Face were whispering to him—"fear not, Ernest; he will come."

More years sped swiftly and tranquilly away. Ernest still dwelt in his native valley and was now a man of middle age. By imperceptible degrees, he had become known among the people. Now, as heretofore, he labored for his bread and was the same simple-hearted man that he had always been. But he had thought and felt so much, he had given so many of the best hours of his life to unworldly hopes for some great good to mankind, that it seemed as though he had been talking with the angels and had imbibed a portion of their wisdom unawares. It was visible in the calm and well-considered beneficence of his daily life, the quiet stream of which had made a wide green margin all along its course. Not a day passed by that the world was not the better because this man, humble as he was, had lived. He never stepped aside from his own path, yet would always reach a blessing to his neighbor. Almost involuntarily, too, he had become a preacher. The pure and high simplicity of his thought, which, as one of its manifestations, took shape in the good deeds that dropped silently from his hand, flowed also forth in speech. He uttered truths that wrought upon and molded the lives of those who heard him. His auditors, it may be, never suspected that Ernest, their own neighbor and familiar friend, was more than an ordinary man; least of all did Ernest himself suspect it; but, inevitably as the murmur of a rivulet, came thoughts out of his mouth that no other human lips had spoken.

When the people's minds had had a little time to cool, they were ready enough to acknowledge their mistake in imagining a similarity between General Blood-and-Thunder's truculent physiognomy and the benign visage on the mountain-side. But now, again, there were reports and many paragraphs in the newspapers, affirming that the likeness of the Great Stone Face had appeared upon the broad shoulders of a certain eminent statesman. He, like Mr. Gathergold and Old Blood-and-Thunder, was a native of the valley, but had left it in his early days and taken up the trades of law and politics. Instead of the rich man's wealth and the warrior's sword, he had but a tongue, and it was mightier than both together. So wonderfully eloquent was he that, whatever he might choose to say, his auditors had no choice but to believe him; wrong looked like right, and right like wrong; for when it pleased him, he could make a kind of illuminated fog with his mere breath and obscure the natural daylight with it. His tongue, indeed, was a magic instrument: sometimes it rumbled like the thunder; sometimes it warbled like the sweetest music. It was the blast of war— the song of peace; and it seemed to have a heart in it, when there was no such matter. In good truth, he was a wondrous man; and when his tongue had acquired him all other imaginable success— when it had been heard in halls of state and in the courts of princes and potentates—after it had made him known all over the world, even as a voice crying from shore to shore—it finally persuaded his countrymen to select him for the Presidency. Before this time—indeed, as soon as he began to grow celebrated—his admirers had found out the resemblance between him and the Great Stone Face; and so much were they struck by it that throughout the country this distinguished gentleman was known by the name of Old Stony Phiz.[5] The phrase was considered as giving a

---

[5] Some critics have suggested that Old Stony Phiz may in some measure represent Daniel Webster.

highly favorable aspect to his political prospects; for, as is likewise the case with the Popedom, nobody ever becomes President without taking a name other than his own.

While his friends were doing their best to make him President, Old Stony Phiz, as he was called, set out on a visit to the valley where he was born. Of course, he had no other object than to shake hands with his fellow-citizens and neither thought nor cared about the effect which his progress through the country might have upon the election. Magnificent preparations were made to receive the illustrious statesman; a cavalcade of horsemen set forth to meet him at the boundary line of the State, and all the people left their business and gathered along the wayside to see him pass. Among these was Ernest. Though more than once disappointed, as we have seen, he had such a hopeful and confiding nature that he was always ready to believe in whatever seemed beautiful and good. He kept his heart continually open and thus was sure to catch the blessing from on high when it should come. So now again, as buoyantly as ever, he went forth to behold the likeness of the Great Stone Face.

The cavalcade came prancing along the road, with a great clattering of hoofs and a mighty cloud of dust, which rose up so dense and high that the visage of the mountain-side was completely hidden from Ernest's eyes. All the great men of the neighborhood were there on horseback; militia officers, in uniform; the member of Congress; the sheriff of the county; the editors of newspapers, and many a farmer, too, had mounted his patient steed, with his Sunday coat upon his back. It really was a very brilliant spectacle, especially as there were numerous banners flaunting over the cavalcade, on some of which were gorgeous portraits of the illustrious statesman and the Great Stone Face, smiling familiarly at one another, like two brothers. If the pictures were to be trusted, the mutual resemblance, it must be confessed, was marvelous. We must not forget to mention that there was a band of music, which made the echoes of the mountains ring and reverberate with the loud triumph of its strains; so that airy and soul-thrilling melodies broke out among all the heights and hollows, as if every nook of his native valley had found a voice, to welcome the distinguished guest. But the grandest effect was when the far-off mountain precipice flung back the music; for then the Great Stone Face itself seemed to be swelling the triumphant chorus, in acknowledgment that, at length, the man of prophecy was come.

All this while the people were throwing up their hats and shouting, with enthusiasm so contagious that the heart of Ernest kindled up, and he likewise threw up his hat, and shouted, as loudly as the loudest, "Huzza for the great man! Huzza for Old Stony Phiz!" But as yet he had not seen him.

"Here he is, now!" cried those who stood near Ernest. "There! There! Look at Old Stony Phiz and then at the Old Man of the Mountain, and see if they are not as like as two twin brothers!"

In the midst of all this gallant array came an open barouche, drawn by four white horses; and in the barouche, with his massive head uncovered, sat the illustrious statesman, Old Stony Phiz himself.

"Confess it," said one of Ernest's neighbors to him, "the Great Stone Face has met its match at last!"

Now, it must be owned that, at his first glimpse of the countenance which was bowing and smiling from the barouche, Ernest did fancy that there was a resemblance between it and the old familiar face upon the mountain-side. The brow, with its massive depth and loftiness, and all the other features, indeed, were boldly and strongly hewn, as if in emulation of a more than heroic, of a Titanic model. But the sublimity and stateliness, the grand expression of a divine sympathy, that illuminated the mountain visage and etherealized its ponderous granite substance into spirit, might here be sought in vain. Something had been originally left out or had departed. And therefore the marvelously gifted statesman had always a weary gloom in the deep caverns of his eyes, as of a child that has outgrown its playthings or a man of mighty faculties and little aims, whose life, with all its high performances, was vague and empty, because no high purpose had endowed it with reality.

Still, Ernest's neighbor was thrusting his elbow into his side and pressing him for an answer.

"Confess! confess! Is not he the very picture of your Old Man of the Mountain?"

"No!" said Ernest, bluntly, "I see little or no likeness."

"Then so much the worse for the Great Stone Face!" answered the neighbor; and again he set up a shout for Old Stony Phiz.

But Ernest turned away, melancholy, and almost despondent: for this was the saddest of his disappointments, to behold a man who might have fulfilled the prophecy and had not willed to do so. Meantime, the cavalcade, the banners, the music, and the barouches swept past him, with the vociferous crowd in the rear, leaving the dust to settle down and the Great Stone Face to be revealed again, with the grandeur that it had worn for untold centuries.

"Lo, here I am, Ernest!" the benign lips seemed to say. "I have waited longer than thou and am not yet weary. Fear not; the man will come."

The years hurried onward, treading in their haste on one another's heels. And now they began to bring white hairs and scatter them over the head of Ernest; they made reverend wrinkles across his forehead and furrows in his cheeks. He was an aged man. But not in vain had he grown old: more than the white hairs on his head were the sage thoughts in his mind; his wrinkles and furrows were inscriptions that Time had graved and in which he had written legends of wisdom that had been tested by the tenor of a life. And Ernest had ceased to be obscure. Unsought for, undesired, had come the fame which so many seek and made him known in the great world, beyond the limits of the valley in which he had dwelt so quietly. College professors, and even the active men of cities, came from far to see and converse with Ernest; for the report had gone abroad that this simple husbandman had ideas unlike those of other men, not gained from books, but of a higher tone—a tranquil and familiar majesty, as if he had been talking with the angels as his daily friends. Whether it were sage, statesman, or philanthropist, Ernest received these visitors with the gentle sincerity that had characterized him from boyhood and spoke freely with them of whatever came uppermost or lay deepest in his heart or their own. While they talked together, his face would kindle, unawares, and shine upon them, as with a mild evening light. Pensive with the fulness of such discourse, his guests took leave and went their way; and passing up the valley, paused to look at the Great Stone Face, imagining that they had seen its likeness in a human countenance, but could not remember where.

While Ernest had been growing up and growing old, a bountiful Providence had granted a new poet[6] to this earth. He, likewise, was a native of the valley, but had spent the greater part of his life at a distance from that romantic region, pouring out his sweet music amid the bustle and din of cities. Often, however, did the mountains which had been familiar to him in his childhood lift their snowy peaks into the clear atmosphere of his poetry. Neither was the Great Stone Face forgotten, for the poet had celebrated it in an ode, which was grand enough to have been uttered by its own majestic lips. This man of genius, we may say, had come down from heaven with wonderful endowments. If he sang of a mountain, the eyes of all mankind beheld a mightier grandeur reposing on its breast, or soaring to its summit, than had before been seen there. If his theme were a lovely lake, a celestial smile had now been thrown over it, to gleam forever on its surface. If it were the vast old sea, even the deep immensity of its dread bosom seemed to swell the higher, as if moved by the emotions of the song. Thus the world assumed another and a better aspect from the hour that the poet blessed it with his happy eyes. The Creator had bestowed him, as the last best touch to his own handiwork. Creation was not finished till the poet came to interpret, and so complete it.

The effect was no less high and beautiful, when his human brethren were the subject of his verse. The man or woman, sordid with the common dust of life, who crossed his daily path, and the child who played in it were glorified if they beheld him in his mood of poetic faith. He showed the golden links of the great chain that intertwined them with an angelic kindred; he brought out the hidden traits of a celestial birth that made them worthy of such kin. Some, indeed, there were who thought to show the soundness of their judgment by affirming that all the beauty and dignity of the natural world existed only in the poet's fancy. Let such men speak for themselves, who undoubtedly appear to have been spawned forth by Nature with a contemptuous bitterness; she having plastered them up out of her refuse stuff, after all the swine were made. As respects all things else, the poet's ideal was the truest truth.

---

[6] When Hawthorne was creating the character of this poet, he may have had in mind Edgar Allan Poe.

The songs of this poet found their way to Ernest. He read them after his customary toil, seated on the bench before his cottage-door, where for such a length of time he had filled his repose with thought, by gazing at the Great Stone Face. And now as he read stanzas that caused the soul to thrill within him, he lifted his eyes to the vast countenance beaming on him so benignantly.

"O majestic friend," he murmered, addressing the Great Stone Face, "is not this man worthy to resemble thee?"

The face seemed to smile, but answered not a word.

Now it happened that the poet, though he dwelt so far away, had not only heard of Ernest, but had meditated much upon his character, until he deemed nothing so desirable as to meet this man, whose untaught wisdom walked hand in hand with the noble simplicity of his life. One summer morning, therefore, he took passage by the railroad, and, in the decline of the afternoon, alighted from the cars at no great distance from Ernest's cottage. The great hotel, which had formerly been the palace of Mr. Gathergold, was close at hand, but the poet, with his carpetbag on his arm, inquired at once where Ernest dwelt and was resolved to be accepted as his guest.

Approaching the door, he there found the good old man, holding a volume in his hand, which alternately he read, and then, with a finger between the leaves, looked lovingly at the Great Stone Face.

"Good evening," said the poet. "Can you give a traveler a night's lodging?"

"Willingly," answered Ernest, and then he added, smiling, "Methinks I never saw the Great Stone Face look so hospitably at a stranger."

The poet sat down on the bench beside him, and he and Ernest talked together. Often had the poet held intercourse with the wittiest and the wisest, but never before with a man like Ernest, whose thoughts and feelings gushed up with such a natural feeling, and who made great truths so familiar by his simple utterance of them. Angels, as had been so often said, seemed to have wrought with him at his labor in the fields; angels seemed to have sat with him by the fireside; and, dwelling with angels as friend with friends, he had imbided the sublimity of their ideas and imbued it with the sweet and lowly charm of household words. So thought

139

the poet. And Ernest, on the other hand, was moved and agitated by the living images which the poet flung out of his mind and which peopled all the air about the cottage-door with shapes of beauty, both gay and pensive. The sympathies of these two men instructed them with a profounder sense than either could have attained alone. Their minds accorded into one strain and made delightful music, which neither of them could have claimed as all his own nor distinguished his own share from the other's. They led one another, as it were, into a high pavilion of their thoughts, so remote, and hitherto so dim, that they had never entered it before, and so beautiful that they desired to be there always.

As Ernest listened to the poet, he imagined that the Great Stone Face was bending forward to listen too. He gazed earnestly into the poet's glowing eyes.

"Who are you, my strangely gifted guest?" he said.

The poet laid his finger on the volume that Ernest had been reading.

"You have read these poems," said he. "You know me, then—for I wrote them."

Again, and still more earnestly than before, Ernest examined the poet's features; then turned towards the Great Stone Face; then back, with an uncertain aspect, to his guest. But his countenance fell; he shook his head and sighed.

"Wherefore are you sad?" inquired the poet.

"Because," replied Ernest, "all through life I have awaited the fulfilment of a prophecy; and, when I read these poems, I hoped that it might be fulfilled in you."

"You hoped," answered the poet, faintly smiling, "to find in me the likeness of the Great Stone Face. And you are disappointed, as formerly with Mr. Gathergold, and Old Blood-and-Thunder, and Old Stony Phiz. Yes, Ernest, it is my doom. You must add my name to the illustrious three and record another failure of your hopes. For—in shame and sadness do I speak it, Ernest—I am not worthy to be typified by yonder benign and majestic image."

"And why?" asked Ernest. He pointed to the volume. "Are not those thoughts divine?"

"They have a strain of the Divinity," replied the poet. "You can hear in them the far-off echo of a heavenly song. But my life, dear Ernest, has not corresponded with my thought. I have had grand dreams, because I have lived—and that, too, by my own choice—among poor and mean realities. Sometimes, even—shall I dare to say it?—I lack faith in the grandeur, the beauty, and the goodness, which my own works are said to have made more evident in Nature and in human life. Why, then, pure seeker of the good and true, should'st thou hope to find me, in yonder image of the divine?"

The poet spoke sadly, and his eyes were dim with tears. So, likewise, were those of Ernest.

At the hour of sunset, as had long been his frequent custom, Ernest was to discourse to an assemblage of the neighboring inhabitants in the open air. He and the poet, arm in arm, still talking together as they went along, proceeded to the spot. It was a small nook among the hills, with a gray precipice behind, the stern front of which was relieved by the pleasant foliage of many creeping plants that made a tapestry for the naked rock, by hanging their festoons from all its rugged angles. At a small elevation above the ground, set in a rich framework of verdure, there appeared a niche, spacious enough to admit a human figure, with freedom for such gestures as spontaneously accompany earnest thought and genuine emotion. Into this natural pulpit Ernest ascended and threw a look of familiar kindness around upon his audience. They stood or sat or reclined upon the grass, as seemed good to each, with the departing sunshine falling obliquely over them and mingling its subdued cheerfulness with the solemnity of a grove of ancient trees, beneath and amid the boughs of which the golden rays were constrained to pass. In another direction was seen the Great Stone Face, with the same cheer, combined with the same solemnity, in its benignant aspect.

Ernest began to speak, giving to the people of what was in his heart and mind. His words had power, because they accorded with his thoughts; and his thoughts had reality and depth, because they harmonized with the life which he had always lived. It was not mere breath that this preacher uttered; they were the words of life, because a life of good deeds and holy love was melted into them. Pearls, pure and rich, had been dissolved into this precious draught. The poet, as he listened, felt that the being and character of Ernest were a nobler strain of poetry than he had ever written. His eyes glistening with tears, he gazed reverentially at the venerable man and said within himself that never was there an aspect so worthy of a prophet and a sage as that mild, sweet, thoughtful countenance, with the glory of white hair diffused about it. At a distance, but distinctly to be seen, high up in the golden light of the setting sun, appeared the Great Stone Face, with hoary mists around it, like the white hairs around the brow of Ernest. Its look of grand beneficence seemed to embrace the world.

At that moment, in sympathy with a thought which he was about to utter, the face of Ernest assumed a grandeur of expression, so imbued with benevolence, that the poet, by an irresistible impulse, threw his arms aloft and shouted:

"Behold! Behold! Ernest is himself the likeness of the Great Stone Face!"

Then all the people looked and saw that what the deep-sighted poet said was true. The prophecy was fulfilled. But Ernest, having finished what he had to say, took the poet's arm and walked slowly homeward, still hoping that some wiser and better man than himself would by and by appear, bearing a resemblance to the GREAT STONE FACE.

STUDY NOTES

1. At what point in "The Great Stone Face" is the hero first presented?

2. Indicate the methods by which Hawthorne has characterized Gathergold, Old Blood-and-Thunder, Old Stony Phiz, the poet, and Ernest.

3. Though Hawthorne has sometimes been criticized for drawing characters too unrealistic and abstract, show that his characterization in "The Great Stone Face" is noteworthy for one of the earliest pioneers in story writing.

4. Point out the dominance of the subjective method over objective methods in the characterization that appears in this story.

5. State the theme and show its harmony with the characterization and the symbolism employed.

6. Though Hawthorne has sometimes been criticized for creating stories lacking in compact and highly dramatic plot, show that the action in "The Great Stone Face" is interesting in its own right and closely harmonizes with the theme.

7. Point out the resemblances between the two characters in each of the following sets:

    a. Old Blood-and-Thunder and General Winfield Scott

    b. Old Stony Phiz and Daniel Webster

    c. The poet and Edgar Allen Poe

    d. Ernest and Ralph Waldo Emerson.

8. Show that Hawthorne has virtually made the Great Stone Face into a human character, or as nearly human as most of the persons in the story, and that the technique of delineating the Face's personality is largely identical with that used in the other characterizations.

9. Give evidence that if Poe was the prototype of Hawthorne's poet, the latter is an idealized character, his traits and Poe's not perfectly corresponding.

10. Gather the proofs as to whether Emerson was the counterpart of Ernest and as to whether Ernest is also idealized.

11. Point out the traits of character identical between Ernest and the Great Stone Face.

12. Summarize the defects and merits of the story, in structure and style.

FOR THEY KNOW NOT WHAT THEY DO [1]
(1919)
WILBUR DANIEL STEELE

WHEN Christopher Kain told me his story, sitting late in his dressing-room at the Philharmonic, I felt that I ought to say something, but nothing in the world seemed adequate. It was one of those times when words have no weight; mine sounded like a fly buzzing in the tomb of kings. And after all, he did not hear me; I could tell that by the look on his face as he sat there staring into the light, the lank, dark hair framing his waxen brow, his shoulders hanging forward, his lean, strong, sentient fingers wrapped around the brown neck of "Ugo," the 'cello, tightly.

Agnes Kain was a lady, as a lady was before the light of that poor worn word went out. Quiet, reserved, gracious, continent, bearing in face and form the fragile beauty of a rose petal come to its fading on a windless ledge, she moved down the years with the steadfast sweetness of the gentlewoman—gentle, and a woman.

They did not know much about her in the city, where she had come with her son. They did not need to. Looking into her eyes, into the transparent soul behind them, they could ask no other credential for the name she bore and the lavender she wore for the husband of whom she never spoke.

She spoke of him, indeed, but that was in privacy, and to her son. As Christopher grew through boyhood, she watched him; in her enveloping eagerness she forestalled the hour when he would have asked, and told him about his father, Daniel Kain.

It gave them the added bond of secret-sharers. The tale grew as the boy grew. Each night when Christopher crept into his mother's bed for the quiet hour of her voice, it was as if he crept into another world, the wind-blown, sky-encompassed kingdom of the Kains, Daniel, his father, and Maynard, *his* father, another Maynard before *him,* and all the Kains— and the Hill and the House, the Willow Wood, the Moor Under the Cloud, the Beach where the gray seas pounded, the boundless Marsh, the Lilac-hedge standing against the stars.

He knew he would have to be a man of men to measure up to

---

that heritage, a man strong, grave, thoughtful, kind with the kindness that never falters, brave with the courage of that dark and massive folk whose blood ran in his veins. Coming as it did, a world legend growing up side by side with the matter-of-fact world of Concord Street, it was made to fit in with all things natural, and it never occurred to him to question. He, the boy, was *not* massive, strong, or brave; he saw things in the dark that frightened him, his thin shoulders were bound to droop, the hours of practice on his violin left him with no blood in his legs and a queer pallor on his brow.

Nor was he always grave, thoughtful, kind. He did not often lose his temper; the river of his young life ran too smooth and deep. But there were times when he did. Brief passions swept him, blinded him, twisted his fingers, left him sobbing, retching, and weak as death itself. He never seemed to wonder at the discrepancy in things, however, any more than he wondered at the look in his mother's eyes, as she hung over him, waiting, in those moments of nausea after rage. She had not the look of the gentlewoman then; she had more the look a thousand times, of the prisoner led through the last gray corridor in the dawn.

He saw her like that once when he had not been angry. It was on a day when he came into the front hall unexpectedly as a stranger was going out of the door. The stranger was dressed in rough, brown homespun; in one hand he held a brown velour hat, in the other a thorn stick without a ferrule. Nor was there anything more worthy of note in his face, an average-long face with hollowed cheeks, sunken gray eyes, and a high forehead, narrow, sallow, and moist.

No, it was not the stranger that troubled Christopher. It was his mother's look at his own blundering entrance, and, when the man was out of hearing, the tremulous haste of her explanation.

"He came about some papers, you know."

"You mean our *Morning Posts?*" Christopher asked her.

She let her breath out all at once, and color flooded her face.

"Yes," she told him. "Yes, yes."

Neither of them said anything more about it.

It was that same day, toward evening, that Christopher broke one of his long silences, reverting to a subject always near to them both.

145

"Mother, you've never told me where it is—on the *map*, I mean."
She was looking the other way. She did not turn around.

"I—Chris—I—I haven't a map in the house."

He did not press the matter. He went out into the back yard presently, under the grape trellis, and there he stood still for a long time, staring at nothing in particular.

He was growing up.

He went away to boarding school not long after this, taking with him the picture of his adored mother, the treasured epic of his dark, strong fathers, his narrow shoulders, his rare, blind bursts of passion, his newborn wonder, and his violin. At school they thought him a queer one.

The destinies of men are unaccountable things. Five children in the village of Deer Bay came down with diphtheria. That was why the academy shut up for a week, and that was what started Christopher on his way home for an unexpected holiday. And then it was only by one chance in a thousand that he should glimpse his mother's face in the down train halted at the Junction where he himself was changing.

She did not see him till he came striding along the aisle of her coach, his arms full of his things, face flushed, eyes brimming with the surprise and pleasure of seeing her, lips trembling questions.

"Why, Mother, what on earth? Where are you going? I'm to have a week at least, Mother; and here you're going away, and you didn't tell me, and what is it, and everything?"

His eager voice trailed off. The color drained out of his face, and there was a shadow in his eyes. He drew back from her the least way.

"What is it, Mother? *Mother!*"

Somewhere on the platform outside the conductor's droning "——*board*" ran along the coaches. Agnes Kain opened her white lips.

"Get off before it's too late, Christopher. I haven't time to explain now. Go home, and Mary will see you have everything. I'll be back in a day or so. Kiss me, and go quickly. Quickly!"

He did not kiss her. He would not have kissed her for worlds. He was too bewildered, dazed, lost, too inexpressibly hurt. On the platform outside, had she turned ever so little to look, she might

146

have seen his face again for an instant as the wheels ground on the rails. Color was coming back to it again, a murky color like the shadow of a red cloud.

They must have wondered, in the coach with her, at the change in the calm, unobtrusive, well-gowned gentlewoman, their fellow passenger. Those that were left after another two hours saw her get down at a barren station where an old man waited in a carriage. The halt was brief, and none of them caught sight of the boyish figure that slipped down from the rearmost coach to take shelter for himself and his dark, tempest-ridden face behind the shed at the end of the platform. . . .

Christopher walked out across a broad, high, cloudy plain, following a red road, led by the dust feather hanging over the distant carriage.

He walked for miles, creeping antlike between the immensities of the brown plain and the tumbled sky. Had he been less implacable, less intent, he might have noticed many things: the changing conformation of the clouds, the far flight of a gull, the new perfume and texture of the wind that flowed over his hot temples. But as it was, the sea took him by surprise. Coming over a little rise, his eyes focused for another long, dun fold of the plain, it seemed for an instant as if he had lost his balance above a void; for a wink he felt the passing of a strange sickness. He went off a little way to the side of the road and sat down on a flat stone.

The world had become of a sudden infinitely simple, as simple as the inside of a cup. The land broke down under him, a long, naked slope fringed at the foot by a ribbon of woods. Through the upper branches he saw the shingles and chimneys of a pale gray village clinging to a white beach, a beach which ran up to the left in a border flight of cliffs, showing on their crest a cluster of roofs and dull green gable ends against the sea that lifted vast, unbroken, to the rim of the cup.

Christopher was fifteen, and queer even for that queer age. He had a streak of the girl in him at his adolescence, and, as he sat there in a huddle, the wind coming out of this huge new gulf of life seemed to pass through him, bone and tissue, and tears rolled down his face.

The carriage bearing his strange mother was gone, from sight

147

and from mind. His eyes came down from the lilac-crowned hill to the beach, where it showed in white patches through the wood, and he saw that the wood was of willows. And he remembered the plain behind him, the wide, brown moor under the cloud. He got up on his wobbly legs. There were stones all about him in the whispering wire grass, and like them the one he had been sitting on bore a blurred inscription. He read it aloud, for some reason, his voice borne away faintly on the river of air:

MAYNARD KAIN, ESQUIRE

1809—1839

THIS MONUMENT ERECTED IN HIS MEMORY BY HIS SORROWING WIDOW, HARRIET BURNAM KAIN

"THE WINDY GALES OF THE WEST INDIES
LAID CLAIM TO HIS NOBLE SOUL
AND TOOK HIM ON HIGH TO HIS CREATOR
WHO MADE HIM WHOLE."

His gaze went on to another of those worn stones.

HERE LIE THE EARTHLY REMAINS OF
MAYNARD KAIN, SECOND
BORN 1835—DIED 1863 FOR THE PRESERVATION OF THE UNION

There was no moss or lichen on this wind-scored slope. In the falling dusk the old white stones stood up like the bones of the dead themselves, and the only sound was the rustle of the wire-grass creeping over them in a dry tide. The boy had taken off his cap; the sea-wind moving under the mat of his damp hair gave it the look of some somber, outlandish cowl. With the night coming on, his solemnity had an elfin quality. He found at last what he was looking for, and his fingers had to help his eyes.

DANIEL KAIN
BELOVED HUSBAND OF AGNES WILLOUGHBY KAIN
BORN 1860—DIED 1886
"FORGIVE THEM FOR THEY KNOW NOT WHAT THEY DO."

Christopher Kain told me that he left the naked graveyard re-peating it to himself, "Forgive them, for they know not what they do," conscious less of the words than of the august rhythm falling in with the pulse of his exaltation.

The velvet darkness that hangs under clouds had come down over the hill and the great marsh stretching away to the south of it. Agnes Kain stood in the open doorway, one hand on the brown wood, the other pressed to her cheek.

"You heard it *that* time, Nelson?"

"No, ma'am." The old man in the entrance-hall behind her shook his head. In the thin, blown light of the candelabra which he held high, the worry and doubt of her deepened on his singularly unlined face.

"And you might well catch your death in that draft, ma'am."

But she only continued to stare out between the pillars where the lilac-hedge made a wall of deeper blackness across the night.

"What am I thinking of?" she whispered, and then: *"There!"*

And this time the old man heard it; a nearer, wind-blown hail.

"Mother! Oh, Mother!"

The boy came striding through the gap of the gate in the hedge.

"It's I, Mother! Chris! Aren't you surprised?"

She had no answer. As he came she turned and moved away from the door, and the old man, peering from under the flat candle-flames, saw her face like wax. And he saw the boy, Christopher, in the doorway, his hands flung out, his face transfigured.

"Mother! I'm here! Don't you understand?"

He touched her shoulder. She turned to him, as it were lazily.

"Yes," she breathed. "I see."

He threw his arms about her, and felt her shaking from head to foot. But he was shaking, too.

"I knew the way!" he cried. "I knew it, Mother, I knew it! I came down from the Moor and there was the Willow Wood, and I knew the way home. And when I came, Mother, it was like the trees bowing down their branches in the dark. And when I came by the Beach, Mother, it was like a roll of drums, beating for me, and when I came to the Hill I saw the Hedge standing against the sky, and I came, and here I am!"

She expressed no wonder, asked no question.

"Yes," was all she said, and it was as if she spoke of a tree coming to its leaf, the wind to its height, the tide to its flood.

He had been less rapt and triumphant he must have wondered more at that icy lassitude, and at the cloak of ceremony she wrapped

149

about her to hide a terror. It was queer to hear the chill urbanity of her: "This is Christopher, Nelson; Christopher, this is your father's servant, Nelson." It was queerer still to see the fastidious decorum with which she led him over this, the familiar house of his fathers.

He might have been a stranger, come with a guidebook in his hand. When he stood on his heels in the big drawing-room, staring up with all his eyes at the likenesses of those men he had known so well, it was strange to hear her going on with all the patter of the gallery attendant, names of painters, prices, dates. He stood before the portrait of Daniel Kain, his father, a dark-skinned, longish face with a slightly protruding nether lip, hollow temples, and a round chin, deeply cleft. As in all the others, the eyes, even in the dead pigment, seemed to shine with an odd, fixed luminosity of their own, and like the others from first to last of the line, it bore upon it the stamp of an imperishable youth. And all the while he stood there, drinking it in, detail by detail, his mother spoke, not of the face, but of the frame, some obscure and unsuspected excellence in the gold-leaf on the frame.

More than once in that stately tour of halls and chambers he found himself protesting gaily, "I know, Mother! I know, I know!"

But the contagion of his glory did not seem to touch her. Nothing seemed to touch her. Only once was the fragile, bright shell of her punctilio penetrated for a moment, and that was when Christopher, lagging, turned back to a door they were about to pass and threw it open with the happy laugh of a discoverer. And then, even before she could have hushed him, the laughter on his lips died of itself.

A man lay on a bed in the room, his face as colorless and still as the pillow behind it. His eyes were open, but they did not move from the three candles burning on the high bureau, and he seemed unconscious of any intrusion.

"I didn't know!" Christopher whispered, shocked, and shamed.

When the door was closed again his mother explained. She explained at length, concisely, standing quite still, with one frail, fine hand worrying the locket she wore at her throat. Nelson stood quite still too, his attention engrossed in his candle-wicks. And Christopher stood quite still, and all their shadows— That man was the caretaker, the man, Christopher was to understand, who had been looking after the place. His name was Sanderson. He had fallen ill, very ill. In fact he was dying. And that was why Christopher's mother had to come down, post-haste, without warning. To see about some papers. Some papers. Christopher was to understand—

Christopher understood. Indeed there was not much to understand. And yet, when they had gone on, he was bothered by it. Already, so young he was, so ruthless, and so romantic, he had begun to be a little ashamed of that fading, matter-of-fact world of Concord Street. And it was with just that world which he wished to forget that the man lying ill in the candlelit chamber was linked in Christopher's memory. For it was the same man he had seen in the doorway that morning months ago, with a brown hat in one hand and a thorn stick in the other.

Even a thing like that may be half put aside, though—for a while. And by the time Christopher went to his room for the night, the thought of the interloper had returned into the back of his mind, and they were all Kains there on the Hill, inheritors of Romance. He found himself bowing to his mother with a courtliness he had never known, and an "I wish you a good night," sounding a century old on his lips. He saw the remote, patrician figure bow as gravely in return, a petal of color as hard as paint on the whiteness of either cheek. He did not see her afterward, though—when the merciful door was closed.

Before he slept he explored the chamber, touching old objects with reverent finger-tips. He came on a leather case like an absurdly overgrown beetle, hidden in a corner, and a violoncello was in it. He had seen such things before, but he had never touched one, and when he lifted it from the case he had a moment of feeling very odd at the pit of his stomach. Sitting in his under-things on the edge of the bed, he held the wine-colored creature in the crook of his arm for a long time, the look in his round eyes, half eagerness, half pain, of one pursuing the shadow of some ghostly and elusive memory.

He touched the C-string by-and-by with an adventuring thumb. I have heard "Ugo" sing, myself, and I know what Christopher meant when he said that the sound did not come *out* of the instrument, but that it came *in* to it, sweeping home from all the walls and corners of the chamber, a slow, rich, concentric wind of tone.

151

He felt it about him, murmurous, pulsating, like the sound of surf borne from some far-off coast.

And then it was like drums, still farther off. And then it was the feet of marching men, massive, dark, grave men with luminous eyes, and the stamp on their faces of an imperishable youth.

He sat there so lost and rapt that he heard nothing of his mother's footsteps hurrying in the hall; knew nothing till he saw her face in the open doorway. She had forgotten herself this time; that fragile defense of gentility was down. For a moment they stared at each other across a gulf of silence, and little by little the boy's cheeks grew as white as hers, his hands as cold, his lungs as empty of breath.

"What is it, Mother?"

"Oh Christopher, Christopher—Go to bed, dear."

He did not know why, but of a sudden he felt ashamed and a little frightened, and, blowing out the candle, he crept under the covers.

The afternoon was bright with a rare sun, and the world was quiet. Christopher lay full-spread on the turf, listening idly to the "clip-clop" of Nelson's shears as the old man trimmed the hedge.

"And was my father *very* strong?" he asked with a drowsy pride.

"No, not so very." Nelson stopped clipping and was immediately lost in the past.

"Only when he was *that* way five strong men couldn't turn him. I'll say that. No, if they had to get him with a shotgun that day, 'twas nobody's fault nor sin. If Guy Bullard seen Daniel there on the sand with an ax in his hand and foam-like on his lips, and the little ones cornered where he caught them between cliff and water— Guy's own baby amongst them—and knowing the sickness of the Kains as he and everybody else did—why, I'm free and willing to say 'twas his bounden duty to hold a true aim and pull a steady trigger on Daniel, man of his though I was, and man of his poor father before him—"

Nelson was a queer fellow. His age was really greater than his unlined face would have told, and his mind, laden with the burden of misty years, had grown tired. It is charitable to think that, once launched on the river of memory, the dreaming fellow forgot where he was and to what audience he spoke, that audience lying quiet, so very quiet, in the deep grass behind his back.

"No, I can't make it right to lay blame on any man for it, no more than I can on them, his brother officers, that broke Maynard's neck with their tent-pegs the night after Gettysburg. No, no—"

It was evidently a time-worn theme, an argument, an *apologia*, accepted after years of bitterness and self-searching. He went on with the remote serenity of age, that has escaped the toils of passion, pursuing the old, worn path of his mind, his eyes buried in vacancy.

"No, 'twas a mercy to the both of them, father and son, and a man must see it so. 'Twould be better of course if they could have gone easier, same as the *old* Maynard went, thinking himself the Lord our God to walk on the water and calm the West Indy gale. That's better, better for all hands round. But if it had to come so, in violence and fear, then nobody need feel the sin of it on his soul—nobody excepting the old man Bickers, him that told Daniel. For 'twas from that day he began to take it on.

"I saw it myself. There was Daniel come home from other parts where his mother had kept him, out of gossip's way, bright as you please and knowing nothing wrong with the blood of the Kains. And so I say the sin lays on the loose-wagging tongue of Bickers, for from the day he let it out to Daniel, Daniel changed. 'Twas like he'd heard his doom, and went to it. Bickers is dead a long time now, but may the Lord God lay eternal damnation on his soul!"

Even then there was no heat; the curse had grown a formula. Having come to the end, the old man's eyes tumbled down painlessly out of the void and discovered the shears in his hand.

"Dear me, that's so," he said to himself. One thought was enough at a time. He fell to work again. The steady "clip-clip-clip" moved off slowly along the hedge. Not once did he remember; not once as the indefatigable worker shuffled himself out of sight around the house did he look back with any stirring of recollection at the boyish figure lying there as still as a shadow cast in the deep grass.

A faintly lopsided moon swam in the zenith. For three days now that rare clarity had hung in the sky, and for three nights the moon had grown. Its benign, poisonous illumination flowed down steeply through the windows of the dark chamber where Christopher huddled on the bed's edge, three pale, chill islands spread on the polished floor.

Once again the boy brought the bow home across the shivering strings, and, as if ears could be thirsty as a drunkard's throat, he drank his fill of the 'cello's deep, full-membered chord. The air was heavy with the resonance of marching feet, ghostly feet marching and marching down upon him in slow, inexorable crescendo as the tides ebbed later among the sedges on the marsh and the moon grew big. And above the pulse of the march he seemed to hear another cadence, a thin laughter.

He laughed too, giving himself up to that spectral contagion. He saw the fat, iridescent bubble with the Hill in it, the House of his dreams, the Beach and the Moor and Willow Wood of fancy, and all the grave, strong, gentle line of Kains to whom he had been made bow down in worship. He saw himself taken in, soul and body, by a thin-plated fraud, a cheap trick of mother's words, as, before him, his father had been. And the faint exhalations from the moon-patches on the floor showed his face contorted with a still, set grimace of mirth.

Anger came over him in a white veil, twitching his lips and his toes and bending his fingers in knots. Through the veil a sound crept, a sound he knew well by this time, secret footfalls in the hall, faltering, retreating, loitering, returning to lag near the door.

How he hated her! It is curious that not once did his passion turn against his blighted fathers; it was against the woman who had borne him, the babe, and lied to him, the boy—against her, and against that man, that interloper, dying in a room below.

The thought that had been willing to creep out of sight into the back-country of his mind on that first night, came out now like a red, devouring cloud. Who was that man?

What was he dying of—or *supposed* to be dying of? What had he been doing that morning in Concord Street? What was he doing here, in the house of the men who would never grow old? Why had his mother come down here, where he was, so queerly, so secretly, so frightened?

Christopher would have liked to kill that man. He shivered and licked his lips. He would have liked to do something bloody and abominable to that face with the hollow cheeks, the sunken gray eyes, and the forehead, high, sallow, and moist. He would have liked to take an ax in his hand and run along the thundering beach and catch that face in a corner somewhere between cliff and water. The desire to do this thing possessed him and blinded him like the kiss of lightning.

He found himself on the floor at the edge of the moonlight, full of weakness and nausea. He felt himself weeping as he crawled back to the bed, his cheeks and neck bathed in a flood of painless tears. He threw himself down, dazed with exhaustion.

It seemed to him that his mother had been calling a long while. "Christopher! What is it? What is it, boy?"

He had heard no footsteps, going or coming; she must have been there all the time, waiting, listening, her ear pressed to the thick, old paneling of the door. The thought was like wine; the torment of her whispering was sweet in his ears.

"Oh, Chris, Chris! You're making yourself sick!"

"Yes," he said. He lifted on an elbow and repeated it in a voice which must have sounded strange enough to the listener beyond the door. "Yes!" he said. "Yes!"

"Go away!" he cried of a sudden, making a wide, dim, imperious gesture in the dark.

"No, no," the imploring whisper crept in. "You're making yourself sick—Christopher—all over nothing—nothing in the world. It's so foolish—so foolish—foolish! Oh, if I could only tell you, Christopher—if I could tell you—"

"Tell me *what?*" He shuddered with the ecstacy of his own irony. "Who that man is? That 'caretaker'? What he's doing here? What *you're* doing here?—" He began to scream in a high, brittle voice. *"Go away from that door! Go away!"*

This time she obeyed. He heard her retreating, soft-footed and frightened, along the hall. She was abandoning him—without so much as trying the door, just once again, to see if it were still bolted against her.

She did not care. She was sneaking off—down the stairs—Oh, yes, he knew where.

His lips began to twitch again and his finger-nails scratched on the bed-clothes. If only he had something, some weapon, an ax, a broad, keen, glittering ax! He would show them! He was strong,

155

incredibly strong! Five men could not have turned him back from what he was going to do—if only he had something.

His hand, creeping, groping, closed on the neck of the 'cello leaning by the bed. He laughed.

Oh, yes, he would stop her from going down there; he would hold her just where she was on the dark stair, nerveless, breathless, as long as he liked; if he liked he would bring her back, cringing, begging.

He drew the bow, and laughed higher and louder yet to hear the booming discord rocking in upon him from the shadows. Swaying from side to side he lashed the hollow creature to madness. They came in the press of the gale, marching, marching, the wild, dark pageant of his fathers, nearer and nearer through the moon-struck night.

"Tell me *what?*" he laughed. *"What?"*

And abruptly he slept, sprawling cross-wise on the covers, half-clothed, dishevelled, triumphant.

It was not the same night, but another, whether the next or the next but one, or two, Christopher can not say. But he was out of doors.

He had escaped from the house at dusk; he knew that. He remembered the wide, hushed mystery of twilight as he paused on the door-sill between the fading pillars, the death of day running crimson in the west; in the east the still, white travail of the sea and the moon—the queer moment.

He had run away, through the hedge and down the back side of the hill, torn between the two, the death, warm and red like life, and the birth, pale, chill, and inexorable as death.

Most of that daft night-running will always be blank in Christopher's mind; moments, and moments only, like islands of clarity, remain. He brings back one vivid interval when he found himself seated on his father's gravestone among the whispering grasses, staring down into the pallid bowl of the world. And in that moment he knew what Daniel Kain had felt, and Maynard Kain before him; a passionate and contemptuous hatred for all the dullards in the world who never dreamed dreams or saw visions or sang wordless songs or ran naked-hearted in the flood of the full-blown moon. He hated them because they could not by any possibility comprehend his magnificent separation, his starry sanity, his—kinship with the gods. And he had a new thirst to obliterate the whole creeping race of dust-dwellers with one wide, incomparably bloody gesture.

It was late when he found himself back again before the house, and an ink-black cloud touched the moon's edge. After the airless evening a wind had sprung up in the east; it thrashed among the lilac-stems as he came through them and across the turf, silent-footed as an Indian. In his right hand he had a bread knife, held butt to thumb, dagger-wise. Where he had come by the rust-bitten thing no one knows, least of all himself. In the broken light his eyes shone with a curious luminosity of their own, absorbed, introspective.

All the windows were dark, and the entrance-hall, when he slipped in between the pillars; but across its floor he saw light thrown in a yellow ribbon from the half-closed door of the drawing-room.

It took his attention, laid hands on his imagination. He began to struggle against it.

He would *not* go into that room. He was going to *another* room. To stay him, he made a picture of that other room in his tumbled mind—the high, bleak walls, the bureau with the three candles burning wanly, the bed, the face of the man on the bed. And when his rebellious feet, surrendering him up to the lure of that beckoning ribbon, had edged as far as the door, and he had pushed it a little further ajar to get his head in, he saw that the face itself was there in the drawing room.

He stood there for some time, his shoulder pressed against the door-jamb, his eyes blinking.

His slow attention moved from the face to the satin pillows that wedged it in, and then to the woman that must have been his mother, kneeling beside the casket with her arms crooked on the shining cover and her head down between them. And across from her leaned "Ugo," the 'cello, come down from his chamber to stand vigil at the other shoulder of the dead.

The first thing that came into his groping mind was a bitter sense of abandonment. The little core of candle-light hanging in the gloom left him out. Its unstirring occupants, the woman, the 'cello, and the clay, seemed sufficient to themselves. His mother had forgotten him.

Bruised, sullen, moved by some deep-lying instinct of the clan, his eyes left them and sought the wall beyond, where there were those who would not forget him, come what might, blood of his blood and mind of his own queer mind. And there among the shadowed faces he searched for one in vain. As if that candlelit tableau, somehow holy and somehow abominable, were not for the eyes of one of them, the face of Daniel, the wedded husband, had been turned to the wall.

Here was something definite, something Christopher could take hold of, and something that *he would not have.*

His mother seemed not to have known he was near till he flung the door back and came stalking into the light with the rusty bread-knife in his hand. None would have imagined there was blood enough left in her wasted heart, but her face went crimson when she lifted it and saw him.

It brought him up short—the blush, where he had looked for fright. It shocked him, and, shocking him, more than by a thousand labored words of explanation it opened a window in his disordered brain. He stood gawking with the effort of thought, hardly conscious of his mother's cry.

"Christopher, I never meant you to know!"

He kept on staring at the ashen face between the pillows, long (as his own was long), sensitive, worn; and at the 'cello keeping incorruptible vigil over its dead. And then slowly his eyes went down to his own left hand, to which that same old wine-brown creature had come home from the first with a curious sense of fitness and authority and right.

"Who is this man?"

"Don't look at me so! Don't, Chris!"

But he did look at her. Preoccupied as he was, he was appalled at sight of the damage the half-dozen days had done. She had been so much the lady, so perfectly the gentlewoman. To no one had the outward gesture and symbol of purity been more precious. No whisper had ever breathed against her. If there had been secrets behind her, they had been dead; if a skeleton, the closet had been closed. And now, looking down on her, he was not only appalled, he was a little sickened, as one might be to find squalor and decay creeping into a familiar and once immaculate room.

"Who is this man?" he repeated.

"He grew up with me." She half raised herself on her knees in the eagerness of her appeal. "We were boy and girl togther at home in Maryland. We were meant for each other, Chris. We were always to marry—always, Chris. And when I went away, and when I married your—when I married Daniel Kain, *he* hunted and he searched and he found me here. He was with me, he stood by me through that awful year—and—that was how it happened. I tell you, Christopher, darling, we were meant for each other. John Sanderson and I. He loved me more than poor Daniel ever did or could, loved me enough to throw away a life of promise, just to hang on here after every one else was gone, alone with his 'cello and his one little memory. And I loved him enough to—to—*Christopher, don't look at me so!*"

His eyes did not waver. You must remember his age, the immaculate, ruthless, mid-Victorian 'teens; and you must remember his bringing-up.

"And so this was my father," he said. And then he went on without waiting, his voice breaking into falsetto with the fierceness of his charge. "And you would have kept on lying to me! If I hadn't happened, just happened to find you here, now, you would have gone on keeping me in the dark! You would have stood by and seen me—well—*go crazy!* Yes, go crazy, thinking I was—well, thinking I was meant for it! And all to save your precious—"

She was down on the floor again, what was left of the gentle-woman, wailing.

"But you don't know what it means to a woman, Chris! You don't know what it means to a woman!"

A wave of rebellion brought her up and she strained toward him across the coffin.

Isn't it something, then, that I gave you a father with a *mind?* And if you think you've been sinned against, think of me! Sin! You call it *sin!* Well, isn't it *anything at all* that by my 'sin' my son's blood came down to him *clean?* Tell me that!"

He shook himself, and his flame turned to sullenness.

159

"It's not so," he glowered.

All the girl in him, the poet, the hero-worshiping boy, rebelled. His harassed eyes went to the wall beyond and the faces there, the ghosts of the doomed, glorious, youth-ridden line, priceless possessions of his dreams. He would not lose them; he refused to be robbed of a tragic birthright. He wanted some gesture puissant enough to turn back and blot out all that had been told him.

"It's not his!" he cried. And reaching out fiercely he dragged the 'cello away from the coffin's side. He stood for an instant at bay, bitter, defiant.

"It's not his! It's mine. It's—it's—*ours!*"

And then he fled out into the dark of the entrance-hall and up the black stairs. In his room there was no moonlight now, for the cloud ran over the sky, and the rain had come.

"It isn't so, it isn't so!" It was like a sob in his throat.

He struck on the full strings. And listening—breathless—through the dying discord he heard—the liquid whispers of the rain, nothing more. He lashed with a wild bow, time and again. But something was broken, something was lost; out of the surf of sound he could no longer fashion the measure of marching feet. The mad Kains had found him out, and cast him out. No longer could he dream them in dreams or run naked-hearted with them in the flood of the moon, for he was no blood of theirs, and they were gone. And huddling down on the edge of the bed, he wept.

The tears washed his eyes and falling down bathed his strengthless hands. And beyond the fantom windows, over the Marsh and the Moor and the Hill that were not his, the graves of strangers and the lost Willow Wood, lay the healing rain. He heard it in gurgling rivulets along the gutters overhead. He heard the soft impact, like a kiss, brushing the reedy cheeks of the Marsh, the showery shouldering of branches, the aspiration of myriad drinking grasses, the far whisper of waters coming home to the waters of the sea—the long, low melody of the rain.

And by and by he found it was "Ugo," the 'cello, and he was playing.

They went home the following afternoon, he and his mother. Or, rather, she went home, and he with her as far as the Junction, where he changed for school.

160

They had not much to say to each other through the journey. The boy had to be given time. Five years younger, or fifteen years older, it would have been easier for him to look at his mother. You must remember what his mother had meant to him, and what, bound up still in the fierce and somber battle of adolescence, she must mean to him now.

As for Agnes Kain, she did not look at him, either. Through the changing hours her eyes rested on the transparent hands lying crossed in her lap. She seemed very tired and very white. Her hair was done up less tidily, her lace cuffs were less fresh than they had been wont to be. About her whole presence there was a troubling hint of let-down, something obscurely slatternly, a kind of awkward and unlovely nakedness.

She really spoke to him for the first time at the Junction, when he stood before her, slim and uncouth under the huge burden of "Ugo," fumbling through his leave-taking.

"Christopher," she said. "Try not to think of me—always—as—as—well, when you're older, Christopher, you'll know what I mean."

That was the last time he ever heard her speak. He saw her once again—two days later—but the telegram was delayed and his train was late, and when he came beside her bed she said nothing. She looked into his eyes searchingly—for a long while—and died.

That space stands for the interval of silence that fell after Christopher had told me the story. I thought he had quite finished. He sat motionless, his shoulders fallen forward, his eyes fixed in the heart of the incandescent globe over the dressing-table, his long fingers wrapped around the neck of the 'cello.

"And so she got me through those years," he said. "Those nip-and-tuck years that followed. By her lie."

"Insanity is a queer thing," he went on, still brooding into the light. "There's more of it about than we're apt to think. It works in so many ways. In hobbies, arts, philosophies. Music is a kind of insanity. I know. I've got *mine* penned up in music now, and I think I can keep it there now, and save my soul."

"*Yours?*"

"Yes, mine. I know now—now that it's safe for me to know. I was down at that village by the Beach a year or so ago. I'm a Kain, of course, one of the crazy Kains, after all. John Sanderson was born in the village and lived there till his death. Only once that folks could remember had he been away, and that was when he took some papers to the city for Mrs. Kain to sign. He was caretaker at the old 'Kain place' the last ten years of his life, and deaf, they said, since his tenth year—'deaf as a post.' And they told me something else. They said there was a story that before my father, Daniel, married her, my mother had been an actress. An actress! You'll understand that *I* needed no one to tell me *that!*

"One told me he had heard that she was a *great* actress. Dear God, if they could only know! When I think of that night and that setting, that scene! It killed her—and it got me over the wall—"

STUDY NOTES

1. Point out the use of the *in-medias-res* beginning in "For They Know Not What They Do."

2. List all the elements that Steele employs in this story for creating the atmosphere of impending madness, such as the shining of the moon, the discordant tone of the 'cello, and the sound of the marching feet of Christopher's insane ancestors.

3. Show that romanticism is present in this story in the play of Christopher's imagination.

4. Inasmuch as Pattee has mentioned Steele's "seemingly realistic methods," indicate the extent to which this story is romantic and the extent to which it is realisic.

5. Outline the plot, making clear that all the action concerns one main situation or crisis.

6. Cite instances of implication of meaning in this story and discover as many of the devices by which the suggested effect is produced as possible.

7. By what methods does Steele characterize Agnes Kain and Christopher and Nelson?

8. What purpose does the insanity scene, in which Christopher appears before his mother with a bread-knife in his hand, serve?

9. List as many of the qualities of Steele's artistic style as you can discover in this story.

10. Collect evidence that the locale of Christopher's ancestral home was either the Massachusetts coastal region that had served for the narratives of Steele's *Land's End* volume or a similar region.

11. Combining the epitaphs with Nelson's ruminations, state the method by which death came to Christopher's father, grandfather, and great-grandfather.

12. Formulate the theme, the underlying philosophical idea, of "For They Know Not What They Do"; also state the secondary theme, if you find one; and show that the theme, the atmosphere, the plot, and the characters harmonize.

COMPARISON EXERCISES

1. Compare "The Great Stone Face" and "For They Know Not What They Do" for their combination of realism and romanticism.

2. Judging from these two stories, which writer, Hawthorne or Steele, has given his fancy the freer play?

3. Which story uses the more exotic and vivid atmosphere?

4. Which probably draws its characterization the more heavily from real-life persons?

5. Which more strikingly impresses a moral or a philosophical truth and by what techniques does the story achieve this result?

WRITING SUGGESTION

Prepare a story that in its plot and implication supports some important truth or ethical principle, avoiding too obvious preaching and trying to make the action as interesting as the theme.

ATMOSPHERE

Introduction to Stories That Make
Atmosphere Prominent

A LL short stories have some measure of atmosphere, according to any commonly assigned definition. In most stories, however, atmosphere is less prominent than either plot or character. A story dominated by atmosphere is difficult to write for two reasons: first, such a narrative subordinates plot; second, it subordinates character. It is not usual for setting or mood or atmosphere to dominate a story. For atmosphere to be predominant, the chief character must be freakish or inhuman or abnormal.

Some textbook writers do not distinguish *tone, mood,* and *atmosphere,*[1] but others attach varying shades of meaning to these terms.[2] When differentiations are attempted, these names are defined approximately as follows: Tone is the author's emotional attitude toward his materials, for example, the characters and the situations that he places in a story. Among the kinds of tone that critics mention are comedy, cynicism, dreaminess, foreboding, melancholy, mock seriousness, romanticism, seriousness, tragedy, and wit. Mood is the emotional attitude of a fictitious character toward some action or person or other object. Among the moods commonly named are devotion, disillusion, expectancy, joy, moroseness, mystery, remorse, sadness, weariness, and whimsicality. Atmosphere is the emotional reaction of the reader to locale or setting, to the "world in which the events" occur, to "time, place, conditions, and the attendant mood." Types of atmosphere mentioned include anxiety, dread, fantasy, gloom, horror, irreverence, mystery, mysticism, rapture, resignation, and unreality.

---

[1] See Robert Witbeck Babcock and Others, *Creative Writing for College Students,* New York: American Book Company, 1938, pp. 324-5 and 357.
[2] West and Stallman, *op. cit.,* pp. 95-8 and 271.

If one needs a definition for *atmosphere,* that already presented will serve. Whether a person uses *tone, mood,* and *atmosphere* interchangeably or distinguishes their meanings is probably not greatly important. The attempted differentiations perhaps somewhat overlap. The emotional attitudes of an author, a character, and a reader toward a particular piece of story material are likely, at least in many cases, to be almost identical.

More important than the definitions or than distinguishing the terms or using them interchangeably is a knowledge of the methods by which tone or mood or atmosphere may be produced. Dialogue, setting, action, and style are useful techniques for engendering atmosphere. In dialogue, the nature of the topics discussed, the ideas expressed, and the manner of speaking may all have an emotional effect upon the reader. Imaginative description of landscape or of any scene or even of a person evokes atmosphere. The writer should visualize the setting clearly and select the details that will help the reader to obtain the image. Actions can create or strengthen atmosphere; for example, in Hawthorne's "Rappaccini's Daughter" the supernatural incidents produce a sense of mystery, and in Poe's "Fall of the House of Usher" such violence as the premature burial of Madeline and the sudden death of Roderick intensifies in the reader a feeling of horror. Stylistic features that may stimulate emotional reaction are connotative diction, repetition of color, realistic oaths, contrast between somewhat dissimilar elements, and instances of emotion-exciting symbolism. Connotative adjectives of color, either drab or flashing, and concrete verbs may produce striking images or make definite emotional suggestions. Repeated mentions of color, red for example, utilizing such synonyms as cerise, cherry, damask, rose, scarlet, and vermilion, may arouse emotion. The use of a few realistic oaths such as a callous, irreligious, profane person might employ may produce, even in the reader, either irreverence or disgust over someone else's irreverence. Some magazines, of course, frown on the use of the oath device. Contrasts between periods of time or between characters, their social standings or their personalities, can induce attitudes toward these times or these persons. Symbolism can contribute to the reader's emotional impression, as occurs in "The Fall of the House of Usher," when the widening of the fissure in the Usher mansion from roof to base represents the death of Roderick—his giving up his soul. It is possible, of course, for certain methods of creating atmosphere, for example dialogue and description, to combine in the same story.

Atmosphere should be integrated with plot, characterization, setting, and theme. It should advance the plot. It can foreshadow future action—can prepare the reader against overshock. It can affect the creation of characters and of the activities in which these persons engage. Only such actions should be attributed to any individual as are congruous with his personality. Atmosphere is closely related to the setting. The writer should select the background that will provide the kind of atmosphere suited to the action. And, finally, the emotional impact of the whole narrative should be appropriate to the theme, should help the theme to impart its meaning and the reader to grasp the implication of the story.

THE MASQUE OF THE RED DEATH [1]
(1842)
EDGAR ALLAN POE

THE "Red Death" had long devastated the country. No pestilence had ever been so fatal or so hideous. Blood was its Avatar and its seal—the redness and the horror of blood. There were sharp pains and sudden dizziness, and then profuse bleeding at the pores, with dissolution. The scarlet stains upon the body, and especially upon the face, of the victim were the pest ban which shut him out from the aid and from the sympathy of his fellow men. And the whole seizure, progress, and termination of the disease were the incidents of half an hour.

But the Prince Prospero was happy and dauntless and sagacious. When his dominions were half depopulated, he summoned to his presence a thousand hale and lighthearted friends from among the knights and dames of his court, and with these retired to the deep seclusion of one of his castellated abbeys. This was an extensive and magnificent structure, the creation of the prince's own eccentric yet august taste. A strong and lofty wall girdled it in. This wall had gates of iron. The courtiers, having entered, brought furnaces and massy hammers and welded the bolts. They resolved to leave means neither of ingress nor egress to the sudden impulses of despair or of frenzy from within. The abbey was amply provisioned. With such precautions the courtiers might bid defiance to contagion. The external world could take care of itself. In the mean time it was folly to grieve or to think. The prince had provided all the appliances of pleasure. There were buffoons, there were improvisatori, there were ballet dancers, there were musicians, there was beauty, there was wine. All these and security were within. Without was the "Red Death."

It was toward the close of the fifth or sixth month of his seclusion, and while the pestilence raged most furiously abroad, that the Prince Prospero entertained his thousand friends at a masked ball of the most unusual significance.

It was a voluptuous scene, that masquerade. But first let me tell

---

[1] First published in *Graham's Magazine* (May, 1842).

of the rooms in which it was held. There were seven—an imperial suite. In many palaces, however, such suites form a long and straight vista, while the folding doors slide back nearly to the walls on either hand, so that the view of the whole extent is scarcely impeded. Here the case was very different, as might have been expected from the prince's love of the bizarre. The apartments were so irregularly disposed that the vision embraced but little more than one at a time. There was a sharp turn at every twenty or thirty yards, and at each turn a novel effect. To the right and left, in the middle of each wall, a tall and narrow Gothic window looked out upon a closed corridor which pursued the windings of the suite. These windows were of stained glass, whose color varied in accordance with the prevailing hue of the decorations of the chamber into which it opened. That at the eastern extremity was hung, for example, in blue, and vividly blue were its windows. The second chamber was purple in its ornaments and tapestries, and here the panes were purple. The third was green throughout, and so were the casements. The fourth was furnished and lighted with orange, the fifth with white, the sixth with violet. The seventh apartment was closely shrouded in black velvet tapestries that hung all over the ceiling and down the walls, falling in heavy folds upon a carpet of the same material and hue. But, in this chamber only, the color of the windows failed to correspond with the decorations. The panes here were scarlet—a deep blood-color. Now in no one of the seven apartments was there any lamp or candelabrum amid the profusion of golden ornaments that lay scattered to and fro or depended from the roof. There was no light of any kind emanating from lamp or candle within the suite of chambers. But in the corridors that followed the suite there stood, opposite to each window, a heavy tripod, bearing a brazier of fire that projected its rays through the tinted glass and so glaringly illumined the room. And thus were produced a multitude of gaudy and fantastic appearances. But in the western or black chamber the effect of the firelight that streamed upon the dark hanging through the blood-tinted panes was ghastly in the extreme and produced so wild a look upon the countenances of those who entered that there were few of the company bold enough to set foot within its precincts at all.

It was in this apartment, also, that there stood against the western

169

wall a gigantic clock of ebony. Its pendulum swung to and fro with a dull, heavy, monotonous clang; and when the minute hand made the circuit of the face and the hour was to be stricken, there came from the brazen lungs of the clock a sound which was clear and loud and deep and exceedingly musical, but of so peculiar a note and emphasis that, at each lapse of an hour, the musicians of the orchestra were constrained to pause momentarily in their performance, to hearken to the sound; and thus the waltzers perforce ceased their evolutions; and there was a brief disconcert of the whole gay company; and, while the chimes of the clock yet rang, it was observed that the giddiest grew pale, and the more aged and sedate passed their hands over their brows as if in confused reverie or meditation. But when the echoes had fully ceased, a light laughter at once pervaded the assembly; the musicians looked at each other and smiled as if at their own nervousness and folly and made whispering vows each to the other that the next chiming of the clock should produce in them no similar emotion; and then, after the lapse of sixty minutes (which embrace three thousand and six hundred seconds of the Time that flies), there came yet another chiming of the clock, and then were the same disconcert and tremulousness and meditation as before.

But in spite of these things it was a gay and magnificent revel. The tastes of the prince were peculiar. He had a fine eye for colors and effects. He disregarded the *decora* of mere fashion. His plans were bold and fiery, and his conceptions glowed with barbaric lustre. There are some who would have thought him mad. His followers felt that he was not. It was necessary to hear and see and touch him to be *sure* that he was not.

He had directed in great part the movable embellishments of the seven chambers upon occasion of this great fête; and it was his own guiding taste which had given character to the masqueraders. Be sure they were grotesque. There were much glare and glitter and piquancy and phantasm—much of what has been since seen in *Hernani.*[2] There were arabesque figures with unsuited limbs and appointments. There were delirious fancies such as the madman fashions. There was much of the beautiful, much of the wanton, much of the bizarre, something of the terrible, and not a little of

[2] A romantic, melodramatic play by Victor Hugo.

that which might have excited disgust. To and fro in the seven chambers there stalked, in fact, a multitude of dreams. And these —the dreams—writhed in and about, taking hue from the rooms and causing the wild music of the orchestra to seem as the echo of their steps. And, anon, there strikes the ebony clock which stands in the hall of the velvet. And then for a moment all is still, and all is silent save the voice of the clock. The dreams are stiff-frozen as they stand. But the echoes of the chime die away—they have endured but an instant—and a light, half-subdued laughter floats after them as they depart. And now again the music swells, and the dreams live and writhe to and fro more merrily than ever, taking hue from the many tinted windows through which stream the rays from the tripods. But to the chamber which lies most westwardly of the seven there are now none of the maskers who venture: for the night is waning away, and there flows a ruddier light through the blood-colored panes; and the blackness of the sable drapery appalls; and to him whose foot falls upon the sable carpet there comes from the near clock of ebony a muffled peal more solemnly emphatic than any which reaches *their* ears who indulge in the more remote gayeties of the other apartments.

But these other apartments were densely crowded, and in them beat feverishly the heart of life. And the revel went whirlingly on, until at length there commenced the sounding of midnight upon the clock. And then the music ceased, as I have told; and the evolutions of the waltzers were quieted; and there was an uneasy cessation of all things as before. But now there were twelve strokes to be sounded by the bell of the clock; and thus it happened, perhaps, that more of thought crept, with more of time, into the meditations of the thoughtful among those who reveled. And thus too it happened, perhaps, that before the last echoes of the last chime had utterly sunk into silence, there were many individuals in the crowd who had found leisure to become aware of the presence of a masked figure which had arrested the attention of no single individual before. And the rumor of this new presence having spread itself whisperingly around, there arose at length from the whole company a buzz or murmur expressive of disapprobation and surprise—then, finally, of terror, of horror, and of disgust.

In an assembly of phantasms such as I have painted, it may well be supposed that no ordinary appearance could have excited such sensation. In truth the masquerade license of the night was nearly unlimited; but the figure in question had out-Heroded Herod and gone beyond the bounds of even the prince's indefinite decorum. There are chords in the hearts of the most reckless which cannot be touched without emotion. Even with the utterly lost, to whom life and death are equally jests, there are matters of which no jests can be made. The whole company, indeed, seemed now deeply to feel that in the costume and bearing of the stranger neither wit nor propriety existed. The figure was tall and gaunt and shrouded from head to foot in the habiliments of the grave. The mask which concealed the visage was made so nearly to resemble the countenance of a stiffened corpse that the closest scrutiny must have had difficulty in detecting the cheat. And yet all this might have been endured, if not approved, by the mad revelers around. But the mummer had gone so far as to assume the type of the Red Death. His vesture was dabbled in *blood;* and his broad brow, with all the features of the face, was besprinkled with the scarlet horror.

When the eyes of Prince Prospero fell upon this spectral image (which with a slow and solemn movement, as if more fully to sustain its rôle, stalked to and fro among the waltzers), he was seen to be convulsed in the first moment with a strong shudder either of terror or distaste; but in the next his brow reddened with rage.

"Who dares," he demanded hoarsely of the courtiers who stood near him—"who dares insult us with this blasphemous mockery? Seize him and unmask him that we may know whom we have to hang at sunrise from the battlements!"

It was in the eastern or blue chamber in which stood the Prince Prospero as he uttered these words. They rang throughout the seven rooms loudly and clearly; for the prince was a bold and robust man, and the music had become hushed at the waving of his hand.

It was in the blue room where stood the prince, with a group of pale courtiers by his side. At first, as he spoke, there was a slight rushing movement of this group in the direction of the intruder, who at the moment was also near at hand, and now with deliberate and stately step made closer approach to the speaker. But, from a certain nameless awe with which the mad assumption of the mummer had inspired the whole party, there were found none who put forth hand to seize him, so that unimpeded he passed within a yard of the prince's person; and, while the vast assembly, as if with one impulse, shrank from the centers of the rooms to the walls, he made his way uninterruptedly, but with the same solemn and measured step which had distinguished him from the first, through the blue chamber to the purple—through the purple to the green—through the green to the orange—through this again to the white—and even thence to the violet, ere a decided movement had been made to arrest him. It was then, however, that the Prince Prospero, maddening with rage and the shame of his own momentary cowardice, rushed hurriedly through the six chambers, while none followed him on account of a deadly terror that had seized upon all. He bore aloft a drawn dagger and had approached in rapid impetuosity to within three or four feet of the retreating figure, when the latter, having attained the extremity of the velvet apartment, turned suddenly and confronted his pursuer. There was a sharp cry—and the dagger dropped gleaming upon the sable carpet, upon which, instantly afterwards, fell prostrate in death the Prince Prospero. Then, summoning the wild courage of despair, a throng of the revelers at once threw themselves into the black apartment, and, seizing the mummer, whose tall figure stood erect and motionless within the shadow of the ebony clock, gasped in unutterable horror at finding the grave cerements and corpselike mask, which they handled with so violent a rudeness, untenanted by any tangible form.

And now was acknowledged the presence of the Red Death. He had come like a thief in the night. And one by one dropped the revelers in the blood-bedewed halls of their revel and died each in the despairing posture of his fall. And the life of the ebony clock went out with that of the last of the gay. And the flames of the tripods expired. And Darkness and Decay and the Red Death held illimitable dominion over all.

STUDY NOTES

1. Cite several of the more pleasing rhythmical passages in "The Masque of the Red Death."

2. Give evidence that this story is rich in sensuous appeal.

3. Although this narrative contains only slight characterization, point out the methods by which Poe communicates such personality as he does attribute to Prince Prospero and the prince's friends.

MANNER

4. Although the story has only a comparatively small amount of plot, show that the actions of Prospero, of his thousand friends, and of the intruder (Red Death himself) contribute to the atmosphere of horror that the story produces.

5. State the implied underlying philosophy and comment on the harmony between the theme and the atmosphere.

6. Show that the atmosphere of horror is present in both the beginning and the denouement.

7. What purpose does the only utterance placed in the mouth of a character (a speech by Prospero) serve?

8. Show that both colors and sounds contribute to the atmosphere of terror.

9. Show that the author's statements of the effect of Red Death's presence upon both Prospero and Prospero's friends help to create a horrific atmosphere.

10. List any other methods that you can discover by which Poe in this story develops within the reader the emotion of horror.

THE SHERATON MIRROR [1]
(1932)

AUGUST DERLETH

BECAUSE the letter was addressed to all of them, Miss Melora, who was oldest, opened it. "Why, it's from a lawyer," she said. "Talliaferro, from a lawyer!"

Talliaferro Pepperall nodded. "What does it say?" he asked.

Miss Tallulah, who had picked up the envelope, looked at the postmark and said, "From Wisconsin. Most likely Aunt Hattie's died—she's been sick long enough."

"Oh, that's what it is," said Miss Melora. "And what do you think," she went on, looking at Talliaferro over the letter, "she's left us the house, and everything!"

Miss Tallulah gasped, then began to chuckle. "Think of it, she hating us so all these years and then leaving us everything!"

Talliaferro took out a snuff-box and opened it gravely. "Seems likely they'd be a catch in that somewhere. You've read it carefully, have you, Melora?"

Melora looked at the letter again and said, "We have to live there—that's all, it seems." Her brow puckered a little, then cleared again. "And that wouldn't be bad, would it, Talliaferro? We could get a good price for this place, too, and we have been in New Orleans for such a long time now. It would be good to go north for a little."

"Oh, but the letter says 'to take up residence for the rest of your natural lives'—and we hope that won't be a little," said Talliaferro, who had taken the letter from his sister's hand and was now reading it carefully.

Tallulah said, "Shall we go, or not? Seems we might as well. With all her money, we'll be a good deal more comfortable than we are now."

Melora added, "We could even afford a maid, and perhaps a butler, Talliaferro."

Talliaferro Pepperall hesitated. "I don't like it," he said. "I've

175

never liked Aunt Hattie, and I don't see that we should accept her money now. And, if I must say it, I don't think we've a right to take it, after the way I've treated her, and after the way she treated us since then."

"You are too proud, Talliaferro," said Melora, and Tallulah nodded in agreement.

"Very well," said Talliaferro. "I think we'd better write the lawyer today."

The Pepperalls came to Wisconsin, and in the small town where their Aunt Hattie had lived and died, "hating" them, as Tallulah said, they took up residence in the old-fashioned Middle Western mansion, there to live secluded lives, as they had done in New Orleans.

The house had two stories, and, best of all, both back and front stairs. It was the largest house in town, and even had servants' quarters; though, to be sure, these were small and cramped. The first floor was taken up largely by a striking drawing-room and a too ornate dining-room. The second floor was mostly bedrooms. Melora, being the oldest, got Aunt Hattie's bedroom, the grand one with the Sheraton mirror to the dressing-table. And Tallulah was content with the guest bedroom just next to her, while Talliaferro slept some distance down the hall.

It took them a time to get used to the house, which was even better than they had hoped, despite its definite atmosphere of past decades.

"And just think, we could have had all this before, but for you, Talliaferro," said Melora, her eyes shining with pleasure.

They were standing in the drawing-room. Talliaferro smiled reminiscently. "It was in this very room that I insulted her," he said. "What did I call her, Melora?"

Melora shook her head, but Tallulah said, "I remember. You said she was a 'homely old witch' and a 'wicked meddler,' and then you told her she'd be better off dead."

Talliaferro nodded, remembering. "I am still not sorry," he said. "She deserved it, and more. She had no business to meddle in Father's affairs as she did." He hesitated, not quite sure of himself. "But she was not right to take it so seriously," he continued presently. "I was quite young, then, and she might have overlooked it in time."

"I don't think she would have been so angry if it hadn't been that Father refused to punish you," said Melora slowly. "I do think that turned her anger into hate finally."

Talliaferro shrugged. "Ah, well, she's dead and gone now, poor soul."

"How she would enjoy hearing you call her 'poor soul,' Talliaferro!" exclaimed Tallulah.

Melora said, as if suddenly remembering, "Did you ever see the letter Aunt Hattie wrote Father just before he died, Talliaferro?"

"I saw no letter."

"It was the most vindictive writing—and that was years after it happened. She said you should be punished still, and that some day if she saw you again, she would punish you—it would be waiting, she promised. And Tallulah and I were to be punished, too, for defending you."

Talliaferro toyed with his snuff-box. "Ah, well," he said, "it doesn't matter. We've got much to thank her for now."

Melora, however, was not listening. She was looking beyond her brother into the hall. "Will you see whether there is some one in the hall, Tallulah?" she asked abruptly. "I thought—"

Tallulah went forward quickly, brushed aside the portieres, and looked into the hall. "There is no one here," she said, coming back into the room.

Melora shrugged. "I thought I saw someone standing there, looking in at us from between the curtains. Couldn't have been the maid, could it?"

Tallulah shook her head. "She won't be here until tomorrow, and the butler comes tonight."

"Curious! I was sure I had seen someone there." She smiled uncertainly. "Time for dinner soon," she said moving away toward the kitchen.

Tallulah said, "I'll be with you in a moment, Melora." Then she turned and began to go up the front stairs, paused a moment to call down to Talliaferro, who was still standing in the drawing-room, and went on.

At the top of the stairs she stood for a moment to look down

177

the carpeted hall. She was just about to go to her room when she saw the flirt of a satin skirt disappearing into Melora's room. She went forward, thinking: I wonder what Melora wants; she should be getting dinner. Just as she came to the door of Melora's room, she heard a slight rustling on the back stairs; turning quickly, she saw Melora, a little breathless, coming up the stairs.

"Why, Melora," she called down in a surprised voice: I could have sworn I just saw you go into your room."

"No, I've been in the kitchen, Tallulah. I've mislaid my handkerchief somewhere, and just came up to get another," explained Melora, as she came toward her sister.

Of course. I should have known you weren't wearing satin today," said Tallulah, smiling.

Melora stopped, standing quite still. "Satin, did you say, Tallulah?"

Tallulah looked at her uncertainly. "I thought I saw a satin skirt just vanishing into your room, Melora," she said. "I swear I did, really."

Melora said, "And I thought a woman in satin was watching us in the drawing-room. I thought I saw her standing in the hall."

Tallulah laughed weakly. "We're seeing things, Melora. I think we're too exhausted with getting things straightened up here. I'll be glad when the maid and butler come."

Melora said no more. She went quickly into her room and got a handkerchief. Together, the sisters went downstairs to prepare dinner.

A few days after the Pepperalls had taken possession, the lawyer called, and they had some conversation over the teacups. Talliaferro was not there.

Tallulah asked, "Was Aunt Hattie taken badly before she died?"

The lawyer blinked a little oddly and said, "Well, I really couldn't say. I wasn't here—that is, not in the house—at the time."

Melora thought the lawyer sounded nervous, "evasive," she said afterward. She put in a question quickly, "Who doctored her? Perhaps you can tell us that?"

The lawyer coughed and said, "Doctor Mason. You'll find him down the street a way. But he hadn't been to see her for ten days before she died."

Tallulah protested, "But that's sheer neglect, I'd say."

Melora nodded in agreement. "It is so," she said. "I think we'd better see that doctor.'"

Then the lawyer spoke again, his words coming very reluctantly. "Why, I thought I told you in the letter, but I guess I didn't after all. You see, your aunt had gotten somewhat better. She'd been up, in fact, and then one day she called the doctor and said she'd got the pains again, and asked him to come up. That he couldn't do until the afternoon; then he came.

"She was dead when he got here. It wasn't his fault, because she hadn't died of the pains. She'd somehow managed to—well, she tied the scarf to the chandelier in her bedroom—it's pretty strong, you see." The lawyer finished in some agitation.

Melora put down her cup with nervous fingers. Her face went suddenly white.

"Hanged herself, did she?" said Tallulah bluntly.

The lawyer nodded.

Melora said, "I'm glad you told us now. I'd rather like it if you said no word to Talliaferro, that is, my brother. He's not so well, and shocks aren't good for him."

"I see. I'll say nothing, then," said the lawyer, smiling. "But it's pretty well known, of course, and you can't keep him from knowing for ever."

Melora nodded. "I suppose not, but I'll thank you to say nothing, just the same. We're not that sociable that we'd hear such talk going about very easily."

The lawyer nodded, smiled, and talked a little more about the change in weather the Pepperalls could expect now in Wisconsin. He went at last and left the sisters sitting alone.

Tallulah gave her older sister a curious look. "It is hard to believe, Melora. She hating us so, and then putting herself out of the way to let us get the property and all." She fingered her bracelet absently.

Melora nodded. "Yes, it is strange. I don't understand, Tallulah. I think there's something wrong somewhere."

"Oh," said Tallulah quickly, "do you feel it, too?"

Melora was startled. "Feel what?" she asked sharply. "What is it, Tallulah?

179

"Nothing," said her sister. "Nothing—that is—yes, it is something, Melora. There's someone here, hiding in this house. I can feel it, someone is watching us. It's frightening me, I'm afraid, Melora."

Melora said, "I've felt that, too. Some one watching—a woman . . . in black satin.

Tallulah swallowed suddenly; then, hearing footsteps in the hall beyond, bent forward and whispered harshly, "Aunt Hattie . . . in black satin."

Talliaferro Pepperall came into the room and sat down. "Lawyer just here, was he? Have anything to say?"

"Not much," said Melora easily.

Tallulah rang for the maid to take away the tea things.

Going up the broad front stairs a little later, Tallulah was suddenly confronted by Melora. For a moment she was startled. Melora motioned her to come on more quickly.

"An odd thing has happened," she said, as they went along down the hall, "a very odd thing, Tallulah. Come into my room; I want you to see it."

They went into Melora's room, but Tallulah could see nothing out of the ordinary. "What is it?" she asked.

"The mirror. Don't you see it?" Melora was agitated.

There was a vague dark spot in the glass of the Sheraton mirror. Instinctively Tallulah moved forward and made an attempt to rub out the spot.

"It won't come out," said Melora. "It wasn't there when we came here, Tallulah. I don't understand what it could be. If you'll look closely, you'll see it isn't *on* the glass—it's *in* the glass. "

"Likely a defect in the glass, Melora."

"Odd that it should show itself first now, after all these years," said Melora dubiously. "Aunt Hattie had the mirror before we were born."

"It is odd," said Tallulah, going slowly from the room, "but nothing to worry about—just so it doesn't spoil the mirror."

In the night Tallulah heard her sister's light tap on her door, and Melora's muffled voice, "Are you awake, Tallulah?"

In a moment she was out of bed and in her dressing-gown, and in another she had opened the door and was confronting Melora, who was standing there in her kimono, her face white and drawn, her hands twisting nervously.

"What has happened?" asked Tallulah quickly.

"Come into my room right away. I want you to look at the mirror again."

Tallulah wanted to brush aside her sister's fear, but the expression on Melora's face prevented her. Without a word, she followed her sister.

Melora's room was brilliantly lit. Melora strode before Tallulah, pointing dramatically at the mirror. Tallulah gasped. There had been a perceptible change in the dark spot in the glass. It had grown somewhat larger, and had taken on a form, a vague, suggestive shape. . . . Tallulah felt suddenly afraid, but looking at her sister's apprehensisve face, she knew she must not show her own fear.

"It looks like a reflection, doesn't it?" she said presently.

Melora nodded.

"Like something hanging in the room somewhere," continued Tallulah, looking hard at her sister.

"Tallulah, what are you saying!" protested Melora, but she was waiting to hear more, was indeed eager to have Tallulah confirm her own secret thought which she was herself afraid to voice.

"It looks like something hanging—from the chandelier, I'd say."

At this Melora became distinctly less agitated, seeming to breathe a little easier, as if the recognition of some impending danger had given way to the less fearful thought of combating it. "Now that we both see it, both feel that way," she began, smiling uncertainly, "perhaps we can do something. I've thought so, watching it grow so strangely, I think we'd better say nothing about it to any one but ourselves—we'd best keep it from Talliaferro, his heart being so bad."

"Of course," said Tallulah. "But why don't you change your room, or sell the mirror, Melora?"

"Talliaferro might wonder why. Besides, it doesn't do any harm just a reflection like that. Not even clear."

"But it's growing clear, Melora."

Melora hesitated, considering the mirror and the horrific suggestion of the shadow in the glass. "We'll wait and see," she said finally.

MANNER

It was not difficult for the sisters Pepperall to keep all knowledge of the spot in the Sheraton mirror from Talliaferro, but it was not as easy to prevent his noticing the strain and uneasiness growing daily more obvious in the conversation and actions of Melora and Tallulah. Talliaferro soon sensed something wrong in this curious restraint, and took to watching his sisters surreptitiously.

The spot in the glass grew steadily more and more disturbing, gaining shape daily. Melora went as little as possible to her room, and took to going to bed without a light, which the watchful Talliferro did not fail to notice. During all of one day the vague reflection grew very clear and Miss Melora, who had gone into the room just ahead of her sister, screamed involuntarily at the sight of the shadow in the glass.

"Look!" she cried. "She's hanging there. It's Aunt Hattie!"

Tallulah shrank back, tensing herself. "It is," she breathed. Then she took her sister by the arm, holding her tightly, hurting her. "Now I know why *she* wanted us here. Now I know. She hating us all the time. When Talliaferro sees her, the shock—oh, she knew, she knew!"

Talliaferro appeared suddenly in the doorway. "Seeing things again, are you Melora?" He frowned at his sisters. "I don't understand what ails you," he went on in an almost petulant voice. "I overheard you talking days ago. I think you'd better see a doctor. It's madness coming over you."

"Madness! Of course, it's madness," said Melora abruptly, her voice strident, forgetting to think of Talliaferro's heart. "It may well be. I can see something hanging there. Look at it. Look into the mirror. It's there. I know it is. Talliaferro, look into the mirror."

Talliaferro came forward to her side and looked over her shoulder.

"Can you see it?" breathed Melora. "Tell me you can see it, Talliaferro."

Talliaferro looked at her queerly and said, "I can see it."

"What is it? Tell me. I've been seeing it for days, now. It's worse afternoons, seems, and at night. Tell me, isn't it—Aunt Hattie?"

Talliaferro said, "I don't know what it could be."

And Melora, hearing this, knew suddenly that Talliaferro could

182

not see Aunt Hattie hanging there at all, and he the one she'd hated most all her life.

Talliaferro spoke to Tallulah when they were alone together somewhat later. "I'm afraid your sister's losing her mind, Tallulah," he said without preamble. "It's that confounded mirror—she sees things there."

Tallulah said, "Yes, I've seen the same thing." She tried to keep her voice calm, but it trembled just a little in apprehension at his reaction.

"Are both of you mad?"

Tallulah looked at him, her eyes suddenly cold. "If you want to call it that, Talliaferro—yes!"

Talliaferro Pepperall left his sister and stamped up the stairs to his room. He was thinking: She hated me most, she hated me most; and he could not understand that this madness should come to Melora and Tallulah, sparing him. When he heard Melora going down the stairs, he crept silently the length of the hall to her room.

He pushed open the door and looked at the mirror. There was nothing there. He went back to his room, disturbed.

Downstairs, Melora was speaking to Tallulah. "Why can't he see it?" she asked. "Why can't he see it?"

"Oh don't you see, Melora? Don't you see? If it grew on him day by day, perhaps he'd get used to it. But if it came to him suddenly, abruptly. . . . Don't you see now?"

"You mean suddenly she will let him see her there? And his heart. . . . oh, God, Tallulah, do you think she would—*do that?*"

Tallulah nodded, pursing her lips grimly. "She hated him terribly. And she promised that his punishment would be waiting for him—here."

Melora drew herself together. "I'm going to smash that glass, Tallulah."

Talliaferro Pepperall went once more down the hall, pushed open the door of Melora's room, and looked again at the mirror. There was a reflection there—a reflection of something hanging in the glass, and as he looked, it swung around and looked at him. It was Aunt Hattie. Talliaferro pulled the door shut and ran to his room, his heart beating wildly. I didn't see it there, he thought; no, I didn't! Then, abruptly, he ran down the stairs to tell his sisters that he, too, had seen.

183

But they were not there. They had gone through to the back of the house, and were even now going up the back stairs. Talliaferro heard them, and he thought, They will see her now! forgetting that they had seen her there often. He heard them walking slowly along the hall above. He wanted to call out, to warn them, but he stood there silent, waiting. Then he heard the door of Melora's room open, and then a terrible silence.

Abruptly, he heard both of them screaming shrilly, but he could not bring himself to run up there to see what they had seen. He came to the foot of the front stairs and looked up. At the top someone was standing, motioning to him—a woman in black satin. He should come up, the figure motioned. Talliaferro was bewildered. A woman in black satin? Who could it be? Black satin. He had known someone somewhere who always wore black satin. Who, who was it? His mind was not clear, but from somewhere a name came to him—*Aunt Hattie!*

The woman was gone abruptly. Fear had encompassed Talliaferro; it pressed upon him with a multitude of icy fingers, but a greater force was drawing him slowly forward. He went hesitatingly up the stairs, and into Melora's room. Melora and Tallulah were huddled together, staring at the mirror. Talliaferro looked at the glass, and there he saw the face of his dead aunt for the second time. The face was distorted, horrible—and it was moving, moving about at the end of the scarf, fascinating the three of them. Talliaferro sat down heavily; his heart beat loudly, irregularly, and he felt a closeness suffocating him. His sisters did not appear to notice him.

Talliaferro's lips opened, and he began to speak, slowly, and with apparent effort. "She killed herself here," he murmured, "hanged herself where the glass caught the reflection. That's it. She was caught in the glass and couldn't get out."

Melora turned and seemed to notice her brother for the first time. She leaned over and touched Tallulah's arm gently. "He sees her now," she whispered. "He sees her. She's watching him. Oh, look at her eyes!"

The eyes of the thing in the glass had begun to glow, shining out toward Talliaferro, who went on mumbling without noticing, his voice rising steadily. "To be caught like that, a woman caught.

We can't help her, won't help her. Homely old witch-woman. She hates us, hates us, and I hate her!"

He got up abruptly and went straight to the glass. He bent his head and pressed his face close to the swinging figure. And then he saw the eyes of the dead woman open wide. With a terrible cry, Talliaferro caught up Melora's steel-backed brush from the dressing-table and struck at the glass. He struck blindly, until he had broken the mirror into many pieces. Then he stepped back a little, dropped the brush, and passed his hand vaguely over his forehead. He looked at his startled sisters and smiled wanly. From within him a tumult arose suddenly, engulfing him. Then he began to sway gently from side to side.

Melora came to her feet just as he crashed to the floor and sprawled there. She ran to him, coming down on her knees beside him. "Talliaferro," she cried, and touched him. "Talliaferro!" She looked over her shoulder at Tallulah and cried out, "He's dead!"

Then Tallulah began to scream. She was looking beyond Melora, at the space on the wall in the frame of the broken mirror. "It's the woman. There behind you, on the wall!"

Melora sat there, hunched on the floor as if frozen. "No, Tallulah," she said. "Talliaferro killed her. I saw him do it. I saw him."

But Tallulah went on screaming. She was still screaming when the frightened maid made her way into the room, followed by the butler. They found Melora hunched on the floor beside the body of Talliaferro, gently stroking one of his hands. She did not appear to see them, for her eyes never once left the jagged aperture where the mirror had been.

Her lips were moving a little, and when the maid touched her shoulder gently, she heard Melora whimpering in a little child voice, "Go away, please. Talliaferro killed you—homely witch-woman. I saw him. Go away, Aunt Hattie."

STUDY NOTES

1. How is Aunt Hattie's hatred and her desire for revenge motivated?

2. Show that in "The Sheraton Mirror" the dialogue helps to portray character and to advance the plot.

3. Though the characterization is slight, indicate the devices employed in delineating Aunt Hattie, Talliaferro, Melora, and Tallulah.

4. Summarize the plot of this story.

5. Comment on the harmony between the plot and the atmosphere.

6. Show that the dialogue helps to create the combined atmosphere of fear, horror, and weirdness.

7. List the concrete actions that convince the two sisters that their aunt is keeping her promise to take revenge and that convince the reader that the revenge includes the sisters.

8. How effective is the description of Aunt Hattie's image in the mirror toward producing an atmosphere of weirdness and horror?

9. Show that the development of atmosphere is climactic—that the emotional reaction becomes stronger as the plot unfolds.

10. List any parts of plot not already mentioned, or any devices not already named, that are striking for their contribution to the atmosphere.

COMPARISON EXERCISES

1. Compare "The Masque of the Red Death" and "The Sheraton Mirror" as regards the kind of atmosphere conveyed.

2. In which story is the atmosphere aroused the longer lasting and why?

3. Which story places the larger emphasis on supernatural activity?

4. Compare the two stories for their employment of dramatic foreshadowing of the impending doom.

5. Which story makes the more effective use of fantastic setting and which goes the farther toward creating atmosphere through the details chosen for the plot?

WRITING SUGGESTION

Write a story aimed at arousing some definite emotion such as sadness, despair, fear, pity, or horror, and choosing the characters, settings, or events, or some combination of these, to produce the intended reaction, and, if it seems desirable, interpreting the details, either by direct statement or by implication, to contribute to the preconceived effect.

PART II: MATTER

FOR persons who seek enjoyment in reading short stories but are not ambitious to write one or more original specimens, a group of artistically constructed examples in which matter predominates over manner should be attractive. Part II should appeal to this class of people especially. All five subdivisions, emphasizing respectively humor, love, surprise, mystery, and adventure, present narratives chosen for their ineffable qualities of content. Every one of these stories not only contains substance of intrinsic interest but also applies well-established and highly effective principles of structure. Just as pointing out what structural type a story illustrates may be of value in the writing of that type, so focusing one's attention on the nature of the usual short-story techniques and on the presence of craftsmanship and artistry in a particular story may heighten the reader's enjoyment of that selection. The former task (causing the student to consider writing manners primarily) Part I attempted, largely for the purpose of stimulating and improving story construction. The latter task (helping the student to be aware that well-built stories of content apply principles of artistic structure) Part II seeks to achieve, mainly to bring to the student the joy that comes from the kind of reading that richly comprehends. Some knowledge of story-writing manner can enhance the appreciation that arises in even the reader who is primarily intent on matter. This fact anyone who has become acquainted with the stories and the study helps in Part I is in position to know. Part II aims primarily to give pleasure to the student who is reading for content and secondarily to add to his enjoyment by keeping in his mind the truth that manner and matter belong together, that the most delightful short fictions exhibit artistic structure as well as ineffable content.

HUMOR

Introduction to Humorous Stories

A humorous story amuses the reader, whether or not it contains irony. If the irony is too pungent, however, the story will cease to be amusing. Humor may range from the mild or light variety, through burlesque, wit, irony, and satire. The most popular and defensible kinds for story use are light humor and broad humor. The mild is preferable to the hilarious. It is easy to overdo satire. Stories that contain sharp satire are usually unsalable.

Humor is one type of single effect that a story may create. The comic tone may be struck early in the narrative, sometimes in the title, often in the first few sentences or paragraphs. The humor should be spontaneous rather than forced.

The laughable element appears in some of the juvenile stories published in widely circulated "slick" magazines; also in some of the present-day stories written for adults. Fictions concerning young people but aimed at adult readers are quite popular, especially if humorous.

It was Washington Irving who first injected light humor into the American short story. His humor was original, pervasive, and attractive, lacking the satirical tone employed by his coeditor of *Salmagundi*, James K. Paulding, and less pungent than that later contributed by Stockton to his gently ironic pieces.

Examination of America's pioneers in the writing of brief humorous fictions throws light on both the manner and the matter of the comic type of story. Such a study, if reasonably thorough, reveals that the ludicrous effect may be generated by either the subject matter or the manner of treatment.

Stockton's humorous stories are characterized by much fantasy, by wonders, by impossible situations, by absurd adventures, by surprise after surprise for the reader and usually a surprise at the finish.

Unexpected predicaments appear throughout the plot. And Stockton presents his materials in a comparatively restrained, artistic style that nevertheless focuses attention on the nonsensical situations. Mark Twain's method is more lawless, his exaggeration more· unrestrained, than Stockton's.

In Rose Terry Cooke's subtly humorous stories the ludicrous effect arises primarily from the New England life which is her subject matter. They present the whims and perverse fancies of trictly religious Puritans and of miserly,· pertinacious Yankee farmers. Their humor inheres in their substance, particularly in the quaintness of the characters.

John Townsend Trowbridge's humor is the Dickensian kind, broad and abundant, based on distortion and exaggeration. Comicality appears in his handling of commonplace materials, especially in his portraying the cunning, materialistic, and profiteering Yankees and his detailing the somewhat impish activities of the country-boy character, Taddy.

Bret Harte's stories convey the broad Western humor that developed in California during the gold rush era, that belonged to barrooms and camps, boats and coaches, mines and prairies. Its farcical quality appears sometimes in understatement, sometimes in overstatement. This humor is original, concise, pointed, frequently irreverent, often infused with local color, always suggestive, and always distinctively American.

The Western humor that developed in Bret Harte's day was intertwined with incidents and characters. So is the sense of the ludicrous that the twentieth-century stories engender. Plot and characters are always necessary to an artistically constructed comical narrative. A full-dimensional story cannot consist of humor alone. In fact, humor cannot exist in a vacuum or without an origin in incongruity. In stories, the sense of the comic usually arises from incongruities of plot or of character or of both. One type of incongruity ordinarily predominates over the other.

Theme sometimes gives rise to a ludicrous effect. Some commonly used entertaining ideas are a disagreement between persons recently married or an older married couple or even two unmarried persons. One of the most popular types of humorous theme concerns some form of marriage problem.

When the incongruity that amuses belongs to character, the contrast arises from imperfections or eccentricities or from the difference between some trait that appears and one that some intellectual or moral or social standard being applied by the reader would require. When the incongruity is in the plot, the contrast lies between successive events or between some occurrence and one that could more normally be expected.

Amusing stories often have a well-thought-out and increasingly complex complication. Humorous situations are all the more entertaining, if original. Many an amusing story ends with a surprise; the humor rises to a telling climax, as in Mark Twain's "Celebrated Jumping Frog."

Other devices that may contribute to a comic effect are suspense and style. Suspense is sometimes employed for increasing the time within which the reader may find amusement. An odd or eccentric style, language that involves amusing contrasts, can heighten the ludicrous effect of a story. Any delightfully comic treatment of narrative material views the subject matter, whether an event or a character trait, primarily from an objective intellectual focus rather than from a humanitarian attitude. Sympathies are generally left unstimulated. Were they aroused, the humor would likely vanish.

MY DOUBLE, AND HOW HE UNDID ME [1]
(1859)

EDWARD EVERETT HALE

IT IS not often that I trouble the readers of the *Atlantic Monthly*. I should not trouble them now, but for the importunities of my wife, who "feels to insist" that a duty to society is unfulfilled till I have told why I had to have a double, and how he undid me. She is sure, she says, that intelligent persons cannot understand that pressure upon public servants which alone drives any man into the employment of a double. And while I fear she thinks, at the bottom of her heart, that my fortunes will never be remade, she has a faint hope that, as another Rasselas, I may teach a lesson to future publics, from which they may profit, though we die. Owing to the behavior of my double, or, if you please, to that public pressure which compelled me to employ him, I have plenty of leisure to write this communication.

I am, or rather was, a minister of the Sandemanian[2] connection. I was settled in the active, wide-awake town of Naguadavick, on one of the finest water-powers in Maine. We used to call it a Western town in the heart of the civilization of New England. A charming place it was and is. A spirited, brave young parish had I; and it seemed as if we might have all "the joy of eventful living" to our heart's content.

Alas! how little we knew on the day of my ordination, and in those halcyon moments of our first housekeeping! To be the confidential friend in a hundred families in the town—cutting the social trifle, as my friend Haliburton says, "from the top of the whipped-syllabub to the bottom of the sponge-cake, which is the foundation"—to keep abreast of the thought of the age in one's study, and to do one's best on Sunday to interweave that thought with the active life of an active town, and to inspirit both and make both infinite by glimpses of the Eternal Glory, seemed such an exquisite forelook into one's life! Enough to do, and all so real and so grand! If this vision could only have lasted!

---

[1] First published in *The Atlantic* (September, 1859).

[2] An obscure sect named for Robert Sandeman, who came to New England in 1764 and began organizing congregations.

The truth is that this vision as not in itself a delusion, nor, indeed, half bright enough. If one could only have been left to do his own business, the vision would have accomplished itself and brought out new paraheliachal visions, each as bright as the original. The misery was and is, as we found out, I and Polly, before long, that besides the vision, and besides the usual human and finite failures in life (such as breaking the old pitcher that came over in the "Mayflower," and putting into the fire the alpenstock with which her father climbed Mont Blanc)—besides these, I say (imitating the style of Robinson Crusoe), there were pitchforked in on us a great rowen-heap of humbugs, handed down from some unknown seedtime, in which we were expected, and I chiefly, to fulfil certain public functions before the community, of the character of those fulfilled by the third row of supernumeraries[3] who stand behind the Sepoys in the spectacle of the "Cataract of the Ganges." [4] They were the duties, in a word, which one performs as member of one or another social class or subdivision, wholly distinct from what one does as A. by himself A. What invisible power put these functions on me, it would be very hard to tell. But such power there was and is. And I had not been at work a year before I found I was living two lives, one real and one merely functional—for two sets of people, one my parish, whom I loved, and the other a vague public, for whom I did not care two straws. All this was in a vague notion, which everybody had and has, that this second life would eventually bring out some great results, unknown at present, to somebody somewhere.

Crazed by this duality of life, I first read Dr. Wigan[5] on the "Duality of the Brain," hoping that I could train one side of my head to do these outside jobs, and the other to do my intimate and real duties. For Richard Greenough once told me, that, in studying for the statue of Franklin, he found that the left side of the great man's face was philosophic and reflective, and the right side funny and smiling. If you will go and look at the bronze statue, you will find he has repeated this observation there for posterity. The eastern profile is the portrait of the statesman Franklin, the western of Poor

---

[3] Persons present for the effect that large numbers may create.

[4] A drama by William Thomas Moncrieff, which, because of its use of a real waterfall, attracted large audiences when staged in 1823.

[5] Dr. Arthur L. Wigan, English physician, whose book, *A New View of Insanity: the Duality of the Mind,* was published in 1844.

Richard. But Dr. Wigan does not go into these niceties of this subject, and I failed. It was then that, on my wife's suggestion, I resolved to look out for a Double.

I was, at first, singularly successful. We happened to be recreating at Stafford Springs that summer. We rode out one day, for one of the relaxations of that watering-place, to the great Monson Poorhouse. We were passing through one of the large halls, when my destiny was fulfilled!

He was not shaven. He had on no spectacles. He was dressed in a green baize roundabout and faded blue overalls, worn sadly at the knee. But I saw at once that he was of my height, five feet four and a half. He had black hair, worn off by his hat. So have and have not I. He stooped in walking. So do I. His hands were large, and mine. And—choicest gift of Fate in all—he had, not a "strawberry-mark on his left arm," but a cut from a juvenile brickbat over his right eye, slightly affecting the play of that eyebrow. Reader, so have I! My fate was sealed!

A word with Mr. Holley, one of the inspectors, settled the whole thing. It proved that this Dennis Shea was a harmless, amiable fellow, of the class known as shiftless, who had sealed his fate by marrying a dumb wife, who was at that moment ironing in the laundry. Before I left Stafford, I had hired both for five years. We had applied to Judge Pynchon, then the probate judge at Springfield, to change the name of Dennis Shea to Frederic Ingham. We had explained to the Judge, what was the precise truth, that an eccentric gentleman wished to adopt Dennis, under this new name, into his family. It never occurred to him that Dennis might be more than fourteen years old. And thus, to shorten this preface, when we returned at night to my parsonage at Naguadavick, there entered Mrs. Ingham, her new dumb laundress, myself, who am Mr. Frederic Ingham, and my double, who was Mr. Frederic Ingham by as good right as I.

O the fun we had the next morning in shaving his beard to my pattern, cutting his hair to match mine, and teaching him how to wear and how to take off gold-bowed spectacles! Really, they were electro-plate, and the glass was plain (for the poor fellow's eyes were excellent). Then in four successive afternoons I taught him four speeches. I had found these would be quite enough for the supernumerary-Sepoy line of life, and it was well for me they were; for though he was good-natured, he was very shiftless, and it was, as our national proverb says, "like pulling teeth" to teach him. But at the end of the next week he could say, with quite my easy and frisky air—

1. "Very well, thank you. And you?" This for an answer to casual salutations.
2. "I am very glad you liked it."
3. "There has been so much said, and, on the whole, so well said, that I will not occupy the time."
4. "I agree, in general, with my friend the other side of the room."

At first I had a feeling that I was going to be at great cost for clothing him. But it proved, of course, at once, that, whenever he was out, I should be at home. And I went, during the bright period of his success, to so few of those awful pageants which require a black dress-coat and what the ungodly call, after Mr. Dickens, a white choker, that in the happy retreat of my own dressing-gowns and jackets my days went by as happily and cheaply as those of another Thalaba.[6] And Polly declares there was never a year when the tailoring cost so little. He lived (Dennis, not Thalaba) in his wife's room over the kitchen. He had orders never to show himself at that window. When he appeared in the front of the house, I retired to my sanctissimum and my dressing-gown. In short, the Dutchman and his wife, in the old weather-box, had not less to do with each other than he and I.[7] He made the furnace-fire and split the wood before daylight; then he went to sleep again, and slept late; then came for orders, with a red silk bandana tied round his head, with his overalls on, and his dress-coat and spectacles off. If we happened to be interrupted, no one guessed that he was Frederic Ingham as well as I; and, in the neighborhood, there grew up an impression that the minister's Irishman worked daytimes in the factory-village at New

---

[6] A character in Robert Southey's poem, "Thalaba," who was supernaturally aided.

[7] The reference is to the old-time, house-shaped barometer. The appearance of the figure of a man, the Dutchman, at the door indicated the weather would be stormy. The appearance of the wife forecast fair weather. Inasmuch as one of these characters was at the door while the other was inside the room, they had little dealing with each other.

Coventry. After I had given him his orders, I never saw him till the next day.

I launched him by sending him to a meeting of the Enlightenment Board. The Enlightenment Board consisted of seventy-four members, of whom sixty-seven are necessary to form a quorum. One becomes a member under the regulations laid down in old Judge Dudley's will. I became one by being ordained pastor of a church in Naguadavick. You see you cannot help yourself, if you would. At this particular time we had had four successive meetings, averaging four hours each—wholly occupied in whipping in a quorum. At the first only eleven men were present; at the next, by force of three circulars, twenty-seven; at the third, thanks to two days canvassing by Auchmuty and myself, begging men to come, we had sixty. Half the others were in Europe. But without a quorum we could do nothing. All the rest of us waited grimly for our four hours, and adjourned without any action. At the fourth meeting we had flagged, and only got fifty-nine together. But on the first appearance of my double—whom I sent on this fatal Monday to the fifth meeting—he was the sixty-seventh man who entered the room. He was greeted with a storm of applause! The poor fellow had missed his way—read the street signs ill through his spectacles (very ill, in fact, without them)—and had not dared to inquire. He entered the room—finding the president and secretary holding to their chairs two judges of the Supreme Court, who were also members *ex officio,* and were begging leave to go away. On his entrance all was changed. *Presto,* the by-laws were suspended, and the Western property was given away. Nobody stopped to converse with him. He voted, as I had charged him to do, in every instance, with the minority. I won new laurels as a man of sense, though a little unpunctual—and Dennis, *alias* Ingham, returned to the parsonage, astonished to see with how little wisdom the world is governed. He cut a few of my parishioners in the street; but he had his glasses off, and I am known to be near-sighted. Eventually he recognized them more readily than I.

I "set him again" at the exhibition of the New Coventry Academy; and here he undertook a "speaking part"—as, in my boyish, worldly days, I remember the bills used to say of Mlle. Celeste. We are all trustees of the New Coventry Academy; and there has lately been "a good deal of feeling" because the Sandemanian trustees did not

196

regularly attend the exhibitions. It has been intimated, indeed, that the Sandemanians are leaning towards Free-Will, and that we have, therefore, neglected these semiannual exhibitions, while there is no doubt that Auchmuty last year went to Commencement at Waterville.[8] Now the head master at New Coventry is a real good fellow, who knows a Sanskrit root when he sees it, and often cracks etymologies with me—so that, in strictness, I ought to go to their exhibitions. But think, reader, of sitting through three long July days in that Academy chapel, following the programme from

TUESDAY MORNING. *English Composition.* "SUNSHINE." Miss Jones. round to

Trio on Three Pianos. Duel from the Opera of "Midshipmen Easy." *Marryat.*

coming in at nine, Thursday evening! Think of this, reader, for men who know the world is trying to go backward, and who would give their lives if they could help it on! Well! The double had succeeded so well at the Board, that I sent him to the Academy. (Shade of Plato,[9] Pardon!) He arrived early on Tuesday, when, indeed, few but mothers and clergymen are generally expected, and returned in the evening to us, covered with honors. He had dined at the right hand of the chairman, and he spoke in high terms of the repast. The chairman had expressed his interest in the French conversation. "I am very glad you liked it," said Dennis; and the poor chairman, abashed, supposed the accent had been wrong. At the end of the day, the gentlemen present had been called upon for speeches—the Rev. Frederic Ingham first, as it happened; upon which Dennis had risen, and had said: "There has been so much said, and, on the whole, so well said, that I will not occupy the time." The girls were delighted, because Dr. Dabney, the year before, had given them at this occasion a scolding on impropriety of behavior at lyceum lectures. They all declared Mr. Ingham was a love—and *so* handsome! (Dennis is good-looking.) Three of them, with arms behind the others' waists, followed him up to the wagon he rode home in; and a little girl with a blue sash had been sent to give him a rosebud. After this *début* in speaking, he went to the exhibition for two days more, to the mutual satisfaction of all concerned. Indeed, Polly reported that

---

[8] Waterville College, which later became Colby University.
[9] The school of philosophy that Plato conducted near Athens was known as the Academy.

he had pronounced the trustees' dinners of a higher grade than those of the parsonage. When the next term began, I found six of the Academy girls had obtained permission to come across the river and attend our church. But this arrangement did not long continue.

After this he went to several Commencements for me, and ate the dinners provided; he sat through three of our Quarterly Conventions for me—always voting judiciously, by the simple rule mentioned above, of siding with the minority. And I, meanwhile, who had before been losing caste among my friends, as holding myself aloof from the associations of the body, began to rise in everybody's favor. "Ingham's a good fellow—always on hand"; "never talks much, but does the right thing at the right time"; "is not as unpunctual as he used to be—he comes early, and sits through to the end." "He has got over his old talkative habit, too. I spoke to a friend of his about it once; and I think Ingham took it kindly," etc., etc.

This voting power of Dennis was particularly valuable at the quarterly meetings of the proprietors of the Naguadavick Ferry. My wife inherited from her father some shares in that enterprise, which is not yet fully developed, though it doubtless will become a very valuable property. The law of Maine then forbade stockholders to appear by proxy at such meetings. Polly disliked to go, not being, in fact, a "hens'-rights hen," and transferred her stock to me. I, after going once, disliked it more than she. But Dennis went to the next meeting, and liked it very much. He said the arm-chairs were good, the collation good, and the free rides to stockholders pleasant. He was a little frightened when they first took him upon one of the ferry-boats, but after two or three quarterly meetings he became quite brave.

Thus far I never had any difficulty with him. Indeed, being, as I implied, of that type which is called shiftless, he was only too happy to be told daily what to do, and to be charged not to be forthputting or in any way original in his discharge of that duty. He learned, however, to discriminate between the lines of his life, and very much preferred these stockholders' meetings and trustees' dinners and Commencement collations to another set of occasions, from which he used to beg off most piteously. Our excellent brother, Dr. Fillmore, had taken a notion at this time that our Sandemanian churches needed more expression of mutual sympathy. He insisted upon it that we were remiss. He said that if the Bishop came to preach at Naguada-vick, all the Episcopal clergy of the neighborhood were present; if Dr. Pond came, all the Congregational clergymen turned out to hear him; if Dr. Nichols, all the Unitarians; and he thought we owed it to each other, that, whenever there was an occasional service at a San-demanian church, the other brethren should all, if possible, attend. "It looked well," if nothing more. Now this really meant that I had not been to hear one of Dr. Fillmore's lectures on the Ethnology of Religion. He forgot that he did not hear one of my course on the "Sandemanianism of Anselm."[10] But I felt badly when he said it; and afterwards I always made Dennis go to hear all the brethren preach, when I was not preaching myself. This was what he took exceptions to—the only thing, as I said, which he ever did except to. Now came the advantage of his long morning-nap, and of the green tea with which Polly supplied the kitchen. But he would plead, so humbly, to be let off, only from one or two! I never excepted him, however. I knew the lectures were of value, and I thought it best he should be able to keep the connection.

Polly is more rash than I am, as the reader has observed in the outset of this memoir. She risked Dennis one night under the eyes of her own sex. Governor Gorges had always been very kind to us, and, when he gave his great annual party to the town, asked us. I confess I hated to go. I was deep in the new volume of Pfeiffer's "Mystics," which Haliburton had just sent me from Boston. "But how rude," said Polly, "not to return the Governor's civility and Mrs. Gorges's when they will be sure to ask why you are away!" Still I demurred, and at last she, with the wit of Eve and Semiramis conjoined, let me off by saying that, if I would go in with her, and sustain the initial conversations with the Governor and ladies stay-ing there, she would risk Dennis for the rest of the evening. And that was just what we did. She took Dennis in training all that afternoon, instructed him in fashionable conversation, cautioned him against the temptations of the supper-table—and at nine in the evening he drove us all down in the carryall. I made the grand star-*entrée* with Polly and the pretty Walton girls, who were staying with us. We had put Dennis into a great rough top-coat, without his glasses; and the

---

[10] Saint Anselm, founder of Scholasticism, was probably not a Sandemanian. A lecture on his Sandemanianism would, therefore, have been very dry.

girls never dreamed, in the darkness, of looking at him. He sat in the carriage, at the door, while we entered. I did the agreeable to Mrs. Gorges, was introduced to her niece, Miss Fernanda; I complimented Judge Jeffries on his decision in the great case of D'Aulnay *vs.* Laconia Mining Company; I stepped into the dressing-room for a moment, stepped out for another, walked home after a nod with Dennis and tying the horse to a pump; and while I walked home, Mr. Frederic Ingham, my double, stepped in through the library into the Gorges's grand salon.

Oh! Polly died of laughing as she told me of it at midnight! And even here, where I have to teach my hands to hew the beech for stakes to fence our cave, she dies of laughing as she recalls it—and says that single occasion was worth all we have paid for it. Gallant Eve that she is! She joined Dennis at the library-door and in an instant presented him to Dr. Ochterlony, from Baltimore, who was on a visit in town, and was talking with her as Dennis came in. "Mr. Ingham would like to hear what you were telling us about your success among the German population." And Dennis bowed and said, in spite of a scowl from Polly, "I'm very glad you liked it." But Dr. Ochterlony did not observe, and plunged into the tide of explanation; Dennis listening like a prime-minister, and bowing like a mandarin, which is, I suppose, the same thing. Polly declared it was just like Haliburton's Latin conversation with the Hungarian minister, of which he is very fond of telling. *"Quaene sit historia Reformationis in Ungariâ?"*[11] quoth Haliburton, after some thought. And his *confrère* replied gallantly, *"In seculo decimo tertio,"*[12] etc., etc., etc.; and from *decimo tertio* to the nineteenth century and a half lasted till the oysters came. So was it that before Dr. Ochterlony came to the "success," or near it, Governor Gorges came to Dennis, and asked him to hand Mrs. Jeffries down to supper, a request which he heard with great joy.

Polly was skipping round the room, I guess, gay as a lark. Auchmuty came to her "in pity for poor Ingham," who was so bored by the stupid pundit—and Auchmuty could not understand why I stood it so long. But when Dennis took Mrs. Jeffries down, Polly could not resist standing near them. He was a little flustered, till the sight

---

[11] Translation: "What is the history of the Reformation in Hungary?"
[12] Translation: "In the thirteenth century."

of the eatables and drinkables gave him the same Mercian courage which it gave Diggory.[13] A little excited then, he attempted one or two of his speeches to the Judge's lady. But little he knew how hard it was to get in even a *promptu* there edgewise. "Very well, I thank you," said he, after the eating elements were adjusted; "and you?" And then did not he have to hear about the mumps, and the measles, and arnica, and belladonna, and chamomile-flower, and dodecatheon, till she changed oysters for salad; and then about the old practice and the new, and what her sister said, and what her sister's friend said, and what the physician to her sister's friend said, and then what was said by the brother of the sister of the physician of the friend of her sister, exactly as if it had been in Ollendorff?[14] There was a moment's pause, as she declined champagne. "I am very glad you liked it," said Dennis again, which he never should have said but to one who complimented a sermon. "Oh! you are so sharp, Mr. Ingham! No! I never drink any wine at all—except sometimes in summer a little currant shrub—from our own currants, you know. My own mother—that is, I call her my own mother, because, you know, I do not remember," etc., etc., etc.; till they came to the candied orange at the end of the feast, when Dennis, rather confused, thought he must say something, and tried No. 4—"I agree, in general, with my friend the other side of the room"—which he never should have said but at a public meeting. But Mrs. Jeffries, who never listens expecting to understand, caught him up instantly with "Well, I'm sure my husband returns the compliment; he always agrees with you—though we do worship with the Methodists; but you know, Mr. Ingham," etc., etc., etc., till the move up-stairs; and as Dennis led her through the hall, he was scarcely understood by any but Polly, as he said, "There has been so much said, and, on the whole, so well said, that I will not occupy the time."

His great resource the rest of the evening was standing in the library, carrying on animated conversations with one and another in much the same way. Polly had initiated him in the mysteries of a discovery of mine, that it is not necessary to finish your sentence in a crowd, but by a sort of mumble, omitting sibilants and dentals.

[13] In Goldsmith's *She Stoops To Conquer*, a clownish servant, who claimed that the sight of food and drink gave him great boldness.
[14] Heinrich Gottfried Ollendorff, a German teacher, wrote many grammar textbooks, presenting numerous exercises exemplifying his theory of teaching language.

This, indeed, if your words fail you, answers even in public extempore speech, but better where other talking is going on. Thus: "We missed you at the Natural History Society, Ingham." Ingham replies, "I am very gligloglum, that is, that you were mmmmm." By gradually dropping the voice, the interlocutor is compelled to supply the answer. "Mrs. Ingham, I hope your friend Augusta is better." Augusta has not been ill. Polly cannot think of explaining, however, and answers, "Thank you, Ma'am; she is very rearason wewahwewoh," in lower and lower tones. And Mrs. Throckmorton, who forgot the subject of which she spoke as soon as she asked the question, is quite satisfied. Dennis could see into the card-room, and came to Polly to ask if he might not go and play all-fours. But, of course, she sternly refused. At midnight they came home delighted—Polly, as I said, wild to tell me the story of the victory; only both the pretty Walton girls said "Cousin Frederic, you did not come near me all the evening."

We always called him Dennis at home, for convenience, though his real name was Frederic Ingham, as I have explained. When the election-day came round, however, I found that by some accident there was only one Frederic Ingham's name on the voting-list; and as I was quite busy that day in writing some foreign letters to Halle,[15] I thought I would forego my privilege of suffrage, and stay quietly at home, telling Dennis that he might use the record on the voting-list, and vote. I gave him a ticket, which I told him he might use, if he liked to. That was that very sharp election in Maine which the readers of the *Atlantic* so well remember, and it had been intimated in public that ministers would do well not to appear at the polls. Of course, after that, we had to appear by self or proxy. Still, Naguadavick was not then a city, and this standing in a double queue at town-meeting several hours to vote was a bore of the first water; and so when I found that there was but one Frederic Ingham on the list, and that one of us must give up, I stayed at home and finished the letters (which, indeed, procured for Fothergill his coveted appointment of Professor of Astronomy at Leavenworth), and I gave Dennis, as we called him, the chance. Something in the matter gave a good deal of popularity to the Frederic Ingham name; and at the adjourned election, next week, Frederic Ingham was chosen

---

[15] A Prussian city in which was a university.

to the legislature. Whether this was I or Dennis I never really knew. My friends seemed to think it was I; but I felt that as Dennis had done the popular thing, he was entitled to the honor; so I sent him to Augusta when the time came, and he took the oaths. And a very valuable member he made. They appointed him on the Committee on Parishes; but I wrote a letter for him, resigning, on the ground that he took an interest in our claim to the stumpage in the minister's sixteenths of Gore A, next to No. 7, in the 10th Range. He never made any speeches, and always voted with the minority, which was what he was sent to do. He made me and himself a great many good friends, some of whom I did not afterwards recognize as quickly as Dennis did my parishioners. On one or two occasions, when there was wood to saw at home, I kept him at home; but I took those occasions to go to Augusta myself. Finding myself often in his vacant seat at these times, I watched the proceedings with a good deal of care; and once was so much excited that I delivered my somewhat celebrated speech on the Central School-District question, a speech of which the "State of Maine" printed some extra copies: I believe there is no formal rule permitting strangers to speak; but no one objected.

Dennis himself, as I said, never spoke at all. But our experience this session led me to think that if, by some such "general understanding" as the reports speak of in legislation daily, every member of Congress might leave a double to sit through those deadly sessions and answer to roll-calls and do the legitimate party-voting, which appears stereotyped in the regular list of Ashe, Bocock, Black, etc., we should gain decidedly in working-power. As things stand, the saddest State prison I ever visit is that Representatives' Chamber in Washington. If a man leaves for an hour, twenty "correspondents" may be howling, "Where was Mr. Pendergrast when the Oregon bill passed?" And if poor Pendergrast stays there! Certainly the worst use you can make of a man is to put him in prison!

I know, indeed, that public men of the highest rank have resorted to this expedient long ago. Dumas' novel of the "Iron Mask" [16] turns on the brutal imprisonment of Louis the Fourteenth's double. There seems little doubt, in our own history, that it was the real General

---

[16] Alexandre Dumas's novel, *The Man in the Iron Mask*, concerned a prisoner of France, who throughout his confinement wore an iron mask with a black velvet cover and whose identity is unknown.

MATTER

Pierce who shed tears when the delegate from Lawrence explained to him the sufferings of the people there, and only General Pierce's double who had given the orders for the assault on that town, which was invaded the next day.[17] My charming friend, George Withers, has, I am almost sure, a double who preaches his afternoon sermons for him. This is the reason that the theology often varies so from that of the forenoon. But that double is almost as charming as the original. Some of the most well-defined men, who stand out most prominently on the background of history, are in this way stereoscopic men, who owe their distinct relief to the slight differences between the doubles. All this I know. My present suggestion is simply the great extension of the system, so that all public machine work may be done by it.

But I see I loiter in my story, which is rushing to the plunge. Let me stop an instant more, however, to recall, were it only to myself, that charming year while all was yet well. After the double had become a matter of course, for nearly twelve months before he undid me, what a year it was! Full of active life, full of happy love, of the hardest work, of the sweetest sleep, and the fulfilment of so many of the fresh aspirations and dreams of boyhood! Dennis went to every school-committee meeting, and sat through all those late wranglings which used to keep me up till midnight and awake till morning. He attended all the lectures to which foreign exiles sent me tickets begging me to come for the love of Heaven and of Bohemia. He accepted and used all the tickets for charity concerts which were sent to me. He appeared everywhere where it was specially desirable that "our denomination," or "our party," or "our class," or "our family," or "our street," or "our town," or "our county," or "our State," should be fully represented. And I fell back to that charming life which in boyhood one dreams of, when he supposes he shall do his own duty and make his own sacrifices, without being tied up with those of other people. My rusty Sanskrit, Arabic, Hebrew, Greek, Latin, French, Italian, Spanish, German, and English began to take polish. Heavens! how little I had done with them while I attended to my *public* duties! My calls on my parishioners became the friendly, frequent, homelike sociabilities they were meant to be,

---

[17] During Franklin Pierce's term as President, pro-slavery advocates in Kansas sacked the town of Lawrence. Pierce had been an American general during the War with Mexico.

instead of the hard work of a man goaded to desperation by the sight of his lists of arrears. And preaching! what a luxury preaching was when I had on Sunday the whole result of an individual, personal week, from which to speak to a people whom all that week I had been meeting as hand-to-hand friend;—I, never tired on Sunday, and in condition to leave the sermon at home, if I chose, and preach it extempore, as all men should do always. Indeed, I wonder, when I think that a sensible people, like ours—really more attached to their clergy than they were in the lost days, when the Mathers and Nortons were noblemen—should choose to neutralize so much of their ministers' lives, and destroy so much of their early training, by this undefined passion for seeing them in public. It springs from our balancing of sects. If a spirited Episcopalian takes an interest in the almshouse, and is put on the Poor Board, every other denomination must have a minister there, lest the poorhouse be changed into St. Paul's Cathedral. If a Sandemanian is chosen president of the Young Men's Library, there must be a Methodist vice-president and a Baptist secretary. And if a Universalist Sunday-School Convention collects five hundred delegates, the next Congregationalist Sabbath-School Conference must be as large "lest 'they' —whoever *they* may be—should think 'we' whoever *we* may be—are going down."

Freed from these necessities, that happy year I began to know my wife by sight. We saw each other sometimes. In those long mornings, when Dennis was in the study explaining to map-peddlers that I had eleven maps of Jerusalem already, and to school-book agents that I would see them hanged before I would be bribed to introduce their text-books into the schools—she and I were at work together, as in those old dreamy days—and in these of our log-cabin again. But all this could not last—and at length poor Dennis, my double, overtasked in turn, undid me.

It was thus it happened. There is an excellent fellow, once a minister—I will call him Isaacs—who deserves well of the world till he dies, and after, because he once, in a real exigency, did the right thing, in the right way, at the right time, as no other man could do it. In the world's great football match, the ball by chance found him loitering on the outside of the field; he closed with it, "camped" it, charged it home—yes, right through the other side—

not disturbed, not frightened by his own success—and breathless found himself a great man, as the Great Delta [18] rang applause. But he did not find himself a rich man; and the football has never come in his way again. From that moment to this monent he has been of no use, that one can see at all. Still, for that great act we speak of Isaacs gratefully and remember him kindly; and he forges on, hoping to meet the football somewhere again. In that vague hope, he had arranged a "movement" for a general organization of the human family into Debating-Clubs, County Societies, State Unions, etc., etc.,[19] with a view of inducing all children to take hold of the handles of their knives and forks, instead of the metal. Children have bad habits in that way. The movement, of course, was absurd; but we all did our best to forward, not it, but him. It came time for the annual county-meeting on this subject to be held at Naguadavick. Isaacs came round, good fellow! to arrange for it—got the town-hall, got the Governor to preside (the saint!—he ought to have triplet doubles provided him by law), and then came to get me to speak. "No," I said "I would not speak, if ten Governors presided. I do not believe in the enterprise. If I spoke, it should be to say children should take hold of the prongs of the forks and the blades of the knives. I would subscribe ten dollars, but I would not speak a mill." So poor Isaacs went his way sadly, to coax Auchmuty to speak, and Delafield. I went out. Not long after he came back, and told Polly that they had promised to speak, the Governor would speak, and he himself would close with the quarterly report, and some interesting anecdotes regarding Miss Biffin's way of handling her knife and Mr. Nellis's way of footing his fork. "Now if Mr. Ingham will only come and sit on the platform, he need not say one word; but it will show well in the paper—it will show that the Sandemanians take as much interest in the movement as the Armenians or the Mesopotamians, and will be a great favor to me." Polly, good soul! was tempted, and she promised. She knew Mrs. Isaacs was starving, and the babies—she knew Dennis was at home—and she promised! Night came, and I returned. I heard her story. I was sorry. I doubted. But Polly had promised to beg me, and I dared all! I told Dennis to

---

[18] The name of the Harvard football field at the time of writing of this story was the *Delta*. The Great Delta is the world, in which men play the game of life.

[19] A craze for these various kinds of organization swept through the United States about the middle of the nineteenth century.

hold his peace, under all circumstances, and sent him down.

It was not half an hour more before he returned, wild with excitement—in a perfect Irish fury—which it was long before I understood. But I knew at once that he had undone me!

What had happened was this. The audience got together, attracted by Governor Gorges's name. There were a thousand people. Poor Gorges was late from Augusta. They became impatient. He came in direct from the train at last, really ignorant of the object of the meeting. He opened it in the fewest possible words, and said other gentlemen were present who would entertain them better than he. The audience were disappointed, but waited. The Governor, prompted by Isaacs, said "The Honorable Mr. Delafield will address you." Delafield had forgotten the knives and forks, and was playing the Ruy Lopez opening[20] at the chess-club. "The Rev. Mr. Auchmuty will address you." Auchmuty had promised to speak late, and was at the school-committee. "I see Dr. Stearns in the hall; perhaps he wil say a word." Dr. Stearns said he had come to listen and not to speak. The Governor and Isaacs whispered. The Governor looked at Dennis, who was resplendent on the platform; but Isaacs, to give him his due, shook his head. But the look was enough. A miserable lad, ill-bred, who had once been in Boston, thought it would sound well to call for me, and peeped out, "Ingham!" A few more wretches cried, "Ingham! Ingham!" Still Isaacs was firm; but the Governor, anxious, indeed, to prevent a row, knew I would say something, and said, "Our friend Mr. Ingham is always prepared; and, though we had not relied upon him, he will say a word perhaps." Applause followed, which turned Dennis's head. He rose, fluttered, and tried No. 3: "There has been so much said, and, on the whole, so well said, that I will not longer occupy the time!" and sat down, looking for his hat; for things seemed squally. But the people cried, "Go on! go on!" and some applauded. Dennis, still confused, but flattered by the applause, to which neither he nor I are used, rose again, and this time tried No. 2: "I am very glad you liked it!" in a sonorous, clear delivery. My best friends stared. All the pople who did not know me personally yelled with delight at the aspect of the evening; the Governor was beside himself, and poor Isaacs thought he was undone! Alas, it was I! A boy in the

---

[20] A particular sequence of moves in beginning the game of chess.

gallery cried in a loud tone, "It's all an infernal humbug," just as Dennis, waving his hand, commanded silence, and tried No. 4: "I agree, in general, with my friend the other side of the room." The poor Governor doubted his senses and crossed to stop him—not in time, however. The same gallery-boy shouted, "How's your mother?" and Dennis, now completely lost, tried, as his last shot, No. 1, vainly: "Very well, thank you, And you?"

I think I must have been undone already. But Dennis, like another Lockhard, chose "to make sicker." [21] The audience rose in a whirl of amazement, rage, and sorrow. Some other impertinence, aimed at Dennis, broke all restraint, and, in pure Irish, he delivered himself of an address to the gallery, inviting any person who wished to fight to come down and do so—stating, that they were all dogs and cowards and the sons of dogs and cowards—that he would take any five of them single-handed. "Shure, I have said all his Riverence and the Misthress bade me say," cried he, in defiance; and seizing the Governor's cane from his hand, brandished it, quarter-staff fashion, above his head. He was, indeed, got from the hall only with the greatest difficulty by the Governor, the City Marshal, who had been called in, and the Superintendent of my Sunday-School.

The universal impression, of course, was that the Rev. Frederic Ingham had lost all command of himself in some of those haunts of intoxication which for fifteen years I have been laboring to destroy. Till this moment, indeed, that is the impression in Naguadavick. This number of the *Atlantic* will relieve from it a hundred friends of mine who have been sadly wounded by that notion now for years; but I shall not be likely ever to show my head there again.

No! My double has undone me.

We left town at seven the next morning. I came to No. 9, in the Third Range, and settled on the Minister's Lot. In the new towns in Maine, the first settled minister has a gift of a hundred acres of land. I am the first settled minister in No. 9. My wife and little Paulina are my parish. We raise corn enough to live on in summer. We kill bear's meat enough to carbonize it in winter. I work on steadily on my "Traces of Sandemanianism in the Sixth and Seventh Centuries," which I hope to persuade Phillips, Sampson & Co. to

---

[21] According to Sir Walter Scott's *Tales of a Grandfather*, Sir Simon Lockhard of Lee was one of Robert Bruce's followers. In Scott's book, however, it was not Lockhard who said that he would "make sicker" (more certain) but Kirkpatrick.

publish next year. We are very happy, but the world thinks we are undone.

STUDY NOTES

1. From whose point of view is "My Double, and How He Undid Me" narrated and what seem to be the advantages of employing this focus in this story?

2. Point out the use of exposition in the rather long beginning.

3. Point out the use of description in this leisurely introduction.

4. By what methods are Dennis Shea and Polly Ingham characterized?

5. Give reasons why you consider the plot more incongruous and humorous than the characters or otherwise, according to the view you hold.

6. Cite enough realistic detail to establish that this story uses verisimilitude extensively.

7. Indicate the mild satire against the unbusinesslike methods of some public organizations in the account of the meetings of the Enlightenment Board.

8. Indicate the satire against small talk in the account of the governor's annual party in Naguadavick.

9. Cite any other examples of mild satire that you find in the story.

10. Cite all the examples of humor that the story seems to present and explain why they are humorous or what devices are employed in arousing the comic sense.

11. What purpose does Dennis's use of Irish dialect in the climax serve?

12. List all the qualities of Hale's literary style that you can discover in this short narrative and prove that they are present.

MATTER

I'M IN A HURRY[1]
(1925)
WILLIAM HAZLETT UPSON

Dry River Junction, Texas
October 1, 1924

To the Farmers Friend Tractor Company
Earthworm City, Illinois

Dear Sir: I'm in a hurry I want a new main drive gear for my
tractor. This tractor was formerly owned by Joe Banks of Llano,
Texas, and bought by me at the auction after he died. The main drive
gear in the tractor has busted and I just been over and asked the
widow Banks where Joe used to buy parts for his tractors and she
said she aint sure but she thinks it was The Farmers Friend Tractor
Company, Earthworm City, Illinois. So please let me know if you are
the folks, and if so please send the gear at once. As I am in a hurry.
It is the main drive gear. It is the big bull gear in the back end of
the transmission that goes round and round and drives the tractor
excuse this paper as my regular business letter paper has not come
yet yours truly,

David Crockett Suggs

FARMERS' FRIEND TRACTOR COMPANY
MAKERS OF EARTHWORM TRACTORS

Earthworm City, Ill.
October 3, 1924

Mr. David Crockett Suggs
Dry River Junction, Tex.

Dear Sir: This will acknowledge receipt of your letter of October
1, in which we note that you request us to send you a gear for
your tractor.

In this connection we are pleased to advise that an inspection
of our files reveals the fact that Mr. Joseph Banks of Llano, Tex.,

---

was the owner of one of our old-style Model 45 Earthworm Tractors. Mr. Banks acquired this tractor on June 3, 1915. We are changing our records to indicate that this tractor has been purchased by yourself, and we are most happy to assure you that all the resources of the Farmers' Friend Tractor Company are at your service and that we can supply you promptly with everything you may need in the way of spare parts, service and information.

We regret, however, that your description of the gear which you desire is not sufficient for us to identify same, as there are a number of gears in the transmission to which the description "main drive gear" might conceivably apply. Kindly look up this gear in the parts book and advise us the proper part number and name as given therein. When necessary information is received, immediate shipment will be made.

In the meantime, we wish to extend you a most cordial welcome into the happy family of Earthworm users, to congratulate you upon selecting an Earthworm Tractor—even though it be of such an old model—and to assure you of our constant interest and desire to cooperate with you to the fullest extent.

Very truly yours,

Frederick R. Overton
Parts Department

Dry River Junction, Texas
October 6, 1924

To the Farmers Friend Tractor Company
Earthworm City, Illinois

Dear Sir: I got your letter I got no parts book. I asked the widow of Joe Banks, who is the man that owned the tractor before I bought it at the auction after he died, I asked her did they have a parts book for the tractor and she said they once had a parts book but it is lost. I would look up the gear in the parts book if I could, but you can understand that I can't look up the gear in the parts book if I got no parts book. What I want is the big bull gear way at the back. The great big cog wheel with 44 cogs on it that goes round and round and drives the tractor.

I'm in a hurry because the tractor is unfortunately broke down right while I'm doing a very important job for Mr. Rogers of this city. The tractor run fine until 3 P. M. October 1, when there came a loud and very funny noise in the back and the tractor would no longer pull. We took the cover off the transmission case, and this big cog wheel was busted. Six cogs was busted off of it, and the tractor will not pull, only make a funny noise.

I am a young man 24 years of age just starting in business and expect to get married soon, so please send the gear at once as I'm in a hurry and oblige,

David Crockett Suggs

FARMERS' FRIEND TRACTOR COMPANY
MAKERS OF EARTHWORM TRACTORS

Earthworm City, Ill.
October 9, 1924

Mr. David Crockett Suggs
Dry River Junction, Tex.

Dear Sir: This will acknowledge your valued letter of October 6, stating that you desire a gear for your tractor, but are unable to give us the parts number of same owing to the fact that you have no parts book. We have carefully gone over your description of the gear, but we regret that we have been unable positively to identify what gear it is that you desire. We note that you state that the gear has 44 teeth and we feel sure that some mistake has been made, as there is no 44-tooth gear in the tractor.

We are therefore mailing you under separate cover a parts book for the Model 45 Earthworm Tractor, Year 1915, and would suggest that you look up the gear in this book, and let us know the part number so that we can fill your order.

Unfortunately we are not able to supply you with a parts book printed in English.

Nearly all of the old-style Model 45 tractors were sold to the French Government in 1915 to be used in pulling artillery on the western front. As only a few of these tractors were sold in America, the edition of English parts books was very limited and has been exhausted. We are, however, sending you one of the French parts books.

We regret exceedingly that we are obliged to give you a parts book printed in a foreign language; and we realize, of course, that possibly you may be unable to understand it. However, you should be able to find the desired gear in the pictures, which are very plain.

Kindly give us the part number which is given under the picture of the gear, and we will make immediate shipment.

Very truly yours,

Frederick R. Overton
Parts Department

Dry River Junction, Texas
October 12, 1924

To the Farmers Friend Tractor Company
Earthworm City, Illinois

Dear Sir: Your letter has come your book has come you was right when you said I might not understand it. I cant understand the Dago printing and I been looking at the pictures all evening and I cant understand the pictures they dont look like nothing I ever seen. So I cant give you no part number, but I'm in a hurry so please send the gear anyway. It is the one way at the back. You cant miss it. Its not the one that lays down its the one that sets up on edge and has 44 teeth and meshes with the little one with 12 teeth. The little one goes round and round and drives the big one. And the big one is keyed on the main shaft and goes round and round and drives the tractor. Or I should say used to go round and round, but now it has six teeth busted out and wont go round—only makes a funny noise when it gets to the place where the teeth are busted out.

I'm in a hurry and to show you that I need this gear quick, I will explain that the tractor is laid up right in the middle of an important job I'm doing for Mr. Rogers of this city. I'm a young man, age 24 years, and new at the house moving business and I want to make a good impression and also expect to get married soon.

When Mr. Rogers of this city decided to move his house from down by the depot up to the north end of town, and give me the job, I thought it was a fine chance to get started in business and

213

make a good impression. I got the house jacked up, and I put heavy timbers underneath, and trucks with solid wheels that I bought from a contractor at Llano. And I bought this secondhand tractor from Joe Banks at Llano at the auction after he died, and all my money is tied up in this equipment and on October 1, at 3 P. M. we had the house moved half way to where they want it, when the tractor made a funny noise and quit. And if I don't get a new gear pretty soon and move the house the rest of the way I'll be a blowed up sucker.

I'm just starting in business and want to make a good impression and I'm expecting to get married so please hurry with the gear. Excuse paper as my regular business paper has not come yet and oblige,

David Crockett Suggs

FARMERS' FRIEND TRACTOR COMPANY
MAKERS OF EARTHWORM TRACTORS

Earthworm City, Ill.
October 14, 1924

Mr. David Crockett Suggs
Dry River Junction, Tex.

Dear Sir: This will acknowledge your valued favor of October 12, and we regret exceedingly that you have been unable to locate the part which you desire in the parts book, and that consequently you have been subject to annoying delay. As it is always our desire to render the greatest possible service to Earthworm Tractor owners, we have gone into this matter with the greatest of care; and after checking over very thoroughly the descriptions given in your latest letter, we have come to the conclusion that the gear you desire is the 45-tooth intermediate spur gear, symbol number 6843, as illustrated on page 16 of the parts book. We note that you state that the gear has 44 teeth, but as there is no such gear in your model tractor, and as No. 6843 gear fits the description in other particulars, we can only assume that you made a mistake in counting the number of teeth in the gear.

Accordingly we are shipping you by express this afternoon one No. 6843 gear, which we trust will prove to be the part desired.

Assuring you of our constant desire to render you every possible service, efficiently and promptly, I remain,

Very truly yours,

Frederick R. Overton
Parts Department

Dry River Junction, Texas
October 18, 1924

To the Farmers Friend Tractor Company
Earthworm City, Illinois

Dear Sir: Your letter come yesterday your gear come today C. O. D. $41.26 and not only that, but it is no good and it wont fit. It is not like the old gear. It looks like a well made gear but there is nothing like it on my tractor so it is no good to me it is too big it won't go on it won't fit on the shaft. And if it did fit on the shaft, it would not work because it is too big and the teeth would not mesh with the teeth on the little gear, and it ought to have 44 teeth like I said, *not* 45.

So will you look this up again more carefully and send me the right gear and send it quick as possible? I'm in a hurry, and I will explain to you how things stand so you can see I am no liar when I say I got to have this gear right off or I am a blowed up sucker.

I am new in the house moving business and I am moving a house for Mr. Rogers of this city, and Mr. Rogers is a very subborn old cuss and he insisted that the house be moved all together—which includes the main part which is two stories high and built very strong and solid, and also the front porch which sticks out in front and is built pretty weak, and also the one-story kitchen which sticks out behind. The kitchen is very frail.

But Mr. Rogers did not listen to me when I wanted to move the kitchen and front porch separate from the house. So, as I am a young man and new at the house moving business and anxious to make a good impression, I tried to do it like he wanted. I jacked up the whole works all together and put timbers underneath, and heavy trucks that I bought from a contractor at Llano, and we came up from the depot fine—the tractor pulling good and the little old

215

house rolling along smooth and quiet and beautiful. But at 3 P. M. October 1, just as we was going past Jim Ferguson's Drug Store, there come a funny noise in the tractor, and we have been stuck ever since waiting for a new gear because the tractor will not run with six teeth busted out of the old gear.

So you can see that it is no lie that I am in a hurry, and I will explain that for 2 and ½ weeks, no traffic has been able to go past Jim Ferguson's Drug Store. All traffic on the main street of this city has been detoured—turning to the right through the field next to Johnson's Garage, following the back lane past the shed where Harvey Jenkins keeps his cow, and then around Wilson's Hardware Store and back to the main street, and all this owing to the stubbornness of old man Rogers making me take the porch and the kitchen along at the same time.

The porch is now resting two feet from the drug store and the kitchen just three feet from the post office on the other side of the street. If old man Rogers had listened to me and we had taken the kitchen off, there would have been room for traffic to get past, but now we cant take the kitchen off on account of being so jammed up against the post office, but people don't figger on that and everybody in town blames it on me that traffic is held up, which is very wrong as I am doing the best I can.

And now old man Rogers says I contracted to move his house, and I had better hurry up, and he says why don't I hire some horses but I say horses would be unsafe, because when they get to pulling something very heavy they get to jerking and they would be liable to jerk the house and injure it, owing to the fact that Mr. Rogers was so stubborn as to make me leave the kitchen and the porch on the house, thus weakening it. And besides I got no money to waste hiring horses when I got a tractor already, so you can see why I'm in a hurry being anxious to make a good impression and get married.

Please send at once the right gear which has FORTY-FOUR TEETH (44), because the old gear has 38 good teeth, and 6 busted off, making 44 like I said, *not* 45. And the right gear is an inch narrower than the one you sent, and the hole through the middle is smaller. I am making a picture so you can see just what gear it is, so please send it at once and oblige,

David Crockett Suggs

HUMOR

FARMERS' FRIEND TRACTOR COMPANY
MAKERS OF EARTHWORM TRACTORS

Earthworm City, Ill.
October 21, 1924

Mr. David Crockett Suggs
Dry River Junction, Tex.

Dear Sir: This will acknowledge receipt of your letter of October 18, from which we note that you are having trouble in installing in your tractor gear No. 6843, which we shipped you on October 14.

We regret exceedingly that you have had this trouble, and to the end that the basis of the difficulty might be discovered, we have carefully checked over your former correspondence and have at length come to the conclusion that gear No. 6843, which we sent you, is the proper gear. We are therefore at a loss to understand why you have been unable to use it, and can only suggest that you may possibly have made some error in installing it.

To obviate this difficulty we are today mailing you, under separate cover, a copy of our latest instruction book on the care, operation and repair of Earthworm Tractors. We regret that this book was prepared for the new-style tractors, but as the method of installing transmission gears is essentially the same in both old- and new-style tractors, we feel sure that you will have no trouble in applying the instructions to your old-style tractor. Please study carefully the pictures and full descriptions on page 34, and if you proceed as directed we feel sure you will experience no further difficulty in installing the gear.

In case, however, there still remains some minor trouble to interfere with the perfect operation of the tractor, we shall appreciate it if you will notify us, as we are always anxious to give owners of Earthworm Tractors the fullest possible cooperation.

Very truly yours,

Frederick R. Overton
Parts Department

217

MATTER

Dry River Junction, Texas
October 25, 1924

To the Farmers Friend Tractor Company
Earthworm City, Illinois

Dear Sir: Your letter come yesterday your book come today they are
no good to me. It takes more than a book for a new tractor to put
onto an entirely different old tractor a gear wheel that don't belong
to it. I tell you again—you have sent me the wrong gear.

What I want is the big bull gear on the back that has 44 teeth.
FORTY-FOUR. *Not* 45. And it goes round and round and makes
the tractor go. It is the great big cog wheel that meshes with the
little cog wheel. I bet you have sent me a gear for one of your new-
style tractors—how do I know? You told me you had looked it up
what model tractor I got, so why don't you send me the gear that
will fit?

If you people knew what I was up against, you would get busy,
and you would send me that gear in a hurry. The whole town is sore
at me. And I will explain that this is a big place with trolley cars and
everything.

The trolleys here run on a track, but they are not electric, they
are run by gasoline motors inside, and are very modern and up-to-
date like everything else in this city. And for over three weeks now
the trolley from the depot has been coming up almost as far as Jim
Ferguson's Drug Store, and then it has to stop and the conductor
will give the people transfers. And they will get out and squeeze
past old man Rogers's house, and get on the other trolley and ride
on. And it is lucky they have two cars. A few years ago they only
had one.

And old man Rogers says if I don't get action by the first of the
week, he is going to hire horses himself, and pull the house where
he wants it. And if I expect to get a cent for it I can just sue him,
and he says he is tired of living in a house sitting in the middle of the
street with the front porch poking into the drug store window and
the people kidding him all the time. But it's all on account of his
own foolishness and stubbornness, because I told him he had better
go live with his brother in Llano while the house was being moved,
but he is a guy that you can't tell him nothing and so he is living
there with Mrs. Rogers and daughter Mildred, and Mrs. Rogers is

cooking on an oil stove on account they dont know coal is safe in moving, and now they blame it on me because the oil stove smokes up the whole house. So you can see I'm in a hurry, and everybody is sore because the traffic is detoured, and me having to hang red lanterns on the house every night so people wont run into it, and the Police Department has served notice on me that I got until next Thursday to move the house or get pinched. And they had given me a permit to move the house. But they say a permit ain't no 99-year lease. And that just shows how it is—they all try to make mean cracks like that.

And this afternoon, old Mr. Rogers came up to me and he said, "Dave, I hope you ain't still thinking of getting married?"

And I said, "I sure am," because, as I told you in another letter, I'm expecting to get married.

Then Mr. Rogers said, "I may have something to say about that, young man." And I will explain that it is possible that old Mr. Rogers—whose house I am moving with my tractor—may have some influence in the matter, owing to the fact that the girl I expect to marry is named Mildred Rogers, and unfortunately happens to be the daughter of old Mr. Rogers.

So you see, I want that gear, and I want it quick. I am sending back the new gear please credit me with the $41.26 I paid on the C. O. D. I am also sending you the old busted gear. Please look over the old busted gear and send me one just like it, only with the six teeth not busted out. Please hurry and remember FORTY-FOUR TEETH, and oblige yours truly,

David Crockett Suggs

P. S. *Not* 45 teeth.

FARMERS' FRIEND TRACTOR COMPANY
MAKERS OF EARTHWORM TRACTORS

Earthworm City, Ill.
October 29, 1924

Mr. David Crockett Suggs
Dry River Junction, Tex.

Dear Sir: This will acknowledge your valued favor of October 26 in reference to the trouble you are having with your tractor. We regret

219

exceedingly that the misunderstanding in regard to the gear which you need has caused you the annoying delay which you mention.

As soon as your old gear arrives, it will be checked up and every possible effort will be made to supply you promptly with a duplicate of it.

Very truly yours,

Frederick R. Overton
Parts Department

DAVID CROCKETT SUGGS
CONTRACTOR
HOUSES MOVED SAFELY, SPEEDILY AND SURELY

Dry River Junction, Texas
October 31, 1924

To the Farmers Friend Tractor Company
Earthworm City, Illinois

Dear Sir: My new letter paper has come your letter has come please send me the gear as quick as possible I'm in a hurry more than at any time before and unless I get this mess straightened out I'll be more of a blowed up sucker than anybody you ever seen, and in order that you may see what a rush I am in and send the gear as quick as possible, I will explain 2 very unfortunate events which has took place since my last letter. The first was last night.

Being Thursday night and my regular night to call, I went around to see Miss Mildred Rogers, who, as I have explained before, I had expected to marry very soon, and who used to live down by the depot, but is now located temporarily on Main Street just in front of Ferguson's Drug Store. It is not as much fun as it used to be to call at the Rogers's house. Formerly it was possible to sit in the hammock on the front porch, and as the house set back from the street and there was trees around and no street lights, a very pleasant evening could be had.

But at present the front porch is located in a most unfortunate way just two feet from the windows of Ferguson's Drug Store, which is all lighted up—you know how drug store windows is—lots of big white lights, and all kinds of jars full of colored water with more lights shining through. And people squeezing past between the porch and the drug store and going in to get ice cream sodas or stopping to crack bum jokes about me, which I will not repeat. So you can see that it would not be any fun for me and Mildred to sit in the hammock in the evening, even if it was possible to sit in the hammock which it is not, owing to the fact that the porch pillar to which the hammock is fastened has become so weakened by the jacking up of the house that it would take very little to pull it over and let the whole porch roof down with a bang.

So we decided that we better sit in the parlor and we had no sooner entered and I was not doing any harm in any way when old Mr. Rogers came in and there was a very painful scene which I won't describe only to say that he used such expressions as "Get to Hell out of here," and "I dont want my daughter keeping company with any moron," which is a word he got out of the Dallas News.

So after he had hollered around and Mildred had cried, I left the house in a dignified manner. Being a gentleman and always respectful to old age, I did not talk back to him, the dirty crook. But you can see why it is I am in a hurry for the gear.

The other unfortunate event was just this A. M., when old man Rogers went out and hired twelve horses from all over town and also one small flivver tractor to move his house up to where he wants it. He tried to get a big tractor, but there is none in town or near-by except mine which is broke down. But there is plenty of horses and there is this little flivver tractor that would not be big enough to pull the house all by itself.

So this morning they wheeled my poor old tractor out of the way, and they hooked up to the house and there was about a hundred people from the town and from round about that was helping with advice and hollering and yelling and telling Mr. Rogers how to do it. And there was I—the only practical and professional house-mover in the whole city—and none of them asked my advice about anything and so it is not my fault what happened.

When they was all ready, Mr. Rogers he stands up and hollers out, "All ready,—Go!" And the six drivers yelled at the twelve horses, and all the people standing around began to cheer and shout. And the feller on the little flivver tractor started up the motor so quick it made a big noise and scared the horses and all the horses began jumping and heaving and they jerked the house sidewise, and some of the timbers slipped, and the kitchen that I told you about,— it give a little lurch and fell off the house. Just let go, and fell off.

So that scared them, and they unhooked the horses and the flivver tractor and didn't try no more moving, and the house is still there all except the kitchen which was busted up so bad that they finished the job and knocked it to pieces and took it away in wheel barrows.

One good thing is that now the traffic can get in between the house and the post office so they dont have to detour any more. But one very unfortunate thing was that Mrs. Rogers happened to be in the kitchen when it fell off being shaken up considerable but not seriously injured so you can see that I got to have the tractor running again so I can move the house and I hope you will send the gear at once yours truly and oblige,

David Crockett Suggs

FARMERS' FRIEND TRACTOR COMPANY
MAKERS OF EARTHWORM TRACTORS

Earthworm City, Ill.
November 2, 1924

Mr. David Crockett Suggs
Dry River Junction, Tex.

Dear Sir: This will acknowledge your valued favor of October 31 requesting that we use all possible haste in sending you a gear which you need to repair your tractor. We are also pleased to report the receipt of one No. 6843 gear which we shipped you on October 14 and which you returned unused owing to the fact that it will not fit your tractor. We are crediting your account with $41.26 C. O. D. which you paid on this shipment.

The broken gear which you sent as a sample has been carefully checked over by our Engineering Department. They report that they have been unable to identify this gear, and they are of the opinion that no gear similar to this has ever been manufactured by this company. We are, therefore, at a loss to understand how this gear ever came to be in your tractor. We do not make gears similar to the one you have sent in, and it will therefore be impossible for us to supply you with one. However, it is always our policy to be of the greatest possible service to Earthworm owners, and we would suggest that the best thing to do in the circumstances would be for one of our service mechanics to inspect your machine.

Fortunately, it happens that Dry River Junction is the nearest railroad point to the Canyon Ranch, which has just purchased a Ten-Ton Earthworm Tractor. Consequently, Mr. Luke Torkle, one of our service men, will be at Dry River Junction in a few days to unload this tractor and drive it overland to the ranch. If you desire, we will have Mr. Torkle stop off and inspect your machine, advising you what steps to take to put it into first-class running condition; or, if this is impossible, to confer with you in regard to turning in your old machine and purchasing one of our new models. Kindly let us know what you wish us to do in this matter.

Very truly yours,

Frederick R. Overton
Parts Department

TELEGRAM

Dry River Junc Tex Nov 4 1924

Farmers Friend Tractor Co
Earthworm Cy Ills

Have the guy come quick in a hurry.

David Crockett Suggs

FARMERS' FRIEND TRACTOR COMPANY
SERVICE MAN'S REPORT

Written at: Dry River Junction, Tex.
Date: November 7, 1924
Written by: Luke Torkle, Service Man
Subject: Tractor belonging to D. C. Suggs

Reached here 7 A. M. Unloaded tractor for Canyon Ranch, and will drive it over tomorrow.

MATTER

Before I had a chance to look up D. C. Suggs, the mayor and prominent citizens urgently requested me to use the new tractor to move a house that was blocking the main street. This looked like good advertising for us, especially as the county commissioner here is expecting to buy a tractor for road work. Accordingly, I spent the morning moving the house to where they wanted it, and then looked up Mr. Suggs.

Found he has left town. It is reported that he was shot at three times yesterday by a man called Rogers, but escaped. Last night he sold his entire property, consisting of a secondhand tractor, an old fliv, one radio set and the good will in a house-moving business for $450. He then took the train north with a girl called Mildred Rogers of this place.

I inspected the tractor formerly owned by Mr. Suggs. No wonder we couldn't supply him with repairs for it. It is not one of our tractors. It has no name plate, but I was able to identify it as a 1920 Model, Steel Elephant Tractor, made by the S. E. Tractor Company of Indianapolis. I talked on the phone with Mrs. Joseph Banks, whose husband formerly owned the tractor. She says her husband sold the old Earthworm Tractor three years ago to a man in Dallas. Mr. Banks owned four or five different kinds of tractors. Mrs. Banks remembered he had once bought tractor parts from the Farmers' Friend Tractor Company.

In regard to your suggestion that Mr. Suggs might be persuaded to buy a new tractor, I think this is hardly possible. It is reported that before he left, Mr. Suggs stated that he and Miss Rogers would be married and would locate in Chicago. He was uncertain what business he would take up, but said very emphatically it would be nothing in any way connected with house moving, or with tractors or any kind of machinery.

STUDY NOTES

1. Indicate the origin of Upson's interest in writing tractor stories.
2. What type of character is David Crockett Suggs and by what method is his personality made known to the reader?
3. Point out the difference in tone and style of the letters written by Suggs and of those written by Overton.
4. List the main incidents of the plot.
5. State your opinion, and support it with reasons, as to whether the

humor of "I'm in a Hurry" arises chiefly from incongruities of character or of plot or from absurd and monstrous diction.

6. Cite instances of humor arising from the use of slang in Suggs's letters.

7. Give examples of humor caused by Suggs's mention of petty and irrelevant details.

8. Point out instances of humor that springs from his use of barbarisms and colloquialisms.

9. Mention examples of humor created by incongruity between an existing situation and some other that Suggs would prefer.

10. Refer to passages in which the humor is due to incongruity between Suggs's action and his emotional attitude or between his opinion of himself and the reader's opinion of him.

11. In the service man's report, point out humor caused by incongruity between action taken toward Suggs and what he would have desired or between his most recent activity and his earlier intention.

12. List any other methods of creating humor, accompanied by examples, that you find in either Suggs's letters or the service man's report.

COMPARISON EXERCISES

1. Show that "My Double, and How He Undid Me" and "I'm in a Hurry" have some connection with the occupational experiences of Hale and Upson.

2. Compare the two stories for their use of realistic detail.

3. Consider the diction—the levels of language—employed.

4. Compare the stories for the degree of humor present—mild or hilarious.

5. Compare the methods by which the two stories create humor.

WRITING SUGGESTION

Decide whether to produce a story mildly titillating or boisterously funny and, as an experiment, write the story, using the best available methods for creating the type of humor desired.

LOVE

Introduction to Stories with a Love Motif

A LOVE story presents the amorous experiences of imagined human beings, particularly youths, usually experiences connected with some problem of courtship or marriage. Though conjugal love is the kind most frequently treated in brief fictions, other forms of affection, such as parental or filial or fraternal, sometimes serve as the motifs. Whichever form may be used, the love must not be sudden and fleeting but deep-seated and powerfully controlling, if it is to help the story find widespread favor. Romantic stories of teen-agers frequently appear in "slick" or "commercial" magazines. And such publications occasionally print a story of love involving older characters. Of all the stories published in the widely circulated commercial magazines, perhaps two-thirds to three-fourths have the love motif.

According to the usual formula for love stories, a boy and a girl or a man and a woman become acquainted accidentally or otherwise, then the two must somehow overcome the obstacles to their marrying, and eventually the marriage must be consummated. In "quality" magazines, not nearly all the romantic stories represent young love as arriving at a successful consummation. The lovers may reach an impasse. Their affinity may be hopelessly beset by conflicting religious faiths on the part of the couple or by social opposition to intermarriage of different races or by some other social conflict. Not nearly so many love stories appear, however, in the quality magazines as in the commercials; therefore, not nearly so many stories leave young love hopelessly deadlocked as bring it to a happy conclusion.

The tone of love stories is typically sentimental. Not only is the affectionate sentiment essential to the love story but so are plot, character, and setting. A theme is also helpful, and the manner of treating the materials is important. To be successful, such stories should have original plots, characters, and settings. The antiquity of the motif increases the need for originality in the other elements.

The theme is often some variation of one of two very ancient ideas: the preciousness of love in a young couple; the marriage of young lovers after conquering all interfering circumstances. Some other idea, however, such as the failure of young love or either the success or failure of older love, sometimes serves as the theme.

The plot of the love stories in the slick magazines is usually rather intricate and marked by a strong suspense. The plot of any love story, whether of the usual and more popular type or the unusual, should present the step-by-step development of a strong emotional attachment between the two principal characters all the way to a triumph, an inescapable dilemma or whatever the outcome. The climax may be a proposal of marriage, but not necessarily. Love can express itself in various ways, for example, through courtesy or generosity or a rescue from danger. Sometimes the climax presents action expressing one of these forms of love or one of these emotions kindred to love, action either prior to or subsequent to a proposal. Sometimes the apex of the plot could hardly be a proposal, because the story may concern the love of a married couple or of a father or mother for a son or daughter or of a person for a pet or of the pet for the person. Though both the stories deal with conjugal love, Bunner's "Love-Letters of Smith" uses the proposition-for-marriage climax, but Seager's "Second Wedding" has another kind, a wife's returning home with her husband after his courageous defense of himself against insult and her thereby showing her decision to continue living with him.

The characters should be sufficiently unique to command the reader's interest. They must be persons with whose romantic experience he will sympathize. They must be lovable. The reader must be allowed to see their attractive physical features and such spiritual traits as unselfishness and sacrifice.

The settings should result from careful observation, and whatever description of them may appear should be interlaced with the action. A little moonlight or other appropriate background can contribute to atmosphere, to the reader's emotional reaction to the incidents unfolding before his mind's eye.

Of great importance is the method of presenting the love-story elements. The plot must rise to a climax; so must the romantic sentiment. Not through the author's comments analyzing the emotions of his characters nor through descriptions of caresses nor through lengthy speeches of endearment but through a well-constructed plot and the suggestions furnished by certain simple acts, such as the making of a date or the feeding of candy to a lady's dog, love can be indicated as already present or about to develop in a man's heart. The writing should rise above the commonplace and show the artistic quality that results from such techniques as restrained tone and style, the use of suspense and surprise, and the attribution to characters of moods that reveal the interrelationships of characters with one another or with environment. The reader's appreciation of the story can come from originality in the various elements and from artistic handling of the materials.

THE LOVE-LETTERS OF SMITH [1]
(1890)

HENRY CUYLER BUNNER

W HEN the little seamstress had climbed to her room in the story over the top story of the great brick tenement house in which she lived, she was quite tired out. If you do not understand what a story over a top story is, you must remember that there are no limits to human greed, and hardly any to the height of tenement houses. When the man who owned that seven-story tenement found that he could rent another floor, he found no difficulty in persuading the guardians of our building laws to let him clap another story on the roof, like a cabin on the deck of a ship; and in the southeasterly of the four apartments on this floor the little seamstress lived. You could just see the top of her window from the street—the huge cornice that had capped the original front, and that served as her window-sill now, quite hid all the lower part of the story on top of the top story.

The little seamstress was scarcely thirty years old, but she was such an old-fashioned little body in so many of her looks and ways that I had almost spelled her sempstress, after the fashion of our grandmothers. She had been a comely body, too; and would have been still, if she had not been thin and pale and anxious-eyed.

She was tired out tonight because she had been working hard all day for a lady who lived far up in the "New Wards" beyond Harlem River, and after the long journey home, she had to climb seven flights of tenement-house stairs. She was too tired both in body and in mind to cook the two little chops she had brought home. She would save them for breakfast, she thought. So she made herself a cup of tea on the miniature stove, and ate a slice of dry bread with it. It was too much trouble to make toast.

But after dinner she watered her flowers. She was never too tired for that; and the six pots of geraniums that caught the south sun on the top of the cornice did their best to repay her. Then she sat down in her rocking-chair by the window and looked out. Her eyrie was high above all the other buildings, and she could look across some low roofs opposite, and see the further end of Tompkins

---

[1] First published in *Puck* (July 23, 1890) ; republished in *Short Sixes,* 1890.

Square, with its sparse Spring green showing faintly through the dusk. The eternal roar of the city floated up to her and vaguely troubled her. She was a country girl, and although she had lived for ten years in New York, she had never grown used to that ceaseless murmur. Tonight she felt the languor of the new season as well as the heaviness of the physical exhaustion. She was almost too tired to go to bed.

She thought of the hard day done and the hard day to be begun after the night spent on the hard little bed. She thought of the peaceful days in the country, when she taught school in the Massachusetts village where she was born. She thought of a hundred small slights that she had to bear from people better fed than bred. She thought of the sweet green fields that she rarely saw nowadays. She thought of the long journey forth and back that must begin and end her morrow's work, and she wondered if her employer would think to offer to pay her fare. Then she pulled herself together. She must think of more agreeable things, or she could not sleep. And as the only agreeable things she had to think about were her flowers, she looked at the garden on top of the cornice.

A peculiar gritting noise made her look down, and she saw a cylindrical object that glittered in the twilight, advancing in an irregular and uncertain manner toward her flower-pots. Looking closer, she saw that it was a pewter beer-mug, which somebody in the next apartment was pushing with a two-foot rule. On top of the beer-mug was a piece of paper, and on this paper was written, in a sprawling, half-formed hand:

porter
pleas excuse the libberty   And
drink it

The seamstress started up in terror, and shut the window. She remembered that there was a man in the next apartment. She had seen him on the stairs, on Sundays. He seemed a grave decent person; but—he must be drunk. She sat down on her bed all a-tremble. Then she reasoned with herself. The man was drunk, that was all. He probably would not annoy her further. And if he did, she had only to retreat to Mrs. Mulvaney's apartment in the rear, and Mr. Mulvaney, who was a highly respectable man and worked in a boiler-shop, would protect her. So, being a poor woman who had already had occasion to excuse—and refuse—two or three "libberties" of like sort, she made up her mind to go to bed like a reasonable seamstress, and she did. She was rewarded, for when her light was out, she could see in the moonlight that the two-foot rule appeared again, with one joint bent back, hitched itself into the mug-handle, and withdrew the mug.

The next day was a hard one for the little seamstress, and she hardly thought of the affair of the night before until the same hour had come around again, and she sat once more by her window. Then she smiled at the remembrance. "Poor fellow," she said in her charitable heart, "I've no doubt he's *awfully* ashamed of it now. Perhaps he was never tipsy before. Perhaps he didn't know there was a lone woman in here to be frightened."

Just then she heard a gritting sound. She looked down. The pewter pot was in front of her, and the two-foot rule was slowly retiring. On the pot was a piece of paper, and on the paper was:

porter
good for the helth
it makes meet

This time the little seamstress shut her window with a bang of indignation. The color rose to her pale cheeks. She thought that she would go down to see the janitor at once. Then she remembered the seven flights of stairs; and she resolved to see the janitor in the morning. Then she went to bed and saw the mug drawn back just as it had been drawn back the night before.

The morning came, but, somehow, the seamstress did not care to complain to the janitor. She hated to make trouble—and the janitor might think—and—and—well, if the wretch did it again she would speak to him herself, and that would settle it.

And so, on the next night, which was a Thursday, the little seamstress sat down by her window, resolved to settle the matter. And she had not sat there long, rocking in the creaking little rocking-chair which she had brought with her from her old home, when the pewter pot hove in sight, with a piece of paper on the top.

This time the legend read:

Perhaps you are afraid i will
adress you
i am not that kind

The seamstress did not quite know whether to laugh or cry. But she felt that the time had come for speech. She leaned out of her window and addressed the twilight heaven.

"Mr.—Mr.—sir—I—will you *please* put your head out of the window so that I can speak to you?"

The silence of the other room was undisturbed. The seamstress drew back, blushing. But before she could nerve herself for another attack, a piece of paper appeared on the end of the two-foot rule.

when I Say a thing i
mene it
i have Sed i would not
Adress you and i
Will not

What was the little seamstress to do? She stood by the window and thought hard about it. Should she complain to the janitor? But the creature was perfectly respectful. No doubt he meant to be kind. He certainly was kind, to waste these pots of porter on her. She remembered the last time—and the first—that she had drunk porter. It was at home, when she was a young girl, after she had had the diphtheria. She remembered how good it was, and how it had given her back her strength. And without one thought of what she was doing, she lifted the pot of porter and took one little reminiscent sip—two little reminiscent sips—and became aware of her utter fall and defeat. She blushed now as she had never blushed before, put the pot down, closed the window, and fled to her bed like a deer in the woods.

And when the porter arrived the next night, bearing the simple appeal:

Dont be afrade of it
drink it all

the little seamstress arose and grasped the pot firmly by the handle, and poured its contents over the earth around her largest geranium. She poured the contents out to the last drop, and then she dropped the pot, and ran back and sat on her bed and cried, with her face hid in her hands.

"Now," she said to herself, "you've done it! And you're just as nasty and hard-hearted and suspicious and mean as—as pusley!"[2]

---

[2] A common plant, a potherb. The comparison is not very appropriate or meaningful. The seamstress seems to have had difficulty completing it.

And she wept to think of her hardness of heart. "He will never give me a chance to say I am sorry," she thought. And, really, she might have spoken kindly to the poor man, and told him that she was much obliged to him, but that he really musn't ask her to drink porter with him.

"But it's all over and done now," she said to herself as she sat at her window on Saturday night. And then she looked at the cornice, and saw the faithful little pewter pot traveling slowly toward her.

She was conquered. This act of Christian forbearance was too much for her kindly spirit. She read the inscription on the paper:

porter is good for Flours
but better for Fokes

and she lifted the pot to her lips, which were not half so red as her cheeks, and took a good, hearty, grateful draught.

She sipped in thoughtful silence after this first plunge, and presently she was surprised to find the bottom of the pot in full view.

On the table at her side a few pearl buttons were screwed up in a bit of white paper. She untwisted the paper and smoothed it out, and wrote in a tremulous hand—she *could* write a very neat hand—

Thanks.

This she laid on the top of the pot, and in a moment the bent two-foot rule appeared and drew the mail-carriage home. Then she sat still, enjoying the warm glow of the porter, which seemed to have permeated her entire being with heat that was not at all like the unpleasant and oppressive heat of the atmosphere, an atmosphere heavy with the Spring damp. A gritting on the tin aroused her. A piece of paper lay under her eyes.

fine groing weather
Smith

it said.

Now it is unlikely that in the whole round and range of conversational commonplaces there was one other greeting that could have induced the seamstress to continue the exchange of communications. But this simple and homely phrase touched her country heart. What did *"groing weather"* matter to the toilers in this waste of brick and mortar? This stranger must be like herself, a country-bred soul, longing for the new green and the upturned brown mold of the country fields. She took up the paper, and wrote under the first message:

Fine

But that seemed curt; *for* she added: *"for"* what? She did not know. At last in desperation she put down *potatoes*. The piece of paper was withdrawn and came back with an addition:

Too mist for potatos

And when the little seamstress had read this, and grasped the fact that *m-i-s-t* represented the writer's pronunciation of "moist," she laughed softly to herself. A man whose mind, at such a time, was seriously bent upon potatoes, was not a man to be feared. She found a half-sheet of note-paper, and wrote:

I lived in a small village before I came to New York, but I am afraid I do not know much about farming. Are you a farmer?

The answer came:

have ben most Every thing
farmed a Spel in Maine
Smith

As she read this, the seamstress heard a church clock strike nine. "Bless me, is it so late?" she cried, and she hurriedly penciled *Good Night,* thrust the paper out, and closed the window. But a few minutes later, passing by, she saw yet another bit of paper on the cornice, fluttering in the evening breeze. It said only *good nite,* and after a moment's hesitation, the little seamstress took it in and gave it shelter.

· · · · ·

After this, they were the best of friends. Every evening the pot appeared, and while the seamstress drank from it at her window, Mr. Smith drank from its twin at his; and notes were exchanged as rapidly as Mr. Smith's early education permitted. They told each other their histories, and Mr. Smith's was one of travel and variety, which he seemed to consider quite a matter of course. He had followed the sea, he had farmed, he had been a logger and a hunter in the Maine woods. Now he was foreman of an East River lumber yard, and he was prospering. In a year or two he would have enough laid by to go home to Bucksport and buy a share in a ship-building business. All this dribbled out in the course of a jerky but variegated correspondence, in which autobiographic details were mixed with reflections, moral and philosophical.

A few samples will give an idea of Mr. Smith's style:

i was one trip to van demens
land[3]

To which the seamstress replied:

It must have been very interesting

But Mr. Smith disposed of this subject very briefly:

it wornt

Further he vouchsafed:

i seen a chinese cook in
hong kong could cook flapjacks
like your Mother

a mishnery that sells Rum
is the menest of Gods crechers

a bulfite is not what it is
cract up to Be

the dagos are wussen the
brutes

i am 6 1¾
but my Father was 6 foot 4

The seamstress had taught school one Winter, and she could not refrain from making an attempt to reform Mr. Smith's orthography. One evening, in answer to this communication:

i killed a Bare in Maine 600
lbs waight

she wrote:

Isn't it generally spelled Bear?

but she gave up the attempt when he responded:

a bare is a mene animle any
way you spel him

---

[3] Van Diemen's Land, the name that Abel Tasman, the discoverer of Tasmania, gave to the island.

The Spring wore on, and the Summer came, and still the evening drink and the evening correspondence brightened the close of each day for the little seamstress. And the draught of porter put her to sleep each night, giving her a calmer rest than she had ever known during her stay in the noisy city; and it began, moreover, to make a little "meet" for her. And then the thought that she was going to have an hour of pleasant companionship somehow gave her courage to cook and eat her little dinner, however tired she was. The seamstress's cheeks began to blossom with the June roses.

And all this time Mr. Smith kept his vow of silence unbroken, though the seamstress sometimes tempted him with little ejaculations and exclamations to which he might have responded. He was silent and invisible. Only the smoke of his pipe, and the clink of his mug as he set it down on the cornice, told her that a living, material Smith was her correspondent. They never met on the stairs, for their hours of coming and going did not coincide. Once or twice they passed each other in the street—but Mr. Smith looked straight ahead of him, about a foot over her head. The little seamstress thought he was a very fine-looking man, with his six feet one and three-quarters and his thick brown beard. Most people would have called him plain.

Once she spoke to him. She was coming home one Summer evening, and a gang of corner-loafers stopped her and demanded money to buy beer, as is their custom. Before she had time to be frightened, Mr. Smith appeared—whence, she knew not—scattered the gang like chaff, and, collaring two of the human hyenas, kicked them with deliberate, ponderous, alternate kicks until they writhed in ineffable agony. When he let them crawl away, she turned to him and thanked him warmly, looking very pretty now, with the color in her cheeks. But Mr. Smith answered no word. He stared over her head, grew red in the face, fidgeted nervously, but held his peace until his eyes fell on a rotund Teuton, passing by.

"Say, Dutchy!" he roared.

The German stood aghast.

"I ain't got nothing to write with!" thundered Mr. Smith, looking him in the eye. And then the man of his word passed on his way.

And so the Summer went on, and the two correspondents chatted silently from window to window, hid from sight of all the world below by the friendly cornice. And they looked out over the roof, and saw the green of Tompkins Square grow darker and dustier as the months went on.

Mr. Smith was given to Sunday trips into the suburbs, and he never came back without a bunch of daisies or black-eyed Susans or, later, asters or golden-rod for the little seamstress. Sometimes, with a sagacity rare in his sex, he brought her a whole plant, with fresh loam for potting.

He gave her also a reel in a bottle, which, he wrote, he had *"maid"* himself, and some coral, and a dried flying-fish, that was somewhat fearful to look upon, with its sword-like fins and its hollow eyes. At first, she could not go to sleep with that flying-fish hanging on the wall.

But he surprised the little seamstress very much one cool September evening, when he shoved this letter along the cornice:

Respected and Honored Madam:

Having long and vainly sought an opportunity to convey to you the expression of my sentiments, I now avail myself of the privilege of epistolary communication to acquaint you with the fact that the Emotions, which you have raised in my breast, are those which should point to Connubial Love and Affection rather than to simple Friendship. In short, Madam, I have the Honor to approach you with a Proposal, the acceptance of which will fill me with ecstatic Gratitude and enable me to extend to you those Protecting Cares, which the Matrimonial Bond makes at once the Duty and the Privilege of him, who would, at no distant date, lead to the Hymeneal Altar one whose charms and virtues should suffice to kindle its Flames, without extraneous Aid.

I remain, Dear Madam,
Your Humble Servant and
Ardent Adorer, J. Smith

The little seamstress gazed at his letter a long time. Perhaps she was wondering in what Ready Letter-Writer of the last century Mr. Smith had found this form. Perhaps she was amazed at the results of his first attempt at punctuation. Perhaps she was thinking of something else, for there were tears in her eyes and a smile on her small mouth.

But it must have been a long time, and Mr. Smith must have grown nervous, for presently another communication came along the line where the top of the cornice was worn smooth. It read:

If not understood will you mary me?

The little seamstress seized a piece of paper and wrote:

If I say Yes, will you speak to me?

Then she rose and passed it out to him, leaning out of the window, and their faces met.

STUDY NOTES

1. With what kind of love motif does "The Love-Letters of Smith" deal?

2. Show that the author's comment concerning the seamstress's attitude toward Smith reflects the character of both Smith and the seamstress.

3. Indicate whether the omniscient point of view—in which an author knows all about his characters—includes both Smith and the woman.

4. By what devices other than author comment does Bunner characterize Smith?

5. By what devices other than author comment does Bunner characterize the seamstress?

6. How does Bunner cause the reader to sympathize with the seamstress and with Smith?

7. How does Smith's love reveal itself—what simple actions suggest the presence of love in his heart?

8. Cite passages from this story that reflect pathos and others that arouse humor.

9. Trace the incidents in the romance between the lumberman and the seamstress from its inception to the marriage proposal.

10. Show that this story employs the usual love-story formula for plot.

11. Point out the instances of suspense, and surprise if any, and the purpose that each instance serves.

12. Make clear that in this story the love sentiment rises to a climax.

SECOND WEDDING[1]
(1949)

ALLAN SEAGER

THE day her husband was arrested, Dorothy was standing by a window, looking out, waiting for him to come home. She had done this every day for three months. It was a habit she only dimly acknowledged—she would not have told him about it for anything. She was not the one who was tender.

She watched his car turn off the main road and into their long, curving driveway between the alley of new, little maple trees, each braced by three wires tied to stakes. Two years before, there had been no trees at all.

They had built the house in a pasture on a hill—from there you could see the whole town, and (she knew it had been part of his plan) the whole town could see the house, severe French in style, modeled after a photograph of a house at Nether Lypiatt in England, the biggest place for miles around. Her living room was thirty feet long, and it was furnished exactly as she had always wanted a room furnished. Yet, when she was alone, it was too big. If she spoke aloud, there seemed to be an actual echo.

She did not know it, but she had formed a conviction that was just at the edge of discovery. She would phrase it this way: Style did not finally depend on décor. But what she meant was that she was a little bored and lonely, and the marvelous fireplace, hooded and carved, and the pearwood chairs did not exercise this in the prompt way she always had expected such things would. To stand by the window and wait for her husband was the only concession she could make to this feeling.

His car stopped. As he got out, she saw that his topcoat was hanging open. This was unusual; he had come to take an extravagant pride in looking neat. He walked slowly into the house, his eyes fixed on the ground. This, too, was unusual. She heard the front door open, but there was no pause in his steps. He walked into the room with his hat and coat on. When he saw her, he seemed to remember himself and swept off the hat.

---

[1] In *Good Housekeeping* (May, 1949). Reprinted by permission of Allan Seager.

240

Never saying anything about it openly, she had arranged that the half hour before dinner should be devoted to conversation—not about what he had been doing at the factory, nor what she had done during the day—but anything to make him forget that he was a businessman making a lot of money, and that she was what other people called a Society Woman. (It was a town of only five thousand people, but if it had been five hundred, there would still have been a Society.)

He kissed her cheek, and started to sit down on the sofa.

"Hello, Perry," she said, "Don't you want to take off your coat?"

He lifted one arm and looked at the sleeve as if it were new. "Coat? Oh. Yeah," he said. He slipped it off and threw it on a chair.

He sat down beside her, his cupped hands between his knees. He looked awkward; he pursed his lips. The posture and the movement of his lips made him seem older, middle-aged, no longer just thirty-five. At last he turned his head toward her and said slowly, "You know that big willow tree down by the bridge? The one where the pair of cardinals nested all last winter?"

Faithfully, he was beginning the conversation proper to the time of day. She was too curious to answer him in kind.

"What's the matter, Perry?"

His gaze fell again. "I got arrested today, Dorothy."

"Arrested? What for?"

"A-a-h!" he said angrily. He looked straight at her. "It's not my fault. I'm not a crook."

"But why did they—"

"Income tax."

"Oh," she said. She was relieved somehow. Her aunts had warned her about him, over and over, at the time of their marriage two years before. He was a roughneck, Aunt Tessa had said, and Aunt Phoebe could remember his father selling vegetables in the street from a wagon. Not that peddling vegetables wasn't an honest occupation, but—

Dorothy was intelligent enough to realize that no woman ever knows her husband completely, but she was afraid there were many facets of Perry's character she could never truly perceive. When he said the word *arrested,* she had a sick feeling that one of them had turned up. He might have, heaven knows why, stolen something obvious like a car, or beaten someone half to death. There was a violence in him she was always trying to keep subdued.

"What happened? Why did they have to arrest you?"

"It's Hatford. But I fixed him."

"What's Clyde got to do with it?"

Clyde Hatford was what Aunt Phoebe called a *scion*. The Hatfords had built the second house in town; that was in 1823. Perry had made Clyde his assistant with a triumphant scorn—Perry had come from the wrong side of the river.

"He did it. I'm too busy to monkey around with income tax. I left it all to him."

"What did he do—make a mistake?"

"See what you think. The Revenue Office sends me a flock of warning letters. I never see them. Then finally they send the auditors around to go over my personal items. I'm in Cleveland that day and Hatford never tells me. The first thing I know is when a U. S. marshal shows up this morning and says, 'Come along.' "

"But why didn't Clyde tell you?"

"*Maybe* he was trying to save me trouble," Perry said nastily. Then he straightened up, smiled, and rubbed his left hand over the right, which was clenched in a tight fist. "I fired him this afternoon."

"But you can tell them it was a mistake and you're willing to pay, can't you."

"I told 'em. I drove back to the city with the marshal this morning. I talked to the judge and offered to fix everything up. It didn't work. He's a new man and he's cracking down on all tax evaders. So I posted my bail and came home."

"That means you're going to have to stand trial."

"That's it." His face was gloomy. "I don't like this standing trial."

"But as long as it's not your fault and you're willing to pay the fine, what difference does it make?'

He stood up, walked to the end of the room, and stopped before the fireplace. "It'll be in the paper tomorrow night."

"It's in the paper when you overpark, too. What of it?"

"We're going to the Parkers' dinner tomorrow night, aren't we?"

"When I was a little girl, the first thing that ever stamped the Parkers on my mind was when the bank examiners caught old Levi. For years I thought Dick Parker must have a sign on him somewhere, like a birthmark, maybe, to show he was the son of a thief. Do you think he's going to say anything? Or Emily? Everybody knows it."

"But why didn't they arrest old Levi? How did he get out of it?"

She could tell what he was trying to say. He wanted to know how Levi Parker's tampering with the bank funds could be hushed up, while he would have to stand trial. Obviously, it was because the Parkers had been there a long time. If you belonged to an old family, your life was cushioned, there were mysterious perquisites and immunities. Perry knew there were, but he could not yet understand why. Not that Dorothy could either, exactly, but she was used to them.

"Oh, I don't know all the details. They kept it quiet somehow."

"And Levi stayed president of the bank until he died."

"Yes, but don't worry. Everybody knew about him. Dick and Emily won't say anything embarrassing tomorrow night."

"I'll pop him one if he does."

"Oh, good. Try and hit him right in front of that confounded antique love seat of Emily's, will you? I'm tired of hearing about it and I'd like to see it broken."

He stopped polishing his fist with his other hand. Then he grinned. "Okay, I won't make any trouble."

"Well, you've got to realize that somebody's going to mention it and you can't just push his face in when he does. A lot of people are jealous of you. You've made too much money."

"Too fast," he finished. After a moment, his face again took on the set frown of concentration and worry.

"Perry—listen to me—don't worry."

He stopped in front of her, his face serious. "You don't know what I'm trying to do. You don't know."

She thought she did know. The theory that women ought to improve their husbands was repugnant to her, but she knew she had been practicing it and Perry was a willing pupil. She watched him leave the room, and then her eyes examined the furniture, making a strangely unrewarding survey of the expensive chairs and the pictures. It was a beautiful room, she told herself, a decorator's room, although she had made the sketches herself, a little aghast at the money she was spending.

The only other living room she had ever known as well as this was at her aunts' where she had grown up. A whir, a soughing noise, was always there because the pine trees outside caught every little breeze. It seemed to her that she had married to get out of that room, away from the tinted photographs of her great-grandfather and grandmother, and the damp, hard candy in the glass bowl, sitting eternally beside a useless oil lamp with a globe of pink china. Even now, the sight of any haircloth sofa could make her heart sink. However, the townspeople, her aunts included, said she had married Perry for his money, this fast money.

After dinner, Perry went back to the factory; she sat down to wait for Aunt Tessa's arrival. Her aunt had said nothing about it, but Dorothy knew she would stop in. The town was too small for the word not to spread, and Aunt Tessa had keen and eager ears, once pierced for earrings.

Aunt Tessa was the active aunt; Aunt Phoebe was passive. When the war brought the first factories to the town, Aunt Tessa had roused herself out of the quiet in which she had expected to end her days and had gone into her capital to buy a mink coat. To keep tab on the wives of the new executives, she joined the women's clubs she had scorned all her life. For her, it meant a new life full of hectic activity and rich variety. Aunt Tessa's new clothes did not fit her very well. She carried a pair of modern-framed eyeglasses, which she didn't need, and by putting them on at special moments, she accentuated the intensity of her gaze, magnifying her usual disapproval.

It was not yet eight o'clock when Dorothy saw the taxi come up the long driveway. As much as she got around, Aunt Tessa could not persuade herself to gouge her capital so far as to buy her own car. Dorothy heard the front door open and Aunt Tessa shout at the taxi driver. "You won't get any more out of me. A dime's enough!" The door closed and Aunt Tessa called, "Anybody home?"

Aunt Tessa came in and stopped still. "Those are new drapes," she said accusingly, pointing toward the windows. She stood looking the antique *toile de Jouy* drapes up and down, a woman seventy years old, feet planted wide apart, her mink coat slipping down off her shoulders, and her hands joined over her stomach. She did not know much about cosmetics, and the folds and crevices of her face were white as plaster. There were two moons of scarlet on her cheeks, and her mouth was a poorly outlined, drab purple.

"When'd you get *them?*" she said, waving her handbag at the windows.

"Oh, last week."

"Humph," Aunt Tessa said, and meant that new drapes were an almost insulting extravagance.

The old woman sat down beside Dorothy on the sofa. She opened the bag and pawed through it, finally taking out the inevitable eyeglasses. She held them ready for instant, strategic use. Dorothy wondered if Aunt Tessa, too, carried a potato; Aunt Phoebe did. Aunt Phoebe carried an Irish potato in a pocket somewhere under her petticoats, and she wore a zinc insole in one shoe, a copper insole in the other, a traditional family remedy against rheumatism. There was no potato, however, in Aunt Tessa's bag.

"Good thing you got those drapes now. You won't be throwing money away on window drapes pretty soon. Have other uses for your money then." She put her glasses on and said clearly, "Won't you?"

"How do you mean?"

"Oh, I don't suppose you know anything about it. Be just like him not to tell you. Shield you," she said sarcastically.

"Are you talking about the mistake in Perry's income tax?"

"Mistake? Well, you can call it a mistake if you want to, but it's the biggest scandal to come out of this town in twenty years. They say he's short thirty-one thousand dollars and they make you pay triple. That's ninety-three thousand dollars it's going to cost him, and maybe a jail sentence on top of that. Some mistake, if you ask me," she finished triumphantly.

Dorothy knew that her aunt told gossip as accurately as a chronometer tells time. "Who told you all this?"

"Sadie Hatford said Clyde told her. He ought to know." Sadie was Clyde Hatford's mother.

245

"Perry didn't tell me how much he owed the Government, but I'm a little surprised that Clyde would be telling it around."

"Why? It'll be in tomorrow night's paper as sure as the world."

"I know it will, but just the same, it's strange that Clyde would start the story."

"Why?"

"Because Perry left all the income tax matters to him. Clyde made the mistake—and he knows it."

"Well, I don't know anything about that," her aunt said snippily, "but I do know that Clyde's very fond of you. That's why he never married."

"What of it? What's his liking me got to do with it?"

Clyde Hatford and she had "gone steady" in high school. He had been manager of the football team and captain of the debating team. They had had a date every Saturday night until he went to college; she had gone to her first house party with him in the early days of the war. She had never much considered whether she liked him or not, because her aunts had encouraged her. Going out with him had seemed inevitable. He was tall, thin, and somehow limber, not like Perry.

"Oh, I don't know. I don't know," her aunt said in an exasperating, high singsong. "Maybe you won't want a jailbird for a husband very long."

Suddenly, a vague idea assumed more definite form in her mind. It was only a wild conjecture, but it might just be true that Clyde had made the mistake deliberately, knowing that Perry would suffer for it, all in a strained farfetched hope that she might divorce him.

"Why do you hate him so?" Dorothy asked Tessa.

"Hate who?" Her aunt was very busy rising, pulling her mink coat around her, meticulously thrusting her hands into her gloves. "I don't hate anybody."

"Yes, you do. You hate him because his father peddled vegetables and couldn't belong to the City Club. You hate him because he worked his way through high school. You hate him because he made a lot of money." This was a routine defense she had made of Perry ever since their marriage—she could reel off the points, one, two, three. Now she had the embarrassing suspicion that she might also be defending her own choice.

Her aunt buttoned her gloves, settled the collar of the mink coat. "I'm going to walk home," she said. "Do me good. I sit around too much." Then, with a vivid warmth of manner Dorothy had never been able to spot as insincere, she said, "Now, dear, don't worry about this dreadful business. It'll come out all right. Phoebe wants to see you. Come down tomorrow morning, will you?" Tessa's glasses were returned to her purse; the visit was over.

Dorothy did not want to see her Aunt Phoebe, but it did not occur to her to say no. "I'll come. Good night."

"Good night. You just keep calm."

If her aunt had wanted to make her nervous, she had done so. What had seemed at first to be an oversight, mere negligence on her husband's part, now had swollen into a crime. She was shrewd enough to see that she had defended him too vehemently; just the saying of the words had made him seem guilty. She tried to shrug off the feeling, and went to bed and read a book. But she did not read very long. After lying awake in the darkness, she pretended to be asleep when Perry came in.

At ten o'clock the next morning, she found her Aunt Phoebe gently swaying back and forth in a horsehair rocker, working slowly and patiently on a petit-point canvas. Aunt Phoebe had done that every morning at ten ever since Dorothy could remember. She was a feeble old lady, her sparse white hair drawn back in a bun, a pair of tortoise-shell side combs at either side of her head. She wore a black dress, a clean white apron, and a cameo brooch at her throat. Although she was shaky, she did her own housework and baked on Thursdays. She saw few people beside her sister and the members of the Ladies' Society. Her manner was courteous and serene, and under its protection she was living exactly as her mother had lived. She was making a retreat into the previous century, composed and determined, as if it were the most natural journey in the world.

"My poor child, sit down, sit down," she sighed in her high, sweet voice.

Dorothy sat down. There was a large rubber plant standing in a tub beside her. Aunt Phoebe carefully wiped the leaves once a month with a rag dipped in castor oil. It seemed to Dorothy that she had grown up under the gloomy indoor shade of that plant.

"I keep thinking of the tremendous shock," Aunt Phoebe quavered. "How *are* you? Did you sleep at all last night?"

A flippant answer occurred to Dorothy, but she did not say it. You do not make flippant answers to these women; they are the voices of your childhood. "Oh, I'm all right, Aunt Phoebe."

"And how is *he* taking the discovery? Is he well?"

The question was asked kindly. Aunt Phoebe's kindness was genuine and embraced everyone, but from her tone it was clear that she was now concerned with the health of a criminal.

"Yes, Perry's very well."

The old lady rocked forward hard and came up standing. "Before we start visiting, I've got something to show you. It's upstairs. Come along, dear." She left the room with quick, little steps, her feet wide apart, as if the floor might lurch under her. Dorothy followed her up the back stairs. At the top, her aunt stopped a moment to pant. There were three bedrooms on the second floor of the old house, one for each aunt and a spare that had once been hers. Aunt Phoebe led her into the spare room.

There was a sharp smell of paste. The wallpaper, with the roses she used to count as a little girl when she was sick, had been replaced by a forget-me-not pattern. The two rush-bottomed chairs were freshly varnished, and there was a new bedspread.

"How do you like the forget-me-nots? Old Mr. Burdick put on that new wallpaper yesterday. Teresa varnished the chairs. My, we worked here till eleven o'clock last night."

"But what for?" Dorothy asked. "You're not taking in a roomer, are you?"

Aunt Phoebe's face lifted in surprise. "A roomer? Heavens and earth, what would we want with a roomer? No, no, no. This is your room. It's always been your room. We were getting it ready for you to come back."

"Come back?"

"My dear child, you're not going on living with that Perry, are you? What would your poor father have said? What if they put him in State's prison?"

"Maybe they will."

"Well, you certainly can't go on being the wife of a convicted felon," the old lady said with an air of finality. "But mind you, no divorce. Divorce is wrong. It's wicked. But you can separate from him and come back home where you belong."

Dorothy sank down on the edge of the bed and her aunt sat down primly beside her. "I'm not going to leave him, Aunt Phoebe."

"I suppose you're going to say he needs you like that fellow did in that movie the other day. He said he *needed* some woman. Need, my foot. That Perry got along without you until two years ago, didn't he?"

Because she remembered this room from her childhood, and this old woman had served as her mother, Dorothy felt that she wanted to cry. "Yes, I suppose he did."

In a grave, portentous tone, Aunt Phoebe said, "Did you ever really *love* that man, Dorothy?" Aunt Phoebe held a high, pure, almost embarrassingly romantic idea of love.

"I'm not going to say I married him for his money, if that's what you mean."

"Why, my dear child, I never blamed you."

It seemed to Dorothy the questions and answers went on forever. At last, when she left her aunt and drove home for lunch, she carried with her an irritating residue from the two meetings with her aunts. She remembered that Aunt Tessa somehow had turned Perry into a thief; Aunt Phoebe had assumed she would leave him. Her husband's innocence, which she had taken for granted at first, was now a diminishing spot of brightness in a cloud of doubt and worry her aunts had cast up. "But they are old and quaint and funny," she said to herself. She had learned that during her two years of marriage; now it made her feel better.

But, pausing at one of the town's stop lights, she had a vision. It was of Madison Avenue in New York, now, in the springtime. The flower shops were filled with color; it spilled out into the street. The mild sun glinted off the silver in the windows.

"I could live there. In New York," she said to herself. She could get a divorce and a big settlement, and live in New York. When the light changed, she began to drive fast, dodging cars and people, berating herself for even thinking of such a thing. But the towers of the city remained in her mind; she could not shame them out of it.

In the afternoon, she discovered that she would not be able to stand going to her bridge club—she stayed at home. At first she tried to take a nap on an impulse that centered vaguely around the phrase "beauty sleep," but she could not sleep. She did her nails carefully, making the job last. She tried listening to the radio, but after a short time she found it irritating and snapped it off. At last she went upstairs and drew a tub, bathed, and began to dress very slowly. She was going to wear a new black gown she had bought the last time she had been in New York. But when she laid it out on the bed, expecting some sense of pleasure, she found she was not even thinking about it. Instead, she was trying to remember precisely how her husband looked.

It was almost six o'clock when she finished dressing, and soon after, she heard Perry come rushing into the house. He shouted a greeting and bounded up the stairs. After a moment she heard the shower. He was a little late and apparently knew it.

As soon as she judged he was partly dressed, she went down the corridor and into his room. The muscles of his big arms and shoulders were rippled and taut with impatience. He was sitting on the edge of the bed, his back toward her, his dress shirt in his lap, and he was trying to put in his studs. When they were first married, he had torn dress shirts into rags on two occasions because the studs would not go in.

"Still playing your zither?" she asked, and giggled.

He whirled around, angry, shamefaced. But when he saw her, a look of surprise spread over his face. He whistled. "Boy, you look good!"

"Why, thank you, Mr. Sutcliffe. Put on your shirt and come over to the mirror—I'll tie your tie."

He had never learned how to put on a bow tie. In fact, he had never worn one until his marriage. He crouched a little before the long mirror in his armoire; she stood behind him, her arms encircling his neck, watching her fingers in the mirror.

He kept looking at her face. "You sure are one good-looking woman."

She evened out the bow. "I'm a lady, drat you," she said. "There you are."

"Thanks, honey."

It was the easy, natural "honey" that made her stiffen and her nails dig into her palms. Still behind him, she looked at his image in the glass. He was buttoning his waistcoat. Handsome, all right. He was handsome, like a good-looking prize fighter, but she could not see his face in one of those group photographs of exclusive, expensive, and suave college societies.

As he was getting into his dinner jacket, she said, "Perry."

"What?"

"Did you find out anything today?"

"About what? I spent all day with a guy from Argentina. Spoke English. Say, we ought to go down there. Buenos Aires is—"

"No. I mean about the trial."

He had just fitted a handkerchief into his breast pocket. He glanced up as she spoke, his face changing. She had never seen anything she could recognize as fear on it before, but maybe this was it. "It'll be next month. I found that out. Bother you?"

"Oh, no. No, it doesn't bother me at all. Why do you think that?" She picked up her purse and looked through it as an excuse to stop this nervous talking. "Only—Clyde Hatford will be at the Parkers' tonight."

He was giving himself a last look. He put on a black homburg hat; she did not tell him to take it off in the house. "He has to eat the same as anybody else," he said coldly.

"No. I mean——"

He looked at her for a long moment. "Come on. Let's go."

On the way to the Parkers,' she made rags of a fine Madeira handkerchief. In a town this small, the assumption, if you can accept it, is that everyone's life is an open book. It is only more or less true, but if all your faults and virtues do lie naked, there isn't any reason they will not be pointed at. Candor, however, requires unusual self-possession to be exercised at all times. Few have it, so most people use indirection—the cryptic compliment, and kidding. And it was the kidding Dorothy feared. She knew what Perry would do if they kidded him.

251

MATTER

In the Parkers' living room, everything that could be covered was done in chintz. The rest of the furniture, surly, dark Victorian pieces of the worst kind, reminded visitors that old Levi Parker had misappropriated the bank's money. But it reminded the Parkers that Grandpa had left some heirlooms. Emily Parker had ineptly brightened things by scattering over the walls some early Picasso prints, poorly reproduced and gaudily framed.

All the men gathered at one end of the room. At the other end, all the women sat about. The only liaison between the two groups was Jules, one of the waiters from the Country Club. He wore a white jacket and carried refreshments back and forth. As soon as Dorothy saw Jules, she knew what the dinner would be—a heavy steak, julienne potatoes, a quarter of a head of lettuce doused with Roquefort dressing, apple pie and cheese. For formal dinners it was easier to hire the Country Club chef to do the catering.

Dorothy went to her proper end of the room and, with a false vivacity, received the ritual compliments of the other ladies. It was a marvelous gown and she knew it. She also knew from experience that she was the only woman in the room anyone would call beautiful. None of this was important. Emily Parker's story, about how she had found genuine Roquefort cheese for the inevitable dressing, flitted past her, barely heard. Her real attention was on her husband.

She seemed to see him very clearly this evening, and she knew her nervousness gave the clarity. His dinner jacket fitted him well; the right amount of cuff was showing at the end of his sleeves. His money could have given him arrogance, but she sensed that he was still afraid of these men who had driven him to earn the money— or, if he was not still afraid, perhaps he suffered a new diffidence, because he was now vulnerable in spite of his wealth. He had joined the men and she hunted their faces for some jibe or sneer; but there was none. Clyde Hatford stood at the fringe of the group. And nothing happened. Perhaps things would go well after all.

There were candles on the table at dinner. The wavering light and the tinkle of the hanging crystals of the candlesticks annoyed her. The talk seemed to make a low roar that pressed against her hearing as she was trying so hard to follow her husband's talk across the table. His face was sober. He did not smile at Mrs. Shaw on his left, nor did he laugh at any of Mrs. Reichman's jokes that came from his right. Dorothy could never quite catch the gist of what they were saying. There was always a clink or a tinkle or a jet of laughter that interrupted. She was listening for insults, and when she realized that, she lowered her head and ate quickly, in shame at her own anxiety. Why was she so tense, she asked herself? Did danger appear in a setting of Spode, crystal, sterling, and expensive meat? She felt it, nevertheless, but she could not put a name to it.

At last dinner was over. In the living room, the men and women resumed their usual groups. Jules, in his white coat, walking softly between them, this time served coffee in demitasse and larger cups. Dorothy stood as close to the men as she dared without inviting criticism, listening, and keeping the thread of her own conversation fairly well in hand. The talk of the men seemed to be normal— corporation profits, bank loans, Russia. Could she relax?

Then, as clearly as if it were printed as a newspaper headline, she heard George Allis say, "Listen, when Uncle Sam wants money, he'll take it. You just try to get out of paying it, just try."

Clyde Hatford said in a soft, caustic voice that made her stomach feel light, "Perry tried, didn't you, Perry? Uncle Sam was going to have to bump along without Perry's contribution, wasn't he?"

A weak, embarrassed laugh came from her husband. This was the time he should have said coolly, "Why, you ought to know—it was your fault, Clyde." But he didn't say that. He was still too much the stranger.

"Great rehabilitation program over there at the prison. Where're you going to work, Perry?" Hatford asked. "In the vegetable garden? In the print shop? In———"

She heard a faint click, like a dry stick breaking. She turned in time to see Clyde Hatford crash into the empty fireplace, overturning a jugful of gladioli on the hearth; a thin stripe of blood appeared on his chin. A pair of brass fire tongs, swinging on the holder, fell off with a clatter in the abrupt silence. The other men stared at Hatford as if he were a strange bird that had flown down the chimney. It was five full seconds before anyone bent to help him or any woman begin to talk.

Dorothy looked at Perry. He did not have his fists clenched and he was not panting. He was not lighting a cigarette with cinematic nonchalance. He was looking straight at her. Then he turned and walked out of the room.

She thought she followed him at once, but she was not quick enough to avoid hearing the shocked gabble of voices that rose around her, or to miss the tableau of her former suitor being raised up, still unconscious, his head lolling. She did not remember saying anything to her hostess or picking up her wrap. She found herself in the darkness outside, a warm spring dark, filled with the faint smell of new leaves. She was thinking, "How dared he? How *dared* he?" After she had recalled the insult of his daring and repeated its signal phrase a few times, she began to laugh softly. Their car was parked half a block away. She followed him, seeing only the white of his collar in the dim light. She began to run. She reached him and touched his arm. "Going somewhere, Mr. Sutcliffe?"

"Home," he said. "You coming?"

She slid her arms around his neck and kissed him. "Of course." She moved back a little. "I guess you fixed them." She meant not only Clyde Hatford, the Parkers, and all those other silly people, but her aunts and the cruelty of her upbringing. "Fixed me, too."

The town clock began to strike. She listened while she counted eleven. "I suppose you could call that our wedding bell really," she said. "Let's go home and sit in the kitchen and I'll get you some coffee."

STUDY NOTES

1. With what kind of love motif does "Second Wedding" deal?
2. From this story cite evidence of Seager's realistic depiction of setting.
3. Utilizing specific data from the story, comment on the lifelikeness of the characters.
4. Contrast Perry Sutcliffe, the husband, with Clyde Hatford, the former suitor, in physical appearance and social standing and personality.
5. Suggest Seager's method of dealing with the emotional element by mentioning the outward expressions of Perry's emotion after his arrest.
6. Also indicate the outward manifestations of Dorothy's emotion in the afternoon before the dinner and on the way to the dinner.
7. Find examples of humor in the story.
8. Also instances of ironic statement.
9. Present the contrast between Dorothy's home environment before marriage and after, as revealed in Seager's descriptions.

10. How does the story foreshadow Perry's slugging of Clyde at the Parkers' dinner?

11. Point out the use of suspense just preceding the scene in which Perry defends his honor.

12. Cite several clues to the genuineness of the love of Perry and Dorothy for each other—dramatic foreshadowings of the triumphant outcome of their romance.

COMPARISON EXERCISES

1. Compare the personal descriptions in "The Love-Letters of Smith" with those in "Second Wedding."

2. Compare the place descriptions in the two stories.

3. Contrast the love affairs in these stories.

4. Contrast the letter-writing method of characterization and plot-building in the former story with the dialogue method of the latter.

5. Indicate the nature of the opposition faced by both Smith and Sutcliffe in their efforts to win the wholehearted love of their respective ladies.

WRITING SUGGESTION

Write a story of a dignified and noble and gradually developing love between either an unmarried or a married couple, creating a fresh and interesting plot, making the principal characters really respectable, and indicating the presence of the romantic sentiment largely through rational suggestions rather than through lengthy descriptions of caresses.

SURPRISE

Introduction to Short Stories That End in Surprise

SURPRISING culminations in American short stories are approximately the age of the American short story itself. Irving ended his *Salmagundi* sketch, "The Little Man in Black" (1807), with a surprise.

In their contribution to the type of story that has an unexpected denouement, Nathaniel Parker Willis and Frank R. Stockton were leading forerunners of O. Henry. Writing near the middle of the nineteenth century, Willis was a pioneer in creating graceful surprise stories. "The Spirit Love of 'Ione S——,'" his best-known story of this type, is touched with finesse, vivacity, humor, wit, and satire against writers for lady's books. Stockton invented a number of surprise-ending stories. "The Transferred Ghost" arouses wonder by representing the ghost as being haunted rather than as haunting. "The Lady or the Tiger?" surprises the reader by ending in a puzzle rather than a definite solution. "The Spectral Mortgage" represents a ghost that has courted a maiden as attending her wedding and sighing over his failure to win her for himself. "Negative Gravity" presents an unexpected element by having gravity pull in the opposite direction from that in which gravity ordinarily pulls. Stockton achieved his surprise effects by such techniques as paradoxes, conundrums, and other different-from-anticipated conclusions. In some aspects of his writing he was an extremist. Extreme whimsicality appears in the plots. His stories have, however, exerted a large influence. Their verisimilitude causes the reader to accept the narrative readily enough until he discovers at the climax that he has been merely entertained, that he has been subjected to a good-natured hoax.

257

Other nineteenth-century American writers of the surprise story were Hawthorne, O'Brien, Aldrich, and Chopin. Hawthorne wrote "Mrs. Bullfrog," which is not very characteristic of him in either its humor or its surprise ending, as an experiment in grotesque style. O'Brien in "A Terrible Night" provided not only a surprising climax but also an uncanny atmosphere and a style of finesse and vivacity. Some of Aldrich's early stories, such as "The Lady with the Balmoral" and "Miss Hepzibah's Lover," and most of the selections in *Marjorie Daw and Other People*, including the title piece and "A Struggle for Life," have an unexpected climax. Besides their surprise endings, these stories exhibit trivial themes, superb craftsmanship, witty style and plot, and enthusiastic enjoyment of life. Chopin's two volumes, *Bayou Folk* and *A Night in Acadie*, usually present a startling climax along with originality, finesse, spontaneous humor, romantic sentiment, and realistic characterization.

O. Henry was unquestionably the master of the type of story that ends with a sharply unexpected twist. Most of his stories culminate in surprise. Typical qualities in his brief fictions are humor or whimsicality or gentle irony, exaggeration, seeming digression, suspense, somewhat artificial characterization (puppets rather than persons), colloquial style, formularized plot, and emotional appeal. His primary purpose was to entertain his reader. In his stories the chief interest lies not in plot construction or characterization but trick endings.

Since O. Henry's day, Henry Sydnor Harrison and Wilbur Daniel Steele have been prominent among the writers of surprise-ending stories. Such specimens by Harrison as "Miss Hinch" and "The White Mole" not only come to an unexpected conclusion but show an ingenious and vital plot, strong suspense, well-developed atmosphere, and realistic characterization. Such examples by Steele as "Blue Murder" and "Footfalls" not only have a satisfying, surprising climax; they deal with the horrible or the terrible; they create suspense and emotional appeal; they possess a distinctive style, vigorous, fanciful, suggestive, largely engaged in communicating atmosphere.

Surprise endings still enjoy fairly wide popularity in storiettes and humorous stories. In serious stories of usual length, the surprise ending is no longer nearly so fashionable as in O. Henry's time.

In short-shorts (not reaching to two thousand words), published in some commercial magazines, trick climaxes are the vogue. Though unexpected endings are not infrequent in pulp and craft magazines for adults and in juvenile magazines, they are almost never found in the quality magazines.

The element of surprise can, of course, appear in parts of a story other than the end. A new incident, a personality trait showing up for the first time, a character's mood toward some other character or toward environment can all be different from what the reader has anticipated. The surprise story is, however, most commonly regarded as the one that concludes with a trick.

A surprise too unexpected is unconvincing. The matter and manner must not be completely artificial. The really clever hoax story must partly foreshadow the finale. Though the skilful writer cannot afford to reveal in advance of the conclusion just how the action will terminate, neither must he make the culmination radically different from what the earlier part of the plot leads the reader to expect. Some of the hints of the outcome must be somewhat misleading or the conclusion can hardly be a surprise. But other clues must sufficiently accord with the concluding action that, when contemplated after the denouement has become known, they will not be regarded as false.

To be most effective, a surprise ending should evolve from both the plot and the characters rather than from the incidents alone. The unexpected climax should be both logical and original. It must make the reader react emotionally—cause him either to laugh or to gasp, amuse him or amaze him. The culmination must, therefore, be brief. One strong, climactic, surprising sentence and the story is at an end.

MATTER

MARJORIE DAW [1]
(1873)

THOMAS BAILEY ALDRICH

I

Dr. Dillon to Edward DeLaney, Esq., at The Pines,
Near Rye, N. H.

August 8, 187—

My Dear Sir: I am happy to assure you that your anxiety is without reason. Flemming will be confined to the sofa for three or four weeks and will have to be careful at first how he uses his leg. A fracture of this kind is always a tedious affair. Fortunately, the bone was very skilfully set by the surgeon who chanced to be in the drugstore where Flemming was brought after his fall, and I apprehend no permanent inconvenience from the accident. *Flemming is doing perfectly well physically;* but I must confess that the irritable and morbid state of mind into which he has fallen causes me a great deal of uneasiness. He is the last man in the world who ought to break his leg. You know how impetuous our friend is ordinarily, what a soul of restlessness and energy, never content unless he is rushing at some object, like a sportive bull at a red shawl; but amiable withal. His temper has become something frightful. Miss Fanny Flemming came up from Newport, where the family are staying for the summer, to nurse him; but he packed her off the next morning in tears. He has a complete set of Balzac's works, twenty-seven volumes, piled up by his sofa, to throw at Watkins whenever that exemplary serving-man appears with his meals. Yesterday I very innocently brought Flemming a small basket of lemons. You know it was a strip of lemon-peel on the curbstone that caused our friend's mischance. Well, he no sooner set his eyes upon these lemons than he fell into such a rage as I cannot describe adequately. This is only one of his moods, and the least distressing.

---

[1] First published in *The Atlantic* (April, 1873). In the "Introduction" of the present anthology, amateurs have been warned that the letters-form of story holds more pitfalls than some other types. Aldrich, however, was hardly an amateur. He had been publishing short stories since 1857. William T. Hastings, *Syllabus of American Literature,* Chicago: The University of Chicago Press, 1925, p. 73, mentions "Marjorie Daw" as "the first genuinely successful short story with a surprise in the last sentence."

At other times he sits with bowed head regarding his splintered limb, silent, sullen, despairing. When this fit is on him—and it sometimes lasts all day—nothing can distract his melancholy. He refuses to eat, does not even read the newspapers; books—except as projectiles for Watkins—have no charms for him. His state is truly pitiable.

Now, if he were a poor man, with a family dependent on his daily labor, this irritability and despondency would be natural enough. But in a young fellow of twenty-four, with plenty of money and seemingly not a care in the world, the thing is monstrous. If he continues to give way to his vagaries in this manner, he will end by bringing on an inflammation of the fibula. It was the fibula he broke. I am at my wits' end to know what to prescribe for him. I have anaesthetics and lotions to make people sleep and to soothe pain; but I've no medicine that will make a man have a little common sense. That is beyond my skill, but maybe it is not beyond yours. You are Flemming's intimate friend, his *fidus Achates*.[2] Write to him, write to him frequently, distract his mind, cheer him up, and prevent him from becoming a confirmed case of melancholia. Perhaps he has some important plans disarranged by his present confinement. If he has you will know, and will know how to advise him judiciously. I trust your father finds the change beneficial? I am, my dear sire, with great respect, etc.

II

Edward DeLaney to John Flemming, West 38th Street, New York

August 9, ——

My Dear Jack:

I had a line from Dillon this morning, and was rejoiced to learn that your hurt is not so bad as reported. Like a certain personage, you are not so black and blue as you are painted. Dillon will put you on your pins again in two or three weeks, if you will only have patience and follow his counsels. Did you get my note of last Wednesday? I was greatly troubled when I heard of the accident. I can imagine how tranquil and saintly you are with your leg in

---

[2] Translation: "faithful Achates." Achates was so faithful a friend to Aeneas (*Aeneid*, i, 312) that the phrase *fidus Achates* became proverbial.

a trough! It is deuced awkward, to be sure, just as we had promised ourselves a glorious month together at the seaside; but we must make the best of it. It is unfortunate, too, that my father's health renders it impossible for me to leave him. I think he has much improved; the sea air is his native element; but he still needs my arm to lean upon in his walks, and requires some one more careful than a servant to look after him. I cannot come to you, dear Jack, but I have hours of unemployed time on hand, and I will write you a whole post-office full of letters, if that will divert you. Heaven knows, I haven't anything to write about. It isn't as if we were living at one of the beach houses; then I could do you some character studies, and fill your imagination with groups of sea-goddesses, with their (or somebody else's) raven and blond manes hanging down their shoulders. You should have Aphrodite in morning wrapper, in evening costume, and in her prettiest bathing suit. But we are far from all that here. We have rooms in a farmhouse, on a cross-road, two miles from the hotels, and lead the quietest of lives.

I wish I were a novelist. This old house, with its sanded floors and high wainscots, and its narrow windows looking out upon a cluster of pines that turn themselves into aeolian harps every time the wind blows, would be the place in which to write a summer romance. It should be a story with the odors of the forest and the beat of the sea in it. It should be a novel like one of that Russian fellow's—what's his name?—Tourguenieff, Turguenef, Turgenif, Toorguniff, Turgenjew—nobody knows how to spell him. Yet I wonder if even a Liza[3] or an Alexandra Paulovna could stir the heart of a man who has constant twinges in his leg. I wonder if one of our own Yankee girls of the best type, haughty and *spirituelle*, would be of any comfort to you in your present deplorable condition. If I thought so, I would hasten down to the Surf House and catch one for you; or, better still, I would find you one over the way.

Picture to yourself a large white house just across the road, nearly opposite our cottage. It is not a house, but a mansion, built, perhaps in the colonial period, with rambling extensions, and gambrel roof, and a wide piazza on three sides—a self-possessed, high-bred piece of architecture, with its nose in the air. It stands back from the road, and has an obsequious retinue of fringed elms and oaks and weep-

---

[3] The pure and gentle heroine of Turgenev's novel, *A House of Gentlefolk.*

ing willows. Sometimes in the morning, and oftener in the afternoon, when the sun has withdrawn from that part of the mansion,
a young woman appears on the piazza with some mysterious Penelope
web of embroidery in her hand, or a book. There is a hammock
over there—of pineapple fibre, it looks from here. A hammock is
very becoming when one is eighteen, and has golden hair, and dark
eyes, and an emerald-colored illusion dress looped up after the
fashion of a Dresden china shepherdess, and is *chaussée* like a belle
of the time of Louis Quatorze. All this splendor goes into that hammock, and sways there like a pond-lily in the golden afternoon. The
window of my bedroom looks down on that piazza—and so do I.

But enough of this nonsense, which ill becomes a sedate young
attorney taking his vacation with an invalid father. Drop me a line,
dear Jack, and tell me how you really are. State your case. Write me
a long quiet letter. If you are violent or abusive, I'll take the
law to you.

III

John Flemming to Edward DeLaney

August 11, ——

Your letter, dear Ned, was a godsend. Fancy what a fix I am in—
I, who never had a day's sickness since I was born. My left leg weighs
three tons. It is embalmed in spices and smothered in layers of fine
linen, like a mummy. I can't move. I haven't moved for five thousand years. I'm of the time of Pharaoh.

I lie from morning till night on a lounge, staring into the hot
street. Everybody is out of town enjoying himself. The brown-stone-
front houses across the street resemble a row of particularly ugly
coffins set up on end. A green mould is settling on the names of
the deceased, carved on the silver door-plates. Sardonic spiders have
sewed up the key-holes. All is silence and dust and desolation. —I
interrupt this a moment, to take a shy at Watkins with the second
volume of *César Birotteau*. Missed him! I think I could bring him
down with a copy of Sainte-Beuve or the *Dictionnaire Universel*, if
I had it. These small Balzac books somehow do not quite fit my hand;
but I shall fetch him yet. I've an idea that Watkins is tapping the
old gentleman's Chateau Yquem. Duplicate key of the wine-cellar.

263

MATTER

Hibernian swarries in the front basement. Young Cheops up-stairs, snug in his cerements. Watkins glides into my chamber, with that colorless, hypocritical face of his drawn out long like an accordion; but I know he grins all the way down-stairs, and is glad I have broken my leg. Was not my evil star in the very zenith when I ran up to town to attend that dinner at Delmonico's? I didn't come up altogether for that. It was partly to buy Frank Livingstone's roan mare Margot. And now I shall not be able to sit in the saddle these two months. I'll send the mare down to you at The Pines—is that the name of the place?

Old Dillon fancies that I have something on my mind. He drives me wild with lemons. Lemons for a mind diseased! Nonsense. I am only as restless as the devil under this confinement—a thing I'm not used to. Take a man who has never had so much as a headache or a toothache in his life, strap one of his legs in a section of water-spout, keep him in a room in the city for weeks, with the hot weather turned on, and then expect him to smile and purr and be happy! It is preposterous. I can't be cheerful or calm.

Your letter is the first consoling thing I have had since my disaster, ten days ago. Send me a screed, Ned, as often as you can, if you love me. Anything will do. Write me more about that little girl in the hammock. That was very pretty, all that about the Dresden china shepherdess and the pond-lily; the imagery a little mixed, perhaps, but very pretty. I didn't suppose you had so much sentimental furniture in your upper story. It shows how one may be familiar for years with the reception-room of his neighbor, and never suspect what is directly under his mansard. I supposed your loft stuffed with dry legal parchments, mortgages, and affidavits; you take down a package of manuscript, and lo! there are lyrics and sonnets and canzonettas. You really have a graphic descriptive touch, Edward Delaney, and I suspect you of anonymous love-tales in the magazines.

I shall be a bear until I hear from you again. Tell me all about your pretty *inconnue* across the road. What is her name? Who is she? Who's her father? Where's her mother? Who's her lover? You cannot imagine how this will occupy me. The more trifling, the better. My imprisonment has weakened me intellectually to such a degree that I find your epistolary gifts quite considerable. I am passing into my second childhood. In a week or two I shall take to India-rubber

264

rings and prongs of coral. A silver cup, with an appropriate inscription would be a delicate attention on your part. In the meantime, write!

IV

August 12, ⸺

Edward Delaney to John Flemming

The sick pasha shall be amused. *Bismillah!* he wills it so. If the story-teller becomes prolix and tedious—the bow-string and the sack, and two Nubians [4] to drop him into the Piscataqua! But truly, Jack, I have a hard task. There is literally nothing here—except the little girl over the way. She is swinging in the hammock at this moment. It is to me compensation for many of the ills of life to see her now and then put out a small kid boot, which fits like a glove, and set herself going. Who is she, and what is her name? Her name is Daw. Only daughter of Mr. Richard W. Daw, ex-colonel and banker. Mother dead. One brother at Harvard, elder brother killed at the battle of Fair Oaks, ten years ago. Old, rich family, the Daws. This is the homestead, where father and daughter pass eight months of the twelve; the rest of the year in Baltimore and Washington. The New England winter too many for the old gentleman. The daughter is called Marjorie—Marjorie Daw. Sounds odd at first, doesn't it? But after you say it over to yourself half a dozen times, you like it. There's a pleasing quaintness to it, something prim and pansy-like. Must be a nice sort of girl to be called Marjorie Daw.

I had mine host of The Pines in the witness-box last night, and drew the foregoing testimony from him. He has charge of Mr. Daw's vegetable-garden, and has known the family these thirty years. Of course I shall make the acquaintance of my neighbors before many days. It will be next to impossible for me not to meet Mr. Daw or Miss Daw in some of my walks. The young lady has a favorite path to the sea beach. I shall intercept her some morning, and touch my hat to her. Then the princess will bend her fair head to me with courteous surprise not unmixed with haughtiness. Will snub me, in fact. All this for thy sake, O Pasha of the Snapt Axle-tree!—How oddly things fall out! Ten minutes ago I was called

[4] The "two Nubians" may be Watkins and the cook, Mary, mentioned in Letter No. **V**.

down to the parlor—you know the kind of parlors in farmhouses on the coast, a sort of amphibious parlor, with sea-shells on the mantel-piece and spruce branches in the chimney-place—where I found my father and Mr. Daw doing the antique polite to each other. He had come to pay his respects to his new neighbors. Mr. Daw is a tall, slim gentleman of about fifty-five, with a florid face and snow-white mustache and side-whiskers. Looks like Mr. Dombey, or as Mr. Dombey would have looked if he had served a few years in the British Army. Mr. Daw was a colonel in the late war, commanding the regiment in which his son was a lieutenant. Plucky old boy, backbone of New Hampshire granite. Before taking his leave, the Colonel delivered himself of an invitation as if he were issuing a general order. Miss Daw has a few friends coming, at 4 P. M., to play croquet on the lawn (parade-ground) and have tea (cold rations) on the piazza. Will we honor them with our company? (or be sent to the guardhouse). My father declines on the plea of ill-health. My father's son bows with as much suavity as he knows, and accepts.

In my next I shall have something to tell you. I shall have seen the little beauty face to face. I have a presentiment, Jack, that this Daw is a *rara avis!* Keep up your spirits, my boy, until I write you another letter—and send me along word how's your leg.

V

Edward Delaney to John Flemming

August 13, ——

The party, my dear Jack, was as dreary as possible. A lieutenant of the navy, the rector of the Episcopal church at Stillwater, and a society swell from Nahant. The lieutenant looked as if he had swallowed a couple of his buttons, and found the bullion rather indigestible; the rector was a pensive youth, of the daffydowndilly sort; and the swell from Nahant was a very weak tidal wave indeed. The women were much better, as they always are; the two Miss Kingsburys of Philadelphia, staying at the Sea-Shell House, two bright and engaging girls. But Marjorie Daw!

The company broke up soon after tea, and I remained to smoke a cigar with the colonel on the piazza. It was like seeing a picture, to see Miss Marjorie hovering around the old soldier, and doing a hundred gracious little things for him. She brought the cigars and lighted the tapers with her own delicate fingers, in the most enchanting fashion. As we sat there, she came and went in the summer twilight, and seemed, with her white dress and pale gold hair, like some lovely phantom that had sprung into existence out of the smoke-wreaths. If she had melted into air, like the statue of Galatea in the play,[5] I should have been more sorry than surprised.

It was easy to perceive that the old colonel worshipped her, and she him. I think the relation between an elderly father and a daughter just blooming into womanhood the most beautiful possible. There is in it a subtile sentiment that cannot exist in the case of mother and daughter, or that of son and mother. But this is going into deep water.

I sat with the Daws until half past ten, and saw the moon rise over the sea. The ocean, that had stretched motionless and black against the horizon, was changed by magic into a broken field of glittering ice, interspersed with marvellous silvery fjords. In the far distance the Isles of Shoals loomed up like a group of huge bergs drifting down on us. The Polar Regions in a June thaw! It was exceedingly fine. What did we talk about? We talked about the weather—and *you!* The weather has been disagreeable for several days past—and so have you. I glided from one topic to the other very naturally. I told my friends of your accident; how it had frustrated all our summer plans, and what our plans were. I played quite a spirited solo on the fibula. Then I described you; or, rather, I didn't. I spoke of your amiability, of your patience under this severe affliction; of your touching gratitude when Dillon brings you little presents of fruit; of your tenderness to your sister Fanny, whom you would not allow to stay in town to nurse you, and how heroically you sent her back to Newport, preferring to remain alone with Mary, the cook, and your man, Watkins, to whom, by the way, you were devotedly attached. If you had been there, Jack, you wouldn't have known yourself. I should have excelled as a criminal lawyer, if I had not turned my attention to a different branch of jurisprudence.

Miss Marjorie asked all manner of leading questions concerning

---

[5] According to classical mythology, Pygmalion, a sculptor of Cyprus, made an ivory statue of which he became enamored and to which Venus gave life. In William S. Gilbert's comedy, *Pygmalion and Galatea,* Pygmalion's wife, Cynisca, became jealous of her husband, but later the two were reconciled and Galatea returned to being a mere statue.

you. It did not occur to me then, but it struck me forcibly afterwards, that she evinced a singular interest in the conversation. When I got back to my room, I recalled how eagerly she leaned forward, with her full, snowy throat in strong moonlight, listening to what I said. Positively, I think I made her like you!

Miss Daw is a girl whom you would like immensely, I can tell you that. A beauty without affectation, a high and tender nature—if one can read the soul in the face. And the old colonel is a noble character, too.

I am glad that the Daws are such pleasant persons. The Pines is an isolated spot, and my resources are few. I fear I should have found life here somewhat monotonous before long, with no other society than that of my excellent sire. It is true, I might have made a target of the defenseless invalid; but I haven't a taste for artillery, *moi*.

VI

John Flemming to Edward Delaney

August 17, ——

For a man who hasn't a taste for artillery, it occurs to me, my friend, you are keeping up a pretty lively fire on my inner works. But go on. Cynicism is a small brass field-piece that eventually bursts and kills the artilleryman.

You may abuse me as much as you like, and I'll not complain; for I don't know what I should do without your letters. They are curing me. I haven't hurled anything at Watkins since last Sunday, partly because I have grown more amiable under your teaching, and partly because Watkins captured my ammunition one night, and carried it off to the library. He is rapidly losing the habit he had acquired of dodging whenever I rub my ear, or make any slight motion with my right arm. He is still suggestive of the wine-cellar, however. You may break, you may shatter Watkins, if you will, but the scent of the Roederer [6] will hang round him still.

Ned, that Miss Daw must be a charming person. I should certainly like her. I like her already. When you spoke in your first letter of seeing a young girl swinging in a hammock under your

---

[6] The name of a champagne.

chamber window, I was somehow strangely drawn to her. I cannot account for it in the least. What you have subsequently written of Miss Daw has strengthened the impression. You seem to be describing a woman I have known in some previous state of existence, or dreamed of in this. Upon my word, if you were to send me her photograph, I believe I should recognize her at a glance. Her manner, that listening attitude, her traits of character, as you indicate them, the light hair and the dark eyes—they are all familiar things to me. Asked a lot of questions, did she? Curious about me? That is strange.

You would laugh in your sleeve, you wretched old cynic, if you knew how I lie awake nights, with my gas turned down to a star, thinking of The Pines and the house across the road. How cool it must be down there! I long for the salt smell in the air. I picture the colonel smoking his cheroot on the piazza. I send you and Miss Daw off on afternoon rambles along the beach. Sometimes I let you stroll with her under the elms in the moonlight, for you are great friends by this time, I take it, and see each other every day. I know your ways and your manners! Then I fall into a truculent mood, and would like to destroy somebody. Have you noticed anything in the shape of a lover hanging around the colonial Lares and Penates? Does that lieutenant of the horse-marines or that young Stillwater parson visit the house much? Not that I am pining for news of them, but any gossip of the kind would be in order. I wonder, Ned, you don't fall in love with Miss Daw. I am ripe to do it myself. Speaking of photographs, couldn't you manage to slip one of her *cartes-de-visite*[7] from her album—she must have an album, you know —and send it to me? I will return it before it could be missed. That's a good fellow! Did the mare arrive safe and sound? It will be a capital animal this autumn for Central Park.

Oh—my leg? I forgot about my leg. It's better.

VII

Edward Delaney to John Flemming

August 20, ——

You are correct in your surmises. I am on the most friendly terms with our neighbors. The colonel and my father smoke their after-

---

[7] Calling cards, at time of story, often displayed photographs.

noon cigar together in our sitting-room or on the piazza opposite, and I pass an hour or two of the day or the evening with the daughter. I am more and more struck by the beauty, modesty, and intelligence of Miss Daw.

You ask me why I do not fall in love with her. I will be frank, Jack: I have thought of that. She is young, rich, accomplished, uniting in herself more attractions, mental and personal, than I can recall in any girl of my acquaintance; but she lacks the something that would be necessary to inspire in me that kind of interest. Possessing this unnamed quantity, a woman neither beautiful nor wealthy nor very young could bring me to her feet. But not Miss Daw. If we were shipwrecked together on an uninhabited island— let me suggest a tropical island, for it costs no more to be picturesque —I would build her a bamboo hut, I would fetch her bread-fruit and coconuts, I would fry yams for her, I would lure the ingenuous turtle and make her nourishing soups, but I wouldn't make love to her—not under eighteen months. I would like to have her for a sister, that I might shield her and counsel her, and spend half my income on old thread-lace and camel's-hair shawls. (We are off the island now.) If such were not my feeling, there would still be an obstacle to my loving Miss Daw. A greater misfortune could scarcely befall me than to love her. Flemming, I am about to make a revelation that will astonish you. I may be all wrong in my premises and consequently in my conclusions; but you shall judge.

That night when I returned to my room after the croquet party at the Daws', and was thinking over the trivial events of the evening, I was suddenly impressed by the air of eager attention with which Miss Daw had followed my account of your accident. I think I mentioned this to you. Well, the next morning, as I went to mail my letter, I overtook Miss Daw on the road to Rye, where the post-office is, and accompanied her thither and back, an hour's walk. The conversation again turned to you, and again I remarked that inexplicable look of interest which had lighted up her face the previous evening. Since then, I have seen Miss Daw perhaps ten times, perhaps oftener, and on each occasion I found that when I was not speaking of you, or your sister, or some person or place associated with you, I was not holding her attention. She would be absent-minded, her eyes would wander away from me to the sea, or to some distant object in the landscape; her fingers would play with the leaves of a book in a way that convinced me she was not listening. At these moments if I abruptly changed the theme—and dropped some remark about my friend Flemming, then the sombre blue eyes would come back to me instantly.

Now, is not this the oddest thing in the world? No, not the oddest. The effect which you tell me was produced on you by my casual mention of an unknown girl swinging in a hammock is certainly as strange. You can conjecture how that passage in your letter of Friday startled me. Is it possible, then, that two persons who have never met, and who are hundreds of miles apart, can exert a magnetic influence on each other? I have read of such psychological phenomena, but never credited them. I leave the solution of the problem to you. As for myself, all other things being favorable, it would be impossible for me to fall in love with a woman who listens to me only when I am talking of my friend!

I am not aware that any one is paying marked attention to my fair neighbor. The lieutenant of the navy—he is stationed at Rivermouth—sometimes drops in of an evening, and sometimes the rector from Stillwater; the lieutenant the oftener. He was there last night. I should not be surprised if he had an eye to the heiress; but he is not formidable. Mistress Daw carries a neat little spear of irony, and the honest lieutenant seems to have a particular facility for impaling himself on the point of it. He is not dangerous, I should say; though I have known a woman to satirize a man for years, and marry him after all. Decidedly, the lowly rector is not dangerous; yet, again, who has not seen Cloth of Frieze victorious in the lists where Cloth of Gold went down?

As to the photograph. There is an exquisite ivorytype of Marjorie, in passe-partout, on the drawing-room mantel-piece. It would be missed at once if taken. I would do anything reasonable for you, Jack; but I've no burning desire to be hauled up before the local justice of the peace, on a charge of petty larceny.

P. S.—Enclosed is a spray of mignonette, which I advise you to treat tenderly. Yes, we talked of you again last night, as usual. It is becoming a little dreary for me.

VIII

Edward Delaney to John Flemming

August 22, ——

Your letter in reply to my last has occupied my thoughts all the morning. I do not know what to think. Do you mean to say that you are seriously half in love with a woman whom you have never seen—with a shadow, a chimera? for what else can Miss Daw be to you? I do not understand it at all. I understand neither you nor her. You are a couple of ethereal beings moving in finer air than I can breathe with my commonplace lungs. Such delicacy of sentiment is something that I admire without comprehending. I am bewildered. I am of the earth earthy, and I find myself in the incongruous position of having to do with mere souls, with natures so finely tempered that I run some risk of shattering them in my awkwardness. I am as Caliban among the spirits!

Reflecting on your letter, I am not sure that it is wise in me to continue this correspondence. But no, Jack; I do wrong to doubt the good sense that forms the basis of your character. You are deeply interested in Miss Daw; you feel that she is a person whom you may perhaps greatly admire when you know her: at the same time you bear in mind that the chances are ten to five that, when you do come to know her, she will fall short of your ideal, and you will not care for her in the least. Look at it in this sensible light, and I will hold back nothing from you.

Yesterday afternoon my father and myself rode over to Rivermouth with the Daws. A heavy rain in the morning had cooled the atmosphere and laid the dust. To Rivermouth is a drive of eight miles, along a winding road lined all the way with wild barberry-bushes. I never saw anything more brilliant than these bushes, the green of the foliage and the faint blush of the berries intensified by the rain. The colonel drove, with my father in front, Miss Daw and I on the back seat. I resolved that for the first five miles your name should not pass my lips. I was amused by the artful attempts she made, at the start, to break through my reticence. Then a silence fell upon her; and then she became suddenly gay. That keenness which I enjoyed so much when it was exercised on the lieutenant was not so satisfactory directed against myself. Miss Daw has great sweetness of disposition, but she can be disagreeable. She is like the young lady in the rhyme, with the curl on her forehead—

> When she is good,
> She is very, very good,
> And when she is bad, she is horrid!

I kept to my resolution, however; but on the return home I relented, and talked of your mare! Miss Daw is going to try a side-saddle on Margot some morning. The animal is a trifle too light for my weight. By the bye, I nearly forgot to say that Miss Daw sat for a picture yesterday to a Rivermouth artist. If the negative turns out well, I am to have a copy. So our ends will be accomplished without crime. I wish, though, I could send you the ivorytype in the drawing-room; it is cleverly colored, and would give you an idea of her hair and eyes, which of course the other will not.

No, Jack, the spray of mignonette did not come from me. A man of twenty-eight doesn't enclose flowers in his letters—to another man. But don't attach too much significance to the circumstance. She gives sprays of mignonette to the rector, sprays to the lieutenant. She has even given a rose from her bosom to your slave. It is her jocund nature to scatter flowers, like Spring.

If my letters sometimes read disjointedly, you must understand that I never finish at a sitting, but write at intervals, when the mood is on me.

The mood is not on me now.

IX

Edward Delaney to John Flemming

August 23, ——

I have just returned from the strangest interview with Marjorie. She has all but confessed to me her interest in you. But with what modesty and dignity! Her words elude my pen as I attempt to put them on paper; and, indeed, it was not so much what she said as her manner; and that I cannot reproduce. Perhaps it was of a piece with the strangeness of this whole business, that she should tacitly acknowledge to a third party the love she feels for a man she has never beheld! But I have lost, through your aid, the faculty of being surprised. I accept things as persons do in dreams. Now that I am again in my room, it all appears like an illusion—the black masses of Rembrandtish shadow under the trees, the fireflies whirling in Pyrrhic dances among the shrubbery, the sea over there, Marjorie sitting in the hammock!

It is past midnight, and I am too sleepy to write more.

Thursday Morning

My father has suddenly taken it into his head to spend a few days at the Shoals. In the meanwhile you will not hear from me. I see Marjorie walking in the garden with the colonel. I wish I could speak to her alone, but shall probably not have an opportunity before we leave.

X

Edward Delaney to John Flemming

August 28, ——

You were passing into your second childhood, were you? Your intellect was so reduced that my epistolary gifts seemed quite considerable to you, did they? I rise superior to the sarcasm in your favor of the 11th instant, when I notice that five days' silence on my part is sufficient to throw you into the depths of despondency.

We returned only this morning from Appledore, that enchanted island—at four dollars per day. I find on my desk three letters from you! Evidently there is no lingering doubt in *your* mind as to the pleasure I derive from your correspondence. These letters are undated, but in what I take to be latest are two passages that require my consideration. You will pardon my candor, dear Flemming, but the conviction forces itself upon me that as your leg grows stronger your head becomes weaker. You ask my advice on a certain point. I will give it. In my opinion you could do nothing more unwise than to address a note to Miss Daw, thanking her for the flower. It would, I am sure, offend her delicacy beyond pardon. She knows you only through me; you are to her an abstraction, a figure in a dream—a dream from which the faintest shock would awaken her. Of course, if you enclose a note to me and insist on its delivery, I shall deliver it; but I advise you not to do so.

You say you are able, with the aid of a cane, to walk about your chamber, and that you purpose to come to The Pines the instant

274

Dillon thinks you strong enough to stand the journey. Again I advise you not to. Do you not see that, every hour you remain away, Marjorie's glamour deepens, and your influence over her increases? You will ruin everything by precipitancy. Wait until you are entirely recovered; in any case, do not come without giving me warning. I fear the effect of your abrupt advent here—under the circumstances.

Miss Daw was evidently glad to see us back again, and gave me both hands in the frankest way. She stopped at the door a moment this afternoon in the carriage; she had been over to Rivermouth for her pictures. Unluckily the photographer had spilt some acid on the plate, and she was obliged to give him another sitting. I have an intuition that something is troubling Marjorie. She had an abstracted air not usual with her. However, it may be only my fancy—I end this, leaving several things unsaid, to accompany my father on one of those long walks which are now his chief medicine—and mine.

XI

Edward Delaney to John Flemming

August 29, ——

I write in great haste to tell you what has taken place here since my letter of last night. I am in the utmost perplexity. Only one thing is plain,—*you* must not dream of coming to The Pines. Marjorie has told her father everything! I saw her for a few moments, an hour ago, in the garden; and, as near as I could gather from her confused statement, the facts are these: Lieutenant Bradley—that's the naval officer stationed at Rivermouth—has been paying court to Miss Daw for some time past, but not so much to her liking, as to that of the colonel, who it seems is an old friend of the young gentleman's father. Yesterday (I knew she was in some trouble when she drove up to our gate) the colonel spoke to Marjorie of Bradley—urged his suit, I infer. Marjorie expressed her dislike for the lieutenant with characteristic frankness, and finally confessed to her father—well, I really do not know what she confessed. It must have been the vaguest of confessions, and must have sufficiently puzzled the colonel. At any rate, it exasperated him. I suppose I am implicated in the matter and that the colonel feels bitterly towards me. I do not see why: I have carried no messages between you and Miss Daw; I have behaved

275

with the greatest discretion. I can find no flaw anywhere in my proceeding. I do not see that anybody has done anything—except the colonel himself.

It is probable, nevertheless, that the friendly relations between the two houses will be broken off. "A plague o' both your houses," say you. I will keep you informed, as well as I can, of what occurs over the way. We shall remain here until the second week in September. Stay where you are, or, at all events, do not dream of joining me—Colonel Daw is sitting on the piazza looking rather wicked. I have not seen Marjorie since I parted with her in the garden.

XII

Edward Delaney to Thomas Dillon, M. D., Madison Square, New York

August 30, ——

My Dear Doctor:

If you have any influence over Flemming, I beg of you to exert it to prevent his coming to this place at present. There are circumstances, which I will explain to you before long, that make it of the first importance that he should not come into this neighborhood. His appearance here, I speak advisedly, would be disastrous to him. In urging him to remain in New York, or to go to some inland resort, you will be doing him and me a real service. Of course you will not mention my name in this connection. You know me well enough, my dear doctor, to be assured that, in begging your secret cooperation, I have reasons that will meet your entire approval when they are made plain to you. We shall return to town on the 15th of next month, and my first duty will be to present myself at your hospitable door and satisfy your curiosity, if I have excited it. My father, I am glad to state, has so greatly improved that he can no longer be regarded as an invalid. With great esteem, I am, etc., etc.

XIII

Edward Delaney to John Flemming

August 31, ——

Your letter, announcing your mad determination to come here, has just reached me. I beseech you to reflect a moment. The step would

276

be fatal to your interests and hers. You would furnish just cause for irritation to R. W. D.; and, though he loves Marjorie devotedly, he is capable of going to any lengths if opposed. You would not like, I am convinced, to be the means of causing him to treat *her* with severity. That would be the result of your presence at The Pines at this juncture. I am annoyed to be obligated to point out these things to you. We are on very delicate ground, Jack; the situation is critical, and the slightest mistake in a move would cost us the game. If you consider it worth the winning, be patient. Trust a little to my sagacity. Wait and see what happens. Moreover, I understand from Dillon that you are in no condition to take so long a journey. He thinks the air of the coast would be the worst thing possible for you; that you ought to go inland, if anywhere. Be advised by me. Be advised by Dillon.

XIV

Telegrams

September 1, ——

1—To Edward Delaney

Letter received. Dillon be hanged. I think I ought to be on the ground.　　J. F.

2—To John Flemming

Stay where you are. You would only complicate matters. Do not move until you hear from me.　　E. D.

3—To Edward Delaney

My being at The Pines could be kept secret. I must see her.　　J. F.

4—To John Flemming

Do not think of it. It would be useless. R. W. D. has locked M. in her room. You would not be able to effect an interview.　　E. D.

5—To Edward Delaney

Locked her in her room. Good God! That settles the question. I shall leave by the twelve-fifteen express.　　J. F.

XV

The Arrival

On the second of September, 187—, as the down express, due at 3:40, left the station at Hampton, a young man, leaning on the shoulder of a servant, whom he addressed as Watkins, stepped from the platform into a hack, and requested to be driven to "The Pines." On arriving at the gate of a modest farmhouse, a few miles from the station, the young man descended with difficulty from the carriage, and, casting a hasty glance across the road, seemed much impressed with some peculiarity in the landscape. Again leaning on the shoulder of the person Watkins, he walked to the door of the farmhouse and inquired for Mr. Edward Delaney. He was informed by the aged man who answered his knock, that Mr. Edward Delaney had gone to Boston the day before, but that Mr. Jonas Delaney was within. This information did not appear satisfactory to the stranger, who inquired if Mr. Edward Delaney had left any message for Mr. John Flemming. There was a letter for Mr. John Flemming, if he were that person. After a brief absence the aged man reappeared with a letter.

XVI

Edward Delaney to John Flemming

September 1, ——

I am horror-stricken at what I have done! When I began this correspondence I had no other purpose than to relieve the tedium of your sick-chamber. Dillon told me to cheer you up. I tried to. I thought that you entered into the spirit of the thing. I had no idea, until within a few days, that you were taking matters *au grand sérieux.*

What can I say? I am in sackcloth and ashes. I am a pariah, a dog of an outcast. I tried to make a little romance to interest you, something soothing and idyllic, and, by Jove! I have done it only too well! My father does not know a word of this, so don't jar the old gentleman any more than you can help. I fly from the wrath to come—when you arrive! For oh, dear Jack, there isn't any colonial mansion on the other side of the road, there isn't any piazza, there isn't any hammock—there isn't any Marjorie Daw!!

STUDY NOTES

1. Investigate and report on the opinion generally held by critics concerning the effectiveness of the epistolary form in short-story writing.
2. Comment on whether a man of Aldrich's artistic ability could prob-

ably have used straight narrative and dialogue more forcefully or more economically than letters in "Marjorie Daw" and give the reasoning that underlies your conclusion.

3. Prove that the plot is both whimsical and commonplace.

4. Show that the story contains much romantic sentiment.

5. Point out devices by which Aldrich forwards the plot yet prevents the story from reaching undue length.

6. Give the evidence for your conclusion as to whether the characterization is chiefly artificial or highly realistic.

7. By what methods are Flemming and Marjorie characterized?

8. Cite instances of humor in this story.

9. Point out the use of verisimilitude in various details of plot and setting and characterization.

10. Cite instances of the foreshadowing of the ending of this story.

11. List the qualities of style, other than these questions have mentioned, that the story reveals.

12. If the ending is foreshadowed, why does it surprise the reader?

MISS HINCH [1]
(1911)

Henry Sydnor Harrison

I N going from a given point on 126th Street to the subway station at 125th, it is not usual to begin by circling the block to the 127th Street, especially in sleet, darkness, and deadly cold. When two people pursue such a course at the same time, moving unobtrusively on opposite sides of the street, in the nature of things the coincidence is likely to attract the attention of one or the other of them.

In the bright light of the entrance to the tube they came almost face to face, and the clergyman took a good look at her. Certainly she was a decent-looking old body, if any woman was: white-haired, wrinkled, spectacled, and stooped. A poor but thoroughly respectable domestic servant of the better class she looked, in her old black hat, wispy veil, and gray shawl; and her brief glance at the reverend gentleman was precisely what it should have been from her to him— open deference itself. Nevertheless, he, going more slowly down the draughty steps, continued to study her from behind with a singular intentness.

An express was just thundering in, which the clergyman, handicapped as he was by his clubfoot and stout cane, was barely in time to catch. He entered the same car with the woman, and chanced to take a seat directly across from her. It must have been then after twelve o'clock, and the wildness of the weather was discouraging to travel. The car was almost deserted. Even in this underground retreat the bitter breath of the night blew and bit, and the old woman shivered under her shawl. At last, her teeth chattering, she got up in an apologetic sort of way, and moved toward the better protected rear of the car, feeling the empty seats as she went, in a palpable search for hot pipes. The clergyman's eyes followed her candidly, and watched her sink down, presently, into a seat on his own side of the car. A young couple sat between them now; he could no longer see the woman, beyond occasional glimpses of her black knees and her ancient bonnet, skewered on with a long steel hatpin.

Nothing could have seemed more natural or more trivial than this change of seats on the part of a thin-blooded and half-frozen pas-

[1] First published in *McClure's Magazine* (September, 1911).

senger. But it happened to be a time of mutual doubt and suspicion, of alert suspicions and hair-trigger watchfulness, when men looked askance into every strange face and the smallest incidents were likely to take on a hysterical importance. Through days of fruitless searching for a fugitive outlaw of extraordinary gifts, the nerve of the city had been slowly strained to the breaking-point. All jumped, now, when anybody cried "Boo!" and the hue and cry went up falsely twenty times a day.

The clergyman pondered; mechanically he turned up his coat collar and fell to stamping his icy feet. He was an Episcopal clergyman, by his garb—rather short, very full-bodied, not to say fat, bearded and somewhat puffy-faced, with heavy cheeks cut by deep creases. Well lined against the cold though he was, however, he, too, began to suffer visibly, and presently was forced to retreat in his turn, seeking out a new place where the heating apparatus gave a better account of itself. He found one two seats beyond the old serving-woman, limped into it, and soon relapsed into his own thoughts.

The young couple, now half the car-length away, were thoroughly absorbed in each other's society. The fifth traveler, a withered old gentleman sitting next the middle door across the aisle, napped fitfully upon his cane. The woman in the hat and shawl sat in a kind of silence; and the train hurled itself roaringly through the tube. After a time, she glanced timidly at the meditating clergyman, and her look fell swiftly from his face to the discarded "ten-o'clock extra" lying by his side. She removed her dim gaze and let it travel casually about the car; but before long it returned again, pointedly, to the newspaper. Then, with some obvious hesitation, she bent forward and said:

"Excuse me, father, but would you please let me look at your paper a minute, sir?"

The clergyman came out of his reverie instantly, and looked up with almost an eager smile.

"Certainly. Keep it if you like: I am quite through with it. But," he said, in a pleasant deep voice, "I am an Episcopal minister, not a priest."

"Oh, sir—I beg your pardon! I thought—"

He dismissed the apology with a smile and a good-natured hand.

The woman opened the paper with decent cotton-gloved fingers. The garish head-lines told the story at a glance: "Earth Opened and Swallowed Miss Hinch—Headquarters Virtually Abandons Case—Even Jessie Dark"—so the bold capitals ran on—"Seems Stumped." Below the spread was a luridly written but flimsy narrative, "By Jessie Dark," which at once confirmed the odd implication of the caption. "Jessie Dark," it appeared, was one of those most extraordinary of the products of yellow journalism, a woman "crime expert," now in action. More than this, she was a "crime expert" to be taken seriously, it seemed—no mere office-desk sleuth, but an actual performer with, unexpectedly enough, a somewhat formidable list of notches on her gun. So much, at least, was to be gathered from her paper's display of "Jessie Dark's Triumphs":

> March 2, 1901. Caught Julia Victorian, *alias* Gregory, the brains of the "Healey Ring" kidnappers.
> October 7-29, 1903. Found Mrs. Trotwood and secured the letter that convicted her of the murder of her lover, Ellis E. Swan.
> December 17, 1903. Ran down Charles Bartsch in a Newark laundry and trapped a confession from him.
> July 4, 1904. Caught Mary Calloran and recovered the Stratford jewels.

And so on—nine "triumphs" in all; and nearly every one of them, as the least observant reader could hardly fail to notice, involved the capture of a woman.

Nevertheless, it could not be pretended that the "snappy" paragraphs in this evening's extra seemed to foreshadow a new or tenth triumph for Jessie Dark at any early date; and the old serving-woman in the car presently laid down the sheet with an irrepressible sigh.

The clergyman glanced toward her kindly. The sigh was so audible that it seemed to be almost an invitation; besides, public interest in the great case was a freemasonry that made conversation between total strangers the rule wherever two or three were gathered together.

"You were reading about this strange mystery, perhaps?"

The woman with a sharp intake of breath, answered: "Yes, sir. Oh, sir, it seems as if I couldn't think of anything else."

"Ah?" he said, without surprise. "It certainly appears to be a remarkable affair."

Remarkable indeed the affair seemed. In a tiny little room within ten steps of Broadway, at half past nine o'clock on a fine evening, Miss Hinch had killed John Catherwood with the light sword she used in her famous representation of the Father of his Country. Catherwood, it was known, had come to tell her of his approaching marriage; and ten thousand amateur detectives, athirst for rewards, had required no further "motive" of a creature so notorious for fierce jealousy. So far the tragedy was commonplace enough, and even vulgar. What had redeemed it to romance from this point on was the extraordinary faculty of the woman, which had made her celebrated while she was still in her teens. Coarse, violent, utterly unmoral she might be, but she happened also to be the most astonishing impersonator of her time. Her brilliant "act" consisted of a series of character changes, many of them done in full view of the audience with the assistance only of a small table of properties half concealed under a net. Some of these transformations were so amazing as to be beyond belief, even after one had sat and watched them. Not her appearance only, but voice, speech, manner, carriage, all shifted incredibly to fit the new part; so that the woman appeared to have no permanent form or fashion of her own, but to be only so much plastic human material out of which her cunning could mould at will man, woman or child, great lady of the Louisan court or Tammany statesman with the modernest of East Side modernisms upon his lip.

With this strange skill, hitherto used only to enthrall huge audiences and wring extortionate contracts from managers, the woman known as Miss Hinch—she appeared to be without a first name—was now fighting for her life somewhere against the police of the world. Without artifice, she was a tall, thin-chested young woman with strongly marked features and considerable beauty of a bold sort. What she would look like at the present moment nobody could venture a guess. Having stabbed John Catherwood in her dressing-room at the Amphitheater, she had put on her hat and coat, dropped two wigs and her make-up kit into a handbag, and walked out into Broadway. Within ten minutes the dead body of Catherwood was found and the chase begun. At the stage door, as she passed out, Miss Hinch had met an acquaintance, a young comedian named Dargis, and exchanged a word of greeting with him. That had been ten days ago. After Dargis, no one had seen her. The earth, indeed, seemed to

283

have opened and swallowed her. Yet her natural features were almost as well known as a President's, and the newspapers of a continent were daily reprinting them in a thousand variations.

"A very remarkable case," repeated the clergyman, rather absently; and his neighbor, the old woman, respectfully agreed that it was. After that she hesitated a moment, and then added with sudden bitterness:

"Oh, they'll never catch her, sir—never! She's too smart for 'em all, Miss Hinch is."

Attracted by her tone, the stout divine inquired if she was particularly interested in the case.

"Yes, sir—I got reason to be. Jack Catherwood's mother and me was at school together, and great friends all our life long. Oh, sir," she went on, as if in answer to his look of faint surprise, "Jack was a fine gentleman, with manners and looks and all beyond his people. But he never grew away from his old mother—no sir, never! And I don't believe ever a Sunday passed that he didn't go up and set the afternoon away with her, talking and laughing just like he was a little boy again. Maybe he done things he hadn't ought, as high-spirited lads will, but oh, sir, he was a good boy in his heart—a good boy. And it does seem too hard for him to die like that—and that hussy free to go her way, ruinin' and killin'—"

"My good woman," said the clergyman presently, "compose yourself. No matter how diabolical this woman's skill is, her sin will assuredly find her out."

The woman dutifully lowered her handkerchief and tried to compose herself, as bidden.

"But oh, she's that clever—diabolical, just as ye say, sir. Through poor Jack we of course heard much gossip about her, and they do say that her best tricks was not done on the stage at all. They say, sir, that, sittin' around a table with her friends, she could begin and twist her face so strange and terrible that they would beg her to stop, and jump up and run from the table—frightened out of their lives, sir, grown-up people, by the terrible faces she could make. And let her only step behind her screen for a minute—for she kept her secrets well, Miss Hinch did—and she'd come walking out to you, and you could go right up to her in the full light and take her hand, and still you couldn't make yourself believe that it was her."

"Yes," said the clergyman, "I have heard that she is remarkably clever—though, as a stranger in this part of the world, I never saw her act. I must say, it is all very interesting and strange."

He turned his head and stared through the rear door of the car at the dark flying walls. At the same moment the woman turned her head and stared full at the clergyman. When he turned back, her gaze had gone off toward the front of the car, and he picked up the paper thoughtfully.

"I'm a visitor in the city, from Denver, Colorado," he said presently, "and knew little or nothing about the case until an evening or two ago, when I attended a meeting of gentlemen here. The men's club of St. Matthias' Church—perhaps you know the place? Upon my word, they talked of nothing else. I confess they got me quite interested in their gossip. So tonight I bought this paper to see what this extraordinary woman detective it employs had to say about it. We don't have such things in the West, you know. But I must say I was disappointed after all the talk about her."

"Yes, sir, indeed, and no wonder, for she's told Mrs. Catherwood herself that she's never made such a failure as this so far. It seemed like she could always catch women, up to this. It seemed like she knew in her own mind just what a woman would do, where she'd try to hide and all, and so she could find them time and time when the men detectives didn't know where to look. But oh, sir, she's never had to hunt for such a woman as Miss Hinch before!"

"No? I suppose not," said the clergman. "Her story here in the paper certainly seems to me very poor."

"*Story,* sir! Bless my soul!" suddenly exploded the old gentleman across the aisle, to the surprise of both. "You don't suppose the clever little woman is going to show her hand in those stories, with Miss Hinch in the city and reading every line of them! In the city, sir—such is my positive belief!"

The approach to his station, it seemed, had roused him from his nap just in time to overhear the episcopate criticism. Now he answered the looks of the old woman and the clergyman with an elderly cackle.

"Excuse my intrusion, I'm sure! But I can't sit silent and hear anybody run down Jessie Dark—Miss Matthewson in private life, as perhaps you don't know. No, sir! Why, there's a man at my boarding-

285

place—astonishing young fellow named Hardy, Tom Hardy—who's known her for *years!* As to those stories, sir, I can assure you that she puts in there *exactly the opposite of what she really thinks!*"

"You don't tell me!" said the clergyman encouragingly.

"Yes, sir! Oh, she plays the game—yes, yes! She has her private ideas, her clues, her schemes. The woman doesn't live who is clever enough to hoodwink Jessie Dark. I look for developments any day—any day, sir!"

A new voice joined in. The young couple down the car, their attention caught by the old man's pervasive tones, had been frankly listening: and it was illustrative of the public mind at the moment that, as they now rose for their station, the young fellow felt perfectly free to offer his contribution:

"Tremendously dramatic situation, isn't it, gentlemen? Those two clever women pitted against each other in a life-and-death struggle, fighting it out silently in the underground somewhere—keen professional pride on one side and the fear of the electric chair on the other. Good heavens, there's—"

"Oh, yes! Oh, yes!" exclaimed the old gentleman rather testily. "But, my dear sir, it's not *professional pride* that makes Jessie Dark so resolute to win. It's *sex jealousy,* if you follow me—no offense, madam! Yes, sir! Women never have the slightest respect for each other's abilities—not the slightest. No mercy for each other, either! I tell you, Jessie Dark'd be ashamed to be beaten by another woman. Read her stories between the lines, sir—as I do. Invincible determination—no weakening—no mercy! You catch my point, sir?"

"It sounds reasonable," answered the Colorado clergyman, with his courteous smile. "All women, we are told, are natural rivals at heart—"

"Oh, I'm for Jessie Dark every time!" the young fellow broke in eagerly—"especially since the police have practically laid down. But—"

"Why, she's told my young friend Hardy," the old gentleman rode him down, "that she'll find Hinch if it takes her lifetime! Knows a thing or two about actresses, she says. Says the world isn't big enough for the creature to hide from her. Well! What do you think of that?"

"Tell what we were just talking about, George," said the young wife, looking at her husband with grossly admiring eyes.

"But oh, sir," began the old woman timidly, "Jack Catherwood's been dead ten days now, and—and—"

"Woman got on my car at nine o'clock tonight," interjected the subway guard, who, having flung open the doors for the station, was listening excitedly to the symposium; "wore a brown veil and goggles. I'd 'a' bet every dollar I had—"

"Ten days, madam! And what is that, pray?" exploded the old gentleman, rising triumphantly. "A lifetime, if necessary! Oh, never fear! Mrs. Victorian was considered pretty clever, eh? Wasn't she? Remember what Jessie Dark did for her? Nan Parmelee, too—though the police did their best to steal her credit. She'll do just as much for Miss Hinch—you may take it from me!"

"But how's she going to make the capture, gentlemen?" cried the young fellow, getting his chance at last. "That's the point my wife and I've been discussing. Assuming that she succeeds in spotting this woman-devil, what will she do? Now—"

"Do! Yell for the police!" burst from the old gentleman at the door.

"And have Miss Hinch shoot her—and then herself, too? Wouldn't she have to—"

"Grand Central!" cried the guard for the second time; and the young fellow broke off reluctantly to find his bride towing him strongly toward the door.

"Hope she nabs her soon, anyway," he called back to the clergyman over his shoulder. "The thing's getting on my nerves. One of these kindergarten reward-chasers followed my wife for five blocks the other day, just because she's got a pointed chin, and I don't know what might have happened if I hadn't come along and—"

Doors rolled shut behind him, and the train flung itself on its way. Within the car a lengthy silence ensued. The clergyman stared thoughtfully at the floor, and the old woman fell back upon her borrowed paper. She appeared to be re-reading the observations of Jessie Dark with considerable care. Presently she lowered the paper and began a quiet search for something under the folds of her shawl; and at length, her hands emerging empty, she broke the silence with a timid request:

"Oh, sir—have you a pencil you could lend me, please? I'd like to mark something in the piece to send to Mrs. Catherwood. It's what she says here about the disguises, sir."

The kindly divine felt in his pockets, and after some hunting produced a pencil—a white one with blue lead. She thanked him gratefully.

"How is Mrs. Catherwood bearing all this strain and anxiety?" he asked suddenly. "Have you seen her today?"

"Oh, yes, sir. I've been spending the evening with her since nine o'clock, and am just back from there now. Oh, she's very much broke up, sir."

She looked at him hesitatingly. He stared straight in front of him, saying nothing, though conceivably he knew, in common with the rest of the reading world, that Jack Catherwood's mother lived, not on 126th Street, but on East Houston Street. Possibly he might have wondered if his silence had not been an error of judgment. Perhaps that mis-statement had not been a slip, but something cleverer?

The woman went on with a certain eagerness: "Oh, sir, I only hope and pray those gentlemen may be right, but it does look to Mrs. Catherwood, and me too, that if Jessie Dark was going to catch her at all, she'd have done it before now. Look at those big, bold blue eyes she had, sir, with lashes an inch long, they say, and that terrible long chin of hers. They do say she can change the color of her eyes, not forever of course, but put a few of her drops into them and make them look entirely different for a time. But that chin, ye'd say—"

She broke off; for the clergyman, without preliminaries of any sort, had picked up his heavy stick and suddenly risen.

"Here we are at Fourteenth Street," he said, nodding pleasantly. "I must change here. Good night. Success to Jessie Dark, I say!"

He was watching the woman's faded face and he saw just that look of respectful surprise break into it that he had expected.

"Fourteenth Street! I'd no notion at all we'd come so far. It's where I get out too, sir, the expresses not stopping at my station."

"Ah?" said the clergyman, with the utmost dryness.

He led the way, limping and leaning on his stick. They emerged upon the chill and cheerless platform, not exactly together, yet still with some reference to their acquaintanceship on the car. But the clergyman, after stumping along a few steps, all at once realized that he was walking alone, and turned. The woman had halted. Over the intervening space their eyes met.

"Come," said the man gently. "Come, let us walk about a little to keep warm."

"Oh, sir—it's too kind of you, sir," said the woman, coming forward.

From other cars two or three blue-nosed people had got off to make the change; one or two more came straggling in from the street; but, scattered over the bleak concrete expanse, they detracted little from the isolation that seemed to surround the woman and the clergyman. Step for step, the odd pair made their way to the extreme northern end of the platform.

"By the way," said the clergyman, halting abruptly, "may I see that paper again for a moment?"

"Oh, yes, sir—of course," said the woman, producing it from beneath her shawl. "I thought you had finished with it, and I—"

He said that he wanted only to glance at it for a moment; but he fell to looking through it page by page, with considerable care. The woman looked at him several times. Finally she said hesitatingly:

"I thought, sir, I'd ask the ticket-chopper could he say how long before the next train. I'm very late as it is, sir, and I still must stop to get something to eat before I go to bed."

"An excellent idea," said the clergyman.

He explained that he, too, was already an hour behind time, and was spending the night with cousins in Newark, to boot. Side by side, they retraced their steps down the platform, questioned the chopper with scant results, and then, as by some tacit consent, started slowly back again. However, before they had gone very far, the woman all at once stopped short and, with a white face, leaned against the wall.

"Oh, sir, I'm afraid I'll just have to stop and get a bite somewhere before I go on. You'll think me foolish, sir, but I missed my supper entirely tonight, and there is quite a faint feeling coming over me."

The clergyman looked at her with apparent concern, "Do you know, my friend, you seem to anticipate all my own wants? Your mentioning something to eat just now reminded me that I myself was all but famishing." He glanced at his watch, appearing to deliberate. "Yes—it will not take long. Come, we will find a modest eating-place together."

"Oh, sir," she stammered, "but—you wouldn't want to eat with a poor old woman like me, sir."

"And why not? Are we not all equal in the sight of God?"

They ascended the stairs together, like any prosperous parson and his poor parishioner, and coming out into Fourteenth Street, started west. On the first block they came to a restaurant, a brilliantly lighted, tiled and polished place of the quick-lunch variety. But the woman timidly preferred not to stop here, saying that the glare of such places was very bad for her old eyes. The divine accepted the objection as valid, without argument. Two blocks farther on they found on a corner a quieter resort, an unpretentious little haven which yet boasted a "Ladies' Entrance" down the side street.

They entered by the front door, and sat down at a table, facing each other. The woman read the menu through, and finally, after some embarrassed uncertainty, ordered poached eggs on toast. The clergyman ordered the same. The simple meal was soon despatched. Just as they were finishing it, the woman said apologetically:

"If you'll excuse me, sir—could I see the bill of fare a minute? I think I'd best take a little pot of tea to warm me up, if they do not charge too high."

"I haven't the bill of fare," said the clergyman.

They looked diligently for the cardboard strip, but it was nowhere to be seen. The waiter drew near.

"Yes, sir! I left it there on the table when I took the order."

"I'm sure I can't imagine what's become of it," repeated the clergyman, rather insistently.

He looked hard at the woman, and found that she was looking hard at him. Both pairs of eyes fell instantly.

The waiter brought another bill of fare; the woman ordered tea; the waiter came back with it. The clergyman paid for both orders with a bill that looked hard-earned.

The tea proved to be very hot: it could not be drunk down at a gulp. The clergyman, watching the woman intently as she sipped, seemed to grow more and more restless. His fingers drummed the tablecloth: he could hardly sit still. All at once he said: "What is that calling in the street? It sounds like newsboys."

The woman put her old head on one side and listened. "Yes, sir. There seems to be an extra out."

"Upon my word," he said, after a pause. "I believe I'll go get one. Good gracious! Crime is a very interesting thing, to be sure!"

He rose slowly, took down his shovel-hat from the hanger near him, and, grasping his heavy stick, limped to the door. Leaving it open behind him, much to the annoyance of the proprietor in the cashier's cage, he stood a moment in the little vestibule, looking up and down the street. Then he took a few slow steps eastward, beckoning with his hand as he went, and so passed out of sight of the woman at the table.

The eating-place was on the corner, and outside the clergyman paused for half a breath. North, east, south, and west he looked, and nowhere he found what his flying glance sought. He turned the corner into the darker cross-street, and began to walk, at first slowly, continually looking about him. Presently his pace quickened, quickened so that he no longer even stayed to use his stout cane. In another moment he was all but running, his club-foot pounding the icy sidewalk heavily as he went. A newsboy thrust an extra under his very nose, and he did not even see it.

Far down the street, nearly two blocks away, a tall figure in a blue coat stood and stamped in the freezing sleet; and the hurrying divine sped straight toward him. But he did not get very near. For, as he passed the side entrance at the extreme rear of the restaurant, a departing guest dashed out so recklessly as to run full into him, stopping him dead.

Without looking at her, he knew who it was. In fact, he did not look at her at all, but turned his head hurriedly east and west, sweeping the dark street with a swift eye. But the old woman, having drawn back with a sharp exclamation as they collided, rushed breathlessly into apologies:

"Oh, sir—excuse me! A newsboy popped his head into the side door just after you went out, and I ran to him to get you the paper. But he got away too quick for me, sir, and so I—"

"Exactly," said the clergyman in his quiet deep voice. "That must have been the very boy I myself was after."

On the other side, two men had just turned into the street, well muffled against the night, talking cheerfully as they trudged along. Now the clergyman looked full at the woman, and she saw that there was a smile on his face.

"As he seems to have eluded us both, suppose we return to the subway?"

"Yes, sir; it's full time I—"

"The sidewalk is so slippery," he went on gently, "perhaps you had better take my arm."

Behind the pair in the dingy restaurant, the waiter came forward to shut the door, and lingered to discuss with the proprietor the sudden departure of his two patrons. However, the score had been paid with a liberal tip for service, so there was no especial complaint to make. After listening to some unfavorable comments on the ways of the clergy, the waiter returned to his table to set it in order.

On the floor in the carpeted aisle between tables lay a white piece of cardboard, which his familiar eye recognized as part of one of his own bills of fare, face downward. He stooped and picked it up. On the back of it was some scribbling, made with a blue lead-pencil.

The handwriting was very loose and irregular, as if the writer had had his eyes elsewhere while he wrote, and it was with some difficulty that the waiter deciphered this message:

Miss Hinch 14th St. subway Get police quick

The waiter carried this curious document to the proprietor, who read it over a number of times. He was a dull man, and had a dull man's suspiciousness of a practical joke. However, after a good deal of irresolute discussion, he put on his overcoat and went out for a policeman. He turned west, and half way up the block met an elderly bluecoat sauntering east. The policeman looked at the scribbling, and dismissed it profanely as a wag's foolishness of the sort that was bothering the life out of him a dozen times a day. He walked along with the proprietor, and as they drew near to the latter's place of business, both became aware of footsteps thudding nearer up the cross-street from the south. As they looked up, two young policemen, accompanied by a man in a uniform like a street-car conductor's, swept around the corner and dashed straight into the restaurant.

The first policeman and the proprietor ran in after them, and found them staring about rather vacantly. One of the arms of the law demanded if any suspicious characters had been seen about the place, and the dull proprietor said no. The officers, looking rather flat, explained their errand. It seemed that a few minutes before, the third man, who was a ticket-chopper at the subway station, had found a mysterious message lying on the floor by his box. Whence it had come, how long it had lain there, he had not the slightest idea. However, there it was. The policeman exhibited a crumpled white scrap torn from a newspaper, on which was scrawled in blue pencil:

Miss Hinch Miller's Restaurant Get police quick

The first policeman, who was both the oldest and the fattest of the three, produced the message on the bill of fare, so utterly at odds with this. The dull proprietor, now bethinking himself, mentioned the clergyman and the old woman who had taken poached eggs and tea together, called for a second bill of fare, and departed so unexpectedly by different doors. The ticket-chopper recalled that he had seen the same pair at his station: they had come up, he remembered, and questioned him about trains. The three policemen were momentarily puzzled by this testimony. But it was soon plain to them that if either the woman or the clergyman really had any information about Miss Hinch—a highly improbable supposition in itself—they would never have stopped with peppering the neighborhood with silly little contradictory messages.

"They're a pair of old fools tryin' to have sport with the police, and I'd like to run them in for it," growled the fattest of the officers; and this was the general verdict.

The little conference broke up. The dull proprietor returned to his cage, the waiter to his table; the subway man departed on the run for his chopping box; the three policemen passed out into the bitter night. They walked together, grumbling, and their feet, perhaps by some subconscious impulse, turned eastward toward the subway. And in the middle of the next block a man came running up to them.

"Officer, look what I found on the sidewalk a minute ago. Read that scribble!"

He held up a white slab which proved to be part of a bill of fare from Miller's Restaurant. On the back of it the three peering officers saw, almost illegibly scrawled in blue pencil:

293

MATTER

The hand trailed off on the *w* as though the writer had been suddenly interrupted. The fat policeman blasphemed and threatened arrests. But the second policeman, who was dark and wiry, raised his head from the bill of fare and said suddenly: "Tim, I believe there's something in this."

"There'd ought to be ten days on the Island [2] in it for thim," growled fat Tim.

"Suppose, now," said the other policeman, staring intently at nothing, "the old woman was Miss Hinch herself, f'r instance, and the parson was shadowing her while pretendin' he never suspicioned her, and Miss Hinch not darin' to cut and run for it till she was sure she had a clean getaway. Well now, Tim, what better could he do—"

"That's right!" exclaimed the third policeman. " 'Specially when ye think that Hinch carries a gun, an'll use it, too! Why not have a look in at the subway station anyway, the three of us?"

The proposal carried the day. The three officers started for the subway, the citizen following. They walked at a good pace and without more talk; and both their speed and their silence had a subtle psychological reaction. As the minds of the four men turned inward upon the odd behavior of the pair in Miller's Restaurant, the conviction that, after all, something important might be afoot grew and strengthened within each one of them. Unconsciously their pace quickened. It was the wiry policeman who first broke into an open run, but the three other men had been for twenty paces on the verge of it.

However, these consultations and vacillations had taken time. The stout clergyman and the poor old woman had five minutes' start of the officers of the law, and that, as it happened, was all that the occasion required. On Fourteenth Street, as they made their way arm in arm to the station, they were seen, and remembered, by a number of belated pedestrians. It was observed by more than one that the woman lagged as if she were tired, while the club-footed divine, supporting her on his arm, steadily kept her up to his own brisk gait.

---

[2] The prison which was maintained on Riker's Island in East River; the island was annexed by New York City in 1884.

So walking, the pair descended the subway steps, came out upon the bare platform again, and presently stood once more at the extreme uptown end of it, just where they had waited half an hour before. Near by a careless porter had overturned a bucket of water, and a splotch of thin ice ran out and over the edge of the concrete. Two young men who were taking lively turns up and down distinctly heard the clergyman warn the woman to look out for this ice. Far away to the north was to be heard the faint roar of an approaching train.

The woman stood nearest the track, and the clergyman stood in front of her. In the vague light their looks met, and each was struck by the pallor of the other's face. In addition, the woman was breathing hard, and her hands and feet betrayed some nervousness. It was difficult now to ignore the too patent fact that for an hour they had been clinging desperately to each other, at all costs; but the clergyman made a creditable effort to do so. He talked ramblingly, in a voice sounding only a little unnatural, for the most part of the deplorable weather and his train to Newark, for which he was now so late. And all the time both of them were incessantly turning their heads toward the station entrances, as if expecting some arrival.

As he talked, the clergyman kept his hands unobtrusively busy. From the bottom edge of his black sack-coat he drew a pin, and stuck it deep into the ball of his middle finger. He took out his handkerchief to dust the hard sleet from his hat; and under his overcoat he pressed the handkerchief against his bleeding finger. While making these small arrangements, he held the woman's eyes with his own, talking on; and, still holding them, he suddenly broke off his random talk and peered at her cheek with concern.

"My good woman, you've scratched your cheek somehow! Why, bless me, it's bleeding quite badly."

"Never mind—never mind," said the woman, and swept her eyes hurriedly toward the entrance.

"But, good gracious, I must mind! The blood will fall on your shawl. If you will permit me—ah!"

Too quick for her, he leaned forward and, through the thin veil, swept her cheek hard with the handkerchief; removing it, he held it up so that she might see the blood for herself. But she did not glance at the handkerchief, and neither did he. His gaze was riveted

295

upon her cheek, which looked smooth and clear where he had smudged the clever wrinkles away.

Down the steps and upon the platform pounded the feet of three flying policemen. But it was evident now that the express would thunder in just ahead of them. The clergyman, standing close in front of the woman, took a firmer grip on his heavy stick and a look of stern triumph came into his face.

"You're not so terribly clever, after all!"

The woman had sprung back from him with an irrepressible exclamation, and in that instant she was aware of the police.

However, her foot slipped upon the treacherous ice—or it may have tripped on the stout cane, when the clergyman shifted its position. And in the next breath the express train roared past.

By one of those curious chances which sometimes refute all experience, the body of the woman was not mangled or mutilated in the least. There was a deep blue bruise on the left temple, and apparently that was all; even the ancient hat remained on her head, skewered fast by the long pin. It was the clergyman who found the body huddled at the side of the dark track where the train had flung it— he who covered the still face and superintended the removal to the platform. Two eye-witnesses of the tragedy pointed out the ice on which the unfortunate woman had slipped, and described their horror as they saw her companion spring forward just too late to save her.

Not wishing to bring on a delirium of excitement among the bystanders, two policemen drew the clergyman quietly aside and showed him the three mysterious messages. Much affected by the shocking end of his sleuthery as he was, he readily admitted having written them. He briefly recounted how the woman's strange movements on 126th Street had arrested his attention and how watching her closely on the car, he had finally detected that she wore a wig. Unfortunately, however, her suspicions had been aroused by his interest in her, and thereafter a long battle of wits had ensued between them—he trying to summon the police without her knowledge, she dogging him close to prevent that, and at the same time watching her chance to give him the slip. He rehearsed how, in the restaurant, when he had invented an excuse to leave her for an instant, she had made a bolt and narrowly missed getting away; and finally how, having brought her back to the subway and seeing the police at last near, he had decided to risk exposing her make-up, with this unexpectedly shocking result.

"And now," he concluded in a shaken voice, "I am naturally most anxious to know whether I am right—or have made some terrible mistake. Will you look at her, officer, and tell me if it is indeed —she?"

But the fat policeman shook his head over the well-known ability of Miss Hinch to look like everybody else in the world but herself.

"It'll take God Almighty to tell ye that, sir—saving your presence. I'll leave it f'r headquarters," he continued, as if that were the same thing. "But, if it is her, she's gone to her reward, sir."

"God pity her!" said the clergyman.

"Amen! Give me your name, sir. They'll likely want you in the morning."

The clergyman gave it: Rev. Theodore Shaler, of Denver; city address, a number on East 126th Street. Having thus discharged his duty in the affair, he started sadly to go away; but, passing by the silent figure stretched on a bench under the ticket-seller's overcoat, he bared his head and stopped for one last look at it.

The parson's gentleness and efficiency had already won favorable comments from the bystanders, and of the first quality he now gave a final proof. The dead woman's balled-up handkerchief, which somebody had recovered from the track and laid upon her breast, had slipped to the floor; and the clergyman, observing it, stooped silently to restore it again. This last small service chanced to bring his head close to the head of the dead woman; and, as he straightened up again, her projecting hatpin struck his cheek and ripped a straight line down it. This in itself would have been a trifle, since scratches soon heal. But it happened that the point of the hatpin caught under the lining of the clergyman's perfect beard and ripped it clean from him; so that, as he rose with a suddenly shrilled cry, he turned upon the astonished onlookers the bare, smooth chin of a woman, curiously long and pointed.

There were not many such chins in the world, and the urchins in the street would have recognized this one. Amid a sudden uproar which ill became the presence of the dead, the police closed in on Miss Hinch and handcuffed her with violence, fearing suicide, if

297

not some new witchery; and at the station-house an unemotional matron divested the famous impersonator of the last and best of her many disguises.

This much the police did. But it was everywhere understood that it was Jessie Dark who had really made the capture, and the papers next morning printed pictures of the unconquerable little woman and of the hatpin with which she had reached back from another world to bring her greatest adversary to justice.

STUDY NOTES

1. Outline the plot of "Miss Hinch."

2. Show that the situation with which the story deals is particularly dramatic.

3. On reading the story a second time, how soon do you discover that the "clergyman" (Miss Hinch) suspects that the "serving-woman" is Jessie Dark?

4. And on the second reading, how soon do you find rather clear indication that the serving-woman supposes the clergyman to be Miss Hinch?

5. What actions and explanations in the first four paragraphs create an atmosphere of mystery?

6. What contribution to the characterization of Jessie Dark do the young couple and the old gentleman, passengers in the subway express car, make?

7. List the methods by which the character of Miss Hinch is portrayed.

8. Mention the clues which suggest that the clergyman is Jessie Dark and that the serving-woman is Miss Hinch.

9. Mention the opposing set of clues—those which hint that the clergyman is Miss Hinch and that the old woman is Jessie Dark.

10. Point out the dramatic foreshadowing of the capture of Miss Hinch.

11. Mention instances of clever use of suspense in this story.

12. After meeting the surprise on the first reading, do you finish the second reading with the impression that false clues unfairly victimized you or that the dramatic and unexpected climax is reasonably logical?

COMPARISON EXERCISES

1. Contrast the letter-writing method of characterization and plot development used in "Marjorie Daw" with the dialogue technique employed in "Miss Hinch."

2. Which of these two stories, on the second reading, reveals the larger amount of foreshadowing of the surprise ending—the larger number of clues or hints that some such ending could occur?

3. Which has the more exciting plot?
4. Which has the more realistic characterization?
5. Which has the more skilfully sustained suspense?

WRITING SUGGESTION

Submit an original story, ending with a dramatic surprise, a narrative that provides some foreshadowing of the climax but keeps the reader confused by conflicting suggestions, letting some of the clues hint only indefinitely at the final action but making the others seem to forecast a different outcome from that at which the story does arrive.

DETECTIVE

Introduction to Stories of Detection

A TYPICAL detective story presents an enigma, usually a crime, frequently a murder, together with the searching and deduction that solve the puzzle. In about the first half of the narrative, the mystery deepens. In the second half, the solution becomes known. Within the last two or three decades, Dashiell Hammett and Raymond Chandler and others have written a type of detective story partly new—placing large emphasis on the lurid activities of depraved characters and on the justice that comes to these bad actors. Such writers give more attention to the effect of crime on the characters than to the solving of a mystery. Usually, even the more recent stories of detection, though they have a new emphasis, do nevertheless present a mystery and its solution.

Poe invented the detective-story *genre* or the tale of ratiocination, publishing five analytical or ratiocinative stories: "The Murders in the Rue Morgue," "The Mystery of Marie Rogêt," "The Purloined Letter," " 'Thou Art the Man,' " and "The Gold-Bug." Poe created most of the devices that have since been employed in tales of detection, such as the use of the microscope and of ballistic tests and the inferior astuteness of policemen to detectives and the discovery of the criminal's identity and method by clever deduction from clues obscure to the casual observer.

Well-known detectives in American short stories belong to at least four classes: (1) the keenly intellectual and deductive, (2) the scientific or pseudo-scientific, (3) the philosophical and psychological, and (4) the hard-working and tough-minded. To the deductive category may be assigned Poe's amateur but scholarly Dupin; Anna Katharine Green's Ebenezer Gryce and the capable woman sleuth Violet Strange; Jacques Futrelle's intellectual, eccentric, and amusing Professor S. F. X. Van Dusen; and Melville Davisson Post's Uncle

301

MATTER

Abner, a grim mountaineer detective. To the scientific or pseudo-scientific group, employing laboratory instruments or methods, belong Luther Trant, created by William MacHarg and Edwin Balmer, and Arthur B. Reeve's Craig Kennedy. In the philosophical-psychological class are Post's Randolph Mason, an unscrupulous lawyer, who helps men evade law and go unpunished; and T. S. Stribling's Henry Poggioli, an American university lecturer on psychology, who solves a murder after being hanged for the crime. In the callous, get-tough-with-the-criminal category are Dashiell Hammett's Samuel Spade, MacHarg's O'Malley, Raymond Chandler's Tony Reseck, and Cornell Woolrich's Dick Gilman and other detectives.

The plot of a detective story must be interesting. It will primarily concern the methods of the criminal and of the sleuth. It must be built mainly (if not exclusively) from commonplace rather than fantastic materials. It must be carefully constructed and end in a satisfying solution. The plot and the setting must harmonize. The solving of the puzzle is usually the main action. In ferreting out a robber or a murderer, the detective's mind is represented as discovering the clues that lead to the solution. He analyzes motives and clues until he finds convincing proof of the criminal's identity.

It must be the detective's skill, not an accident, that solves the mystery. He must employ the inductive investigative method before arriving at his deductions. If the reader is to enjoy the work of detection—both the induction and the deduction—he must not be led to pity the criminal nor to feel that the criminal is treated unjustly. On the contrary, the penalty placed upon the villain must seem well deserved.

Convincing evidence must be given that the person apprehended and punished for the crime is guilty. The detective's deductions must be supported by some such realistic details as the condition of the murdered person's body when found, the significance of footprints discovered near the scene of the crime, the condition of doors and windows in any house represented as entered, or any other appropriate circumstances. The proof of guilt must be unfolded piece by piece, giving time for conviction. The plainest and strongest evidence must be presented near the end of the story. When the reader becomes definitely skeptical or fearful that the sleuth may not discover who committed the crime, the climax should appear.

302

Detective stories have a somewhat different technique from other stories. The typical mystery narrative uses the crime-to-solution order rather than the chronological. The environment must be realistic. Characterization is comparatively slight except in the portraying of the detective. The characters must seem plausible but not be too closely delineated. The detective story usually has less atmosphere, is more intellectual, than other stories. Suspense increases as the action unfolds, with the greatest suspense of all appearing just before the climax. The writer takes pains to keep the reader from knowing the solution until near the end. By one method or another he causes the reader to misplace his suspicions, perhaps by having the villain wear a religious cloak or by apparently placing him above suspicion through his relationship to the other characters or to the plot. The element of probability should be present in the criminal's motive and method. The style should be homely, not too literary or descriptive.

Some writers since Poe's time have somewhat altered the technique of the detective story and reached out to include certain phases of subject matter that he did not touch. The settings in Poe's tales of ratiocination were less realistic than is common in America's twentieth century detective stories. The dialogue was less natural and the characters were more abstract. The language was less terse and lurid than now sometimes appears. Some of the more recent stories place heavier emphasis upon forceful or violent action of underworld characters or of the detective himself than did Poe's.

The detective story is a popular form of literature, read by millions who love the lure of the mysterious and share vicariously in the chase of a criminal and perhaps enjoy a feeling of superiority in not being under scrutiny or even delight in trying to guess the end of the action. People of various social and intellectual classes find entertainment in detective stories. Many specimens of this type of literature appear in both the pulp and the slick magazines. Quantitatively, the story of detection probably exceeds any other class of short fiction and qualitatively the better examples justify the large measure of pride that Americans place in a kind of literature that originated in their own nation.

THE DOCTOR, HIS WIFE, AND THE CLOCK [1]
(1895)
ANNA KATHARINE GREEN

I

ON THE 17th of July, 1851, a tragedy of no little interest occurred in one of the residences of the Colonnade in Lafayette Place.

Mr. Hasbrouck, a well-known and highly respected citizen, was attacked in his room by an unknown assailant, and shot dead before assistance could reach him. His murderer escaped, and the problem offered to the police was how to identify this person who, by some happy chance or by the exercise of the most remarkable forethought, had left no traces behind him or any clue by which he could be followed.

The affair was given to a young man, named Ebenezer Gryce, to investigate, and the story, as he tells it, is this:

When, some time after midnight, I reached Lafayette Place, I found the block lighted from end to end. Groups of excited men and women peered from the open doorways and mingled their shadows with those of the huge pillars which adorn the front of this picturesque block of dwellings.

The house in which the crime had been committed was near the center of the row, and, long before I reached it, I had learned from more than one source that the alarm was first given to the street by a woman's shriek, and secondly by the shouts of an old man-servant who had appeared, in a half-dressed condition, at the window of Mr. Hasbrouck's room, crying, "Murder! murder!"

But when I had crossed the threshold, I was astonished at the paucity of the facts to be gleaned from the inmates themselves. The old servitor, who was the first to talk, had only this account of the crime to give.

The family, which consisted of Mr. Hasbrouck, his wife, and three servants, had retired for the night at the usual hour and under the usual auspices. At eleven o'clock the lights were all extinguished, and the whole household asleep, with the possible exception of Mr.

---

[1] This story was first published as a book, *The Doctor, His Wife, and the Clock,* and was republished in revised form in *The Golden Slipper* (1915).

Hasbrouck himself, who, being a man of large business responsibilities, was frequently troubled with insomnia.

Suddenly Mrs. Hasbrouck woke with a start. Had she dreamed the words that were ringing in her ears or had they been actually uttered in her hearing? They were short, sharp words, full of terror and menace, and she had nearly satisfied herself that she had imagined them, when there came, from somewhere near the door, a sound she neither understood nor could interpret, but which filled her with inexplicable terror and made her afraid to breathe or even to stretch forth her hand towards her husband, whom she supposed to be sleeping at her side. At length another strange sound, which she was sure was not due to her imagination, drove her to make an attempt to rouse him, when she was horrified to find that she was alone in the bed and her husband nowhere within reach.

Filled now with something more than nervous apprehension, she flung herself to the floor and tried to penetrate, with frenzied glances, the surrounding darkness. But the blinds and shutters both having been carefully closed by Mr. Hasbrouck before retiring, she found this impossible, and she was about to sink in terror to the floor, when she heard a low gasp on the other side of the room, followed by the suppressed cry:

"God! what have I done!"

The voice was a strange one, but before the fear aroused by this fact could culminate in a shriek of dismay, she caught the sound of retreating footsteps, and, eagerly listening, she heard them descend the stairs and depart by the front door.

Had she known what had occurred—had there been no doubt in her mind as to what lay in the darkness on the other side of the room—it is likely that, at the noise caused by the closing front door, she would have made at once for the balcony that opened out from the window before which she was standing, and taken one look at the flying figure below. But her uncertainty as to what lay hidden from her by the darkness chained her feet to the floor, and there is no knowing when she would have moved, if a carriage had not at that moment passed down Astor Place, bringing with it a sense of companionship which broke the spell that held her and gave her strength to light the gas, which was in ready reach of her hand.

As the sudden blaze illuminated the room, revealing in a burst the

305

old familiar walls and well-known pieces of furniture, she felt for a moment as if released from some heavy nightmare and restored to the common experiences of life. But in another instant her former dread returned, and she found herself quaking at the prospect of passing around the foot of the bed into that part of the room which was as yet hidden from her eyes.

But the desperation which comes with great crises finally drove her from her retreat; and, creeping slowly forward, she cast one glance at the floor before her, when she found her worst fears realized by the sight of the dead body of her husband lying prone before the open doorway, with a bullet-hole in his forehead.

Her first impulse was to shriek, but, by a powerful exercise of will, she checked herself, and, ringing frantically for the servants, who slept on the top floor of the house, flew to the nearest window and endeavored to open it. But the shutters had been bolted so securely by Mr. Hasbrouck, in his endeavor to shut out light and sound, that by the time she had succeeded in unfastening them, all trace of the flying murderer had vanished from the street.

Sick with grief and terror, she stepped back into the room just as the three frightened servants descended the stairs. As they appeared in the open doorway, she pointed at her husband's inanimate form, and then, as if suddenly realizing in its full force the calamity which had befallen her, she threw up her arms and sank forward to the floor in a dead faint.

The two women rushed to her assistance, but the old butler, bounding over the bed, sprang to the window and shrieked his alarm to the street.

In the interim that followed, Mrs. Hasbrouck was revived, and the master's body laid decently on the bed; but no pursuit was made nor any inquiries started likely to assist me in establishing the identity of the assailant.

Indeed, every one, both in the house and out, seemed dazed by the unexpected catastrophe, and as no one had any suspicions to offer as to the probable murderer, I had a difficult task before me.

I began, in the usual way, by inspecting the scene of the murder. I found nothing in the room, or in the condition of the body itself, which added an iota to the knowledge already obtained. That Mr. Hasbrouck had been in bed; that he had risen upon hearing a noise;

and that he had been shot before reaching the door were self-evident facts. But there was nothing to guide me further. The very simplicity of the circumstances caused a dearth of clues, which made the difficulty of procedure as great as any I ever encountered.

My search through the hall and down the stairs elicited nothing; and an investigation of the bolts and bars by which the house was secured, assured me that the assassin had either entered by the front door or had already been secreted in the house when it was locked up for the night.

"I shall have to trouble Mrs. Hasbrouck for a short interview," I hereupon announced to the trembling old servitor, who had followed me like a dog about the house.

He made no demur, and in a few minutes I was ushered into the presence of the newly made widow, who sat quite alone, in a large chamber in the rear. As I crossed the threshold she looked up, and I encountered a good plain face, without the shadow of guile in it.

"Madame," said I, "I have not come to disturb you. I will ask two or three questions only and then leave you to your grief. I am told that some words came from the assassin before he delivered his fatal shot. Did you hear these distinctly enough to tell me what they were?"

"I was sound asleep," said she, "and dreamt, as I thought, that a fierce, strange voice cried somewhere to someone: 'Ah! you did not expect me!' But I dare not say that these words were really uttered to my husband, for he was not the man to call forth hate, and only a man in the extremity of passion could address such an exclamation in such a tone as rings in my memory in connection with the fatal shot which woke me."

"But that shot was not the work of a friend," I argued. "If, as these words seem to prove, the assassin had some other motive than gain in his assault, then your husband had an enemy, though you never suspected it."

"Impossible!" was her steady reply, uttered in the most convincing tone. "The man who shot him was a common burglar, and, frightened at having been betrayed into murder, fled without looking for booty. I am sure I heard him cry out in terror and remorse: 'God! what have I done!' "

"Was that before you left the side of the bed?"

"Yes; I did not move from my place till I heard the front door close. I was paralyzed by my fear and dread."

"Are you in the habit of trusting to the security of a latch-lock only in the fastening of your front door at night? I am told that the big key was not in the lock, and that the bolt at the bottom of the door was not drawn."

"The bolt at the bottom of the door is never drawn. Mr. Hasbrouck was so good a man he never mistrusted any one. That is why the big lock was not fastened. The key, not working well, he took it some days ago to the locksmith, and when the latter failed to return it, he laughed, and said he thought no one would ever think of meddling with his front door."

"Is there more than one night-key to your house?" I now asked.

She shook her head.

"And when did Mr. Hasbrouck last use his?"

"Tonight, when he came home from prayer-meeting," she answered, and burst into tears.

Her grief was so real and her loss so recent that I hesitated to afflict her by further questions. So returning to the scene of the tragedy, I stepped out upon the balcony which ran in front. Soft voices instantly struck my ears. The neighbors on either side were grouped in front of their own windows and were exchanging the remarks natural under the circumstances. I paused, as in duty bound, and listened. But I heard nothing worth recording and would have instantly re-entered the house if I had not been impressed by the appearance of a very graceful woman who stood at my right. She was clinging to her husband, who was gazing at one of the pillars before him, in a strange, fixed way which astonished me till he attempted to move, and then I saw that he was blind. Instantly I remembered that there lived in this row a blind doctor, equally celebrated for his skill and for his uncommon personal attractions, and, greatly interested not only in his affliction but in the sympathy evinced for him by his young and affectionate wife, I stood still till I heard her say in the soft and appealing tones of love:

"Come in, Constant; you have heavy duties for tomorrow, and you should get a few hours' rest, if possible."

He came from the shadow of the pillar, and for one minute I

saw his face with the lamplight shining full upon it. It was as regular of feature as a sculptured Adonis, and it was as white.

"Sleep!" he repeated, in the measured tones of deep but suppressed feeling. "Sleep! with murder on the other side of the wall!" And he stretched out his hands in a dazed way that insensibly accentuated the horror I myself felt of the crime which had so lately taken place in the room behind me.

She, noting the movement, took one of the groping hands in her own and drew him gently towards her.

"This way," she urged; and, guiding him into the house, she closed the window and drew down the shades, making the street seem darker by the loss of her exquisite presence.

This may seem a digression, but I was at the time a young man of thirty and much under the dominion of woman's beauty. I was therefore slow in leaving the balcony and persistent in my wish to learn something of this remarkable couple before leaving Mr. Hasbrouck's house.

The story told me was very simple. Dr. Zabriskie had not been born blind but had become so after a grievous illness, which had stricken him down after he received his diploma. Instead of succumbing to an affliction which would have daunted most men, he expressed his intention of practising his profession and soon became so successful in it that he found no difficulty in establishing himself in one of the best-paying quarters of the city. Indeed, his intuition seemed to have developed in a remarkable degree after his loss of sight, and he seldom, if ever, made a mistake in diagnosis. Considering this fact and the personal attractions which gave him distinction, it was no wonder that he soon became a popular physician whose presence was a benefaction and whose word a law.

He had been engaged to be married at the time of his illness, and, when he learned what was likely to be its results, had offered to release the young lady from all obligation to him. But she would not be released, and they were married. This had taken place some five years previous to Mr. Hasbrouck's death, three of which had been spent by them in Lafayette Place.

So much for the beautiful woman next door.

There being absolutely no clue to the assailant of Mr. Hasbrouck, I naturally looked forward to the inquest for some evidence upon which to work. But there seemed to be no underlying facts to this tragedy. The most careful study into the habits and conduct of the deceased brought nothing to light save his general beneficence and rectitude, nor was there in his history or in that of his wife any secret or hidden obligation calculated to provoke any such act of revenge as murder. Mrs. Hasbrouck's surmise that the intruder was simply a burglar and that she had rather imagined than heard the words that pointed to the shooting as a deed of vengeance soon gained general credence. But, though the police worked long and arduously in this new direction, their efforts were without fruit, and the case bade fair to remain an unsolvable mystery.

But the deeper the mystery the more persistently does my mind cling to it, and some five months after the matter had been delegated to oblivion, I found myself starting suddenly from sleep, with these words ringing in my ears:

"Who uttered the scream that gave the first alarm of Mr. Hasbrouck's violent death?"

I was in such a state of excitement that the perspiration stood out on my forehead. Mrs. Hasbrouck's story of the occurrence returned to me, and I remembered as distinctly as if she were then speaking that she had expressly stated that she did not scream when confronted by the sight of her husband's dead body. But some one had screamed, and that very loudly. Who was it, then? One of the maids, startled by the sudden summons from below, or some one else—some involuntary witness of the crime, whose testimony had been suppressed at the inquest, by fear or influence?

The possibility of having come upon a clue even at this late day so fired my ambition that I took the first opportunity of revisiting Lafayette Place. Choosing such persons as I thought most open to my questions, I learned that there were many who could testify to having heard a woman's shrill scream on that memorable night just prior to the alarm given by old Cyrus; but no one could tell from whose lips it had come. One fact, however, was immediately settled. It had not been the result of the servant-women's fears. Both of the girls were positive that they had uttered no sound, nor had they themselves heard any, till Cyrus rushed to the window with his wild cries. As the scream, by whomever given, was uttered before they descended the stairs, I was convinced by these assurances that it had issued from one of the front windows, and not from the rear of the house, where their own rooms lay. Could it be that it had sprung from the adjoining dwelling and that—— My thoughts went no further, but I made up my mind to visit the doctor's house at once.

It took some courage to do this, for the doctor's wife had attended the inquest, and her beauty, seen in broad daylight, had worn such an aspect of mingled sweetness and dignity that I hesitated to encounter it under any circumstances likely to disturb its pure serenity. But a clue, once grasped, cannot be lightly set aside by a true detective, and it would have taken more than a woman's frown to stop me at this point. So I rang Dr. Zabriskie's bell.

I am seventy years old now and am no longer daunted by the charms of a beautiful woman, but I confess that when I found myself in the fine reception parlor on the first-floor, I experienced no little trepidation at the prospect of the interview that awaited me. But as soon as the fine commanding form of the doctor's wife crossed the threshold, I recovered my senses and surveyed her with as direct a gaze as my position allowed. For her aspect bespoke a degree of emotion that astonished me; and even before I spoke I perceived her to be trembling, though she was a woman of no little natural dignity and self-possession.

"I seem to know your face," she said, advancing courteously towards me, "but your name"—and here she glanced at the card she held in her hand—"is totally unfamiliar to me."

"I think you saw me some eighteen months ago," said I. "I am the detective who gave testimony at the inquest which was held over the remains of Mr. Hasbrouck."

I had not meant to startle her, but at this introduction of myself I saw her naturally pale cheek turn paler, and her fine eyes, which had been fixed curiously upon me, gradually sink to the floor.

"Great heaven!" thought I, "what is this I have stumbled upon!"

"I do not understand what business you can have with me," she presently remarked, with a show of gentle indifference that did not in the least deceive me.

"I do not wonder," I rejoined. "The crime which took place next door is almost forgotten by the community, and even if it were not, I am sure you will find it difficult to conjecture the nature of the question I have to put to you."

"I am surprised," she began, rising in her involuntary emotion and thereby compelling me to rise also. "How can you have any question to ask me on this subject? Yet if you have," she continued, with a rapid change of manner that touched my heart in spite of myself, "I shall, of course, do my best to answer you."

There are women whose sweetest tones and most charming smiles only serve to awaken distrust in men of my calling; but Mrs. Zabriskie was not of this number. Her face was beautiful, but it was also candid in expression, and beneath the agitation which palpably disturbed her, I was sure there lurked nothing either wicked or false. Yet I held fast by the clue which I had grasped, as it were, in the dark, and without knowing whither I was tending, much less whither I was leading her, I proceeded to say:

"The question which I presume to put to you as the nextdoor neighbor of Mr. Hasbrouck is this: Who was the woman who screamed out so loudly that the whole neighborhood heard her on the night of that gentleman's assassination?"

The gasp she gave answered my question in a way she little realized, and, struck as I was by the impalpable links that had led me to the threshold of this hitherto unsolvable mystery, I was about to press my advantage and ask another question, when she quickly started forward and laid her hand on my lips.

Astonished, I looked at her inquiringly, but her head was turned aside, and her eyes, fixed upon the door, showed the greatest anxiety. Instantly I realized what she feared. Her husband was entering the house, and she dreaded lest his ears should catch a word of our conversation.

Not knowing what was in her mind, and unable to realize the importance of the moment to her, I yet listened to the advance of her blind husband with an almost painful interest. Would he enter the room where we were, or would he pass immediately to his office in the rear? She seemed to wonder, too, and almost held her breath as he neared the door, paused, and stood in the open doorway, with his ear turned toward us.

As for myself, I remained perfectly still, gazing at his face in mingled surprise and apprehension. For besides its beauty, which was of a marked order, as I have already observed, it had a touching expression which irresistibly aroused both pity and interest in the spectator. This may have been the result of his affliction or it may have sprung from some deeper cause; but, whatever its source, this look in his face produced a strong impression upon me and interested me at once in his personality. Would he enter? Or would he pass on? Her look of silent appeal showed me in which direction her wishes lay, but while I answered her glance by complete silence, I was conscious in some indistinct way that the business I had undertaken would be better furthered by his entrance.

The blind have been often said to possess a sixth sense in place of the one they have lost. Though I am sure we made no noise, I soon perceived that he was aware of our presence. Stepping hastily forward he said, in the high and vibrating tones of restrained passion:

"Helen, are you here?"

For a moment I thought she did not mean to answer, but knowing doubtless from experience the impossibility of deceiving him, she answered with a cheerful assent, dropping her hand as she did so from before my lips.

He heard the slight rustle which accompanied the movement, and a look I found it hard to comprehend flashed over his features, altering his expression so completely that he seemed another man.

"You have some one with you," he declared, advancing another step, but with none of the uncertainty which usually accompanies the movements of the blind. "Some dear friend," he went on, with an almost sarcastic emphasis and a forced smile that had little of gaiety in it.

The agitated and distressed blush which answered him could have but one interpretation. He suspected that her hand had been clasped in mine, and she perceived his thought and knew that I perceived it also.

Drawing herself up, she moved towards him, saying in a sweet womanly tone that to me spoke volumes:

"It is no friend, Constant, not even an acquaintance. The person whom I now present to you is an agent from the police. He is here upon a trivial errand which will be soon finished, when I will join you in your office."

I knew she was but taking a choice between two evils. That she would have saved her husband the knowledge of a detective's presence in the house, if her self-respect would have allowed it, but neither she nor I anticipated the effect which this presentation produced upon him.

"A police officer," he repeated, staring with his sightless eyes, as if, in his eagerness to see, he half hoped his lost sense would return. "He can have no trivial errand here; he has been sent by God himself to—"

"Let me speak for you," hastily interposed his wife, springing to his side and clasping his arm with a fervor that was equally expressive of appeal and command. Then turning to me, she explained: "Since Mr. Hasbrouck's unaccountable death, my husband has been laboring under an hallucination which I have only to mention for you to recognize its perfect absurdity. He thinks—oh! do not look like that, Constant; you know it is an hallucination which must vanish the moment we drag it into broad daylight—that he—he, the best man in all the world, was himself the assailant of Mr. Hasbrouck."

"Good God!"

"I say nothing of the impossibility of this being so," she went on in a fever of expostulation. "He is blind and could not have delivered such a shot even if he had desired to; besides, he had no weapon. But the inconsistency of the thing speaks for itself and should assure him that his mind is unbalanced and that he is merely suffering from a shock that was greater than we realized. He is a physician and has had many such instances in his own practice. Why, he was very much attached to Mr. Hasbrouck! They were the best of friends, and though he insists that he killed him, he cannot give any reason for the deed."

At these words the doctor's face grew stern, and he spoke like an automaton repeating some fearful lesson.

"I killed him. I went to his room and deliberately shot him. I had nothing against him, and my remorse is extreme. Arrest me and let me pay the penalty of my crime. It is the only way in which I can obtain peace."

Shocked beyond all power of self-control by this repetition of what she evidently considered the unhappy ravings of a madman, she let go his arm and turned upon me in frenzy.

"Convince him!" she cried. "Convince him by your questions that he never could have done this fearful thing."

I was laboring under great excitement myself, for I felt my youth against me in a matter of such tragic consequence. Besides, I agreed with her that he was in a distempered state of mind, and I hardly knew how to deal with one so fixed in his hallucination and with so much intelligence to support it. But the emergency was great, for he was holding out his wrists in the evident expectation of my taking him into instant custody; and the sight was killing his wife, who had sunk on the floor between us, in terror and anguish.

"You say you killed Mr. Hasbrouck," I began. "Where did you get your pistol and what did you do with it after you left his house?"

"My husband had no pistol; never had any pistol," put in Mrs. Zabriskie, with vehement assertion. "If I had seen him with such a weapon—"

"I threw it away. When I left the house, I cast it as far from me as possible, for I was frightened at what I had done, horribly frightened."

"No pistol was ever found," I answered, with a smile, forgetting for the moment that he could not see. "If such an instrument had been found in the street after a murder of such consequence it certainly would have been brought to the police."

"You forget that a good pistol is valuable property," he went on stolidly. "Some one came along before the general alarm was given and, seeing such a treasure lying on the sidewalk, picked it up and carried it off. Not being honest, he preferred to keep it to drawing the attention of the police upon himself."

"Hum, perhaps," said I; "but where did you get it? Surely you can tell where you procured such a weapon, if, as your wife intimates, you did not own one."

"I bought it that selfsame night of a friend; a friend whom I will not name, since he resides no longer in this country. I"—He paused; intense passion was in his face; he turned towards his wife, and a low cry escaped him, which made her look up in fear.

"I do not wish to go into any particulars," said he. "God forsook me, and I committed a horrible crime. When I am punished, perhaps peace will return to me and happiness to her. I would not wish her to suffer too long or too bitterly for my sin."

"Constant!" What love was in the cry! and what despair! It seemed to move him and turn his thoughts for a moment into a different channel.

"Poor child!" he murmured, stretching out his hands by an irresistible impulse towards her. But the change was but momentary, and he was soon again the stern and determined self-accuser. "Are you going to take me before a magistrate?" he asked. "If so, I have a few duties to perform which you are welcome to witness."

"I have no warrant," I said; "besides, I am scarcely the one to take such a responsibility upon myself. If, however, you persist in your declaration, I will communicate with my superiors, who will take such action as they think best."

"That will be still more satisfactory to me," said he; "for though I have many times contemplated giving myself up to the authorities, I have still much to do before I can leave my home and practise without injury to others. Good day; when you want me, you will find me here."

He was gone, and the poor young wife was left crouching on the floor alone. Pitying her shame and terror, I ventured to remark that it was not an uncommon thing for a man to confess to a crime he had never committed and assured her that the matter would be inquired into very carefully before any attempt was made upon his liberty.

She thanked me, and, slowly rising, tried to regain her equanimity; but the manner as well as the matter of her husband's self-condemnation was too overwhelming in its nature for her to recover readily from her emotions.

"I have long dreaded this," she acknowledged. "For months I have foreseen that he would make some rash communication or insane avowal. If I had dared, I would have consulted some physician about this hallucination of his; but he was so sane on other points that I hesitated to give my dreadful secret to the world. I kept hoping that time and his daily pursuits would have their effect and restore him to himself. But his illusion grows, and now I fear that nothing will ever convince him that he did not commit the deed of which he accuses himself. If he were not blind I would have more hope, but the blind have so much time for brooding."

"I think he had better be indulged in his fancies for the present," I ventured. "If he is laboring under an illusion it might be dangerous to cross him."

"If?" she echoed in an indescribable tone of amazement and

dread. "Can you for a moment harbor the idea that he has spoken the truth?"

"Madame," I returned, with something of the cynicism of my later years, "what caused you to give such an unearthly scream just before this murder was made known to the neighborhood?"

She stared, paled, and finally began to tremble, not, as I now believe, at the insinuation latent in my words, but at the doubts which my question aroused in her own breast.

"Did I?" she asked; then with a great burst of candor, which seemed inseparable from her nature, she continued: "Why do I try to mislead you or deceive myself? I did give a shriek just before the alarm was raised next door; but it was not from any knowledge I had of a crime having been committed, but because I unexpectedly saw before me my husband whom I supposed to be on his way to Poughkeepsie. He was looking very pale and strange, and for a moment I thought I was beholding his ghost. But he soon explained his appearance by saying that he had fallen from the train and had been only saved by a miracle from being dismembered; and I was just bemoaning his mishap and trying to calm him and myself, when that terrible shout was heard next door of 'Murder! murder!' Coming so soon after the shock he had himself experienced, it quite unnerved him, and I think we can date his mental disturbance from that moment. For he began almost immediately to take a morbid interest in the affair next door, though it was weeks, if not months, before he let a word fall of the nature of those you have just heard. Indeed it was not till I repeated to him some of the expressions he was continually letting fall in his sleep that he commenced to accuse himself of crime and talk of retribution."

"You say that your husband frightened you on that night by appearing suddenly at the door when you thought him on his way to Poughkeepsie. Is Dr. Zabriskie in the habit of thus going and coming alone at an hour so late as this must have been?"

"You forget that to the blind night is less full of perils than the day. Often and often has my husband found his way to his patients' houses alone after midnight; but on this especial evening he had Harry with him. Harry was his driver and always accompanied him when he went any distance."

"Well, then," said I, "all we have to do is to summon Harry and hear what he has to say concerning this affair. He surely will know whether or not his master went into the house next door."

"Harry has left us," she said. "Dr. Zabriskie has another driver now. Besides (I have nothing to conceal from you), Harry was not with him when he returned to the house that evening, or the doctor would not have been without his portmanteau till the next day. Something—I have never known what—caused them to separate, and that is why I have no answer to give the doctor when he accuses himself of committing a deed on that very night which is wholly out of keeping with every other act of his life."

"And have you never questioned Harry why they separated and why he allowed his master to come home alone after the shock he had received at the station?"

"I did not know there was any reason for doing so till long after he left us."

"And when did he leave?"

"That I do not remember. A few weeks or possibly a few days after that dreadful night."

"And where is he now?"

"Ah, that I have not the least means of knowing. But," she suddenly cried, "what do you want of Harry? If he did not follow Dr. Zabriskie to his own door, he could tell us nothing that would convince my husband that he is laboring under an illusion."

"But he might tell us something which would convince us that Dr. Zabriskie was not himself after the accident, that he—"

"Hush!" came from her lips in imperious tones. "I will not believe that he shot Mr. Hasbrouck, even if you prove him to have been insane at the time. How could he? My husband is blind. It would take a man of very keen sight to force himself into a house that was closed for the night and kill a man in the dark at one shot."

"Rather," cried a voice from the doorway, "it is only a blind man who could do this. Those who trust to eyesight must be able to catch some glimpse of the mark they aim at, and this room, as I have been told, was without a glimmer of light. But the blind trust to sound, and as Mr. Hasbrouck spoke—"

"Oh!" burst from the horrified wife, "is there no one to stop him when he speaks like that?"

318

II

When I related to my superiors the details of the foregoing interview, two of them coincided with the wife in thinking that Mr. Zabriskie was in an irresponsible condition of mind which made any statement of his questionable. But the third seemed disposed to argue the matter, and, casting me an inquiring look, seemed to ask what my opinion was on the subject. Answering him as if he had spoken, I gave my conclusion as follows: That whether insane or not, Dr. Zabriskie had fired the shot which terminated Mr. Hasbrouck's life.

It was the inspector's own idea, but it was not shared in by the others, one of whom had known the doctor for years. Accordingly they compromised by postponing all opinion till they had themselves interrogated the doctor, and I was detailed to bring him before them the next afternoon.

He came without reluctance, his wife accompanying him. In the short time which had elapsed between their leaving Lafayette Place and entering headquarters, I embraced the opportunity of observing them, and I found the study equally exciting and interesting. His face was calm but hopeless, and his eye, which should have shown a wild glimmer if there was truth in his wife's hypothesis, was dark and unfathomable, but neither frenzied nor uncertain. He spoke but once and listened to nothing, though now and then his wife moved as if to attract his attention, and once even stole her hand toward his, in the tender hope that he would feel its approach and accept her sympathy. But he was deaf as well as blind and sat wrapped up in thoughts which she, I know, would have given worlds to penetrate.

Her countenance was not without its mystery also. She showed in every lineament passionate concern and misery, and a deep tenderness from which the element of fear was not absent. But she, as well as he, betrayed that some misunderstanding, deeper than any I had previously suspected, drew its intangible veil between them and made the near proximity in which they sat, at once a heart-piercing delight and unspeakable pain. What was this misunderstanding? and what was the character of the fear that modified her every look of love in his direction? Her perfect indifference to my presence proved that it was not connected with the position in which he had put himself towards the police by his voluntary confession of crime, nor could I thus interpret the expression of frantic question which now and

319

then contracted her features, as she raised her eyes towards his sight-less orbs and strove to read, in his firm-set lips, the meaning of those assertions she could only ascribe to a loss of reason.

The stopping of the carriage seemed to awaken both from thoughts that separated rather than united them. He turned his face in her direction, and she, stretching forth her hand, prepared to lead him from the carriage, without any of that display of timidity which had been previously evident in her manner.

As his guide, she seemed to fear nothing; as his lover, everything.

"There is another and a deeper tragedy underlying the outward and obvious one," was my inward conclusion, as I followed them into the presence of the gentlemen awaiting them.

Dr. Zabriskie's appearance was a shock to those who knew him; so was his manner, which was calm, straightforward, and quietly determined.

"I shot Mr. Hasbrouck," was his steady affirmation, given without any show of frenzy or desperation. "If you ask me why I did it, I cannot answer; if you ask me how, I am ready to state all that I know concerning the matter."

"But, Dr. Zabriskie," interposed his friend, "the why is the most important thing for us to consider just now. If you really desire to convince us that you committed the dreadful crime of killing a totally inoffensive man, you should give us some reason for an act so opposed to all your instincts and general conduct."

But the doctor continued unmoved:

"I had no reason for murdering Mr. Hasbrouck. A hundred questions can elicit no other reply; you had better keep to the how."

A deep-drawn breath from his wife answered the looks of the three gentlemen to whom this suggestion was offered. "You see," that breath seemed to protest, "that he is not in his right mind."

I began to waver in my own opinion, and yet the intuition which has served me in cases as seemingly impenetrable as this bade me beware of following the general judgment.

"Ask him to inform you how he got into the house," I whispered to Inspector D——, who sat nearest me.

Immediately the inspector put the question I had suggested:

"By what means did you enter Mr. Hasbrouck's house at so late an hour as his murder occurred?"

The blind doctor's head fell forward on his breast, and he hesitated for the first and only time.

"You will not believe me," said he; "but the door was ajar when I came to it. Such things make crime easy; it is the only excuse I have to offer for this dreadful deed."

The front door of a respectable citizen's house ajar at half-past eleven at night. It was a statement that fixed in all minds the conviction of the speaker's irresponsibility. Mrs. Zabriskie's brow cleared, and her beauty became for a moment dazzling as she held out her hands in irrepressible relief towards those who were interrogating her husband. I alone kept my impassibility. A possible explanation of this crime had flashed like lightning across my mind; an explanation from which I inwardly recoiled, even while I was forced to consider it.

"Dr. Zabriskie," remarked the inspector, who was most friendly to him, "such old servants as those kept by Mr. Hasbrouck do not leave the front door ajar at twelve o'clock at night."

"Yet ajar it was," repeated the blind doctor, with quiet emphasis; "and finding it so, I went in. When I came out again, I closed it. Do you wish me to swear to what I say? If so, I am ready."

What could we reply? To see this splendid-looking man, hallowed by an affliction so great that in itself it called forth the compassion of the most indifferent, accusing himself of a cold-blooded crime, in tones that sounded dispassionate because of the will that forced their utterance, was too painful in itself for us to indulge in any unnecessary words. Compassion took the place of curiosity, and each and all of us turned involuntary looks of pity upon the young wife pressing so eagerly to his side.

"For a blind man," ventured one, "the assault was both deft and certain. Are you accustomed to Mr. Hasbrouck's house, that you found your way with so little difficulty to his bedroom?"

"I am accustomed—" he began.

But here his wife broke in with irrepressible passion:

"He is not accustomed to that house. He has never been beyond the first door. Why, why do you question him? Do you not see—"

His hand was on her lips.

"Hush!" he commanded. "You know my skill in moving about a house; how I sometimes deceive those who do not know me into believing that I can see, by the readiness with which I avoid obstacles and find my way even in strange and untried scenes. Do not try to make them think I am not in my right mind or you will drive me into the very condition you deprecate."

His face, rigid, cold and set looked like that of a mask. Hers, drawn with horror and filled with question that was fast taking the form of doubt, bespoke an awful tragedy from which more than one of us recoiled.

"Can you shoot a man dead without seeing him?" asked the superintendent, with painful effort.

"Give me a pistol and I will show you," was the quick reply.

A low cry came from the wife. In a drawer near to every one of us there lay a pistol, but no one moved to take it out. There was a look in the doctor's eye which made us fear to trust him with a pistol just then.

"We will accept your assurance that you possess a skill beyond that of most men," returned the superintendent. And beckoning me forward, he whispered: "This is a case for the doctors and not for the police. Remove him quietly and notify Dr. Southyard of what I say."

But Dr. Zabriskie, who seemed to have an almost supernatural acuteness of hearing, gave a violent start at this and spoke up for the first time with real passion in his voice:

"No, no, I pray you. I can bear anything but that. Remember, gentlemen, that I am blind; that I cannot see who is about me; that my life would be a torture if I felt myself surrounded by spies watching to catch some evidence of madness in me. Rather conviction at once, death, dishonor, and obloquy. These I have incurred. These I have brought upon myself by crime, but not this worse fate—oh! not this worse fate."

His passion was so intense and yet so confined within the bounds of decorum that we felt strangely impressed by it. Only the wife stood transfixed, with a dread growing in her heart, till her white, waxen visage seemed even more terrible to contemplate than his passion-distorted one.

"It is not strange that my wife thinks me demented," the doctor continued, as if afraid of the silence that answered him. "But it is your business to discriminate, and you should know a sane man when you see him."

Inspector D—— no longer hesitated.

"Very well," said he, "give us the least proof that your assertions are true, and we will lay your case before the prosecuting attorney."

"Proof? Is not a man's word—"

"No man's confession is worth much without some evidence to support it. In your case there is none. You cannot even produce the pistol with which you assert yourself to have committed the deed."

"True, true. I was frightened by what I had done, and the instinct of self-preservation led me to rid myself of the weapon in any way I could. But some one found this pistol; some one picked it up from the sidewalks of Lafayette Place on that fatal night. Advertise for it. Offer a reward. I will give you the money." Suddenly he appeared to realize how all this sounded. "Alas!" cried he, "I know the story seems improbable; all I say seems improbable; but it is not the probable things that happen in this life, but the improbable, as you should know, who every day dig deep into the heart of human affairs."

Were these the ravings of insanity? I began to understand the wife's terror.

"I bought the pistol," he went on, "of—alas! I cannot tell you his name. Everything is against me. I cannot adduce one proof; yet she, even she, is beginning to fear that my story is true. I know it by her silence, a silence that yawns between us like a deep and unfathomable gulf."

But at these words her voice rang out with passionate vehemence.

"No, no; it is false! I will never believe that your hands have been plunged in blood. You are my own pure-hearted Constant, cold, perhaps, and stern, but with no guilt upon your conscience, save in your own wild imagination."

"Helen, you are no friend to me," he declared, pushing her gently aside. "Believe me innocent but say nothing to lead these others to doubt my word."

And she said no more, but her looks spoke volumes.

The result was that he was not detained, though he prayed for instant commitment. He seemed to dread his own home and the surveillance to which he instinctively knew he would henceforth be subjected. To see him shrink from his wife's hand as she strove to lead him from the room was sufficiently painful; but the feeling thus aroused was nothing to that with which we observed the keen and agonized expectancy of his look as he turned and listened for the steps of the officer who followed him.

"I shall never again know whether or not I am alone," was his final observation as he left our presence.

* * * * * *

I said nothing to my superiors of the thoughts I had had while listening to the above interrogatories. A theory had presented itself to my mind which explained in some measure the mysteries of the doctor's conduct, but I wished for time and opportunity to test its reasonableness before submitting it to their higher judgment. And these seemed likely to be given me, for the inspectors continued divided in their opinion of the blind physician's guilt, and the district-attorney, when told of the affair, pooh-poohed it without mercy and declined to stir in the matter, unless some tangible evidence were forthcoming to substantiate the poor doctor's self-accusations.

"If guilty, why does he shrink from giving his motives," said he, "and if so anxious to go to the gallows, why does he suppress the very facts calculated to send him there? He is as mad as a March hare, and it is to an asylum he should go and not to jail."

In this conclusion I failed to agree with him, and as time wore on my suspicions took shape and finally ended in a fixed conviction. Dr. Zabriskie had committed the crime he avowed, but—let me proceed a little further with my story before I reveal what lies beyond that "but."

Notwithstanding Dr. Zabriskie's almost frenzied appeal for solitude, a man had been placed in surveillance over him in the shape of a young doctor skilled in the diseases of the brain. This man communicated more or less with the police, and one morning I received from him the following extracts from the diary he had been ordered to keep:

"The doctor is settling into a deep melancholy from which he tries to rise at times, but with only indifferent success. Yesterday he rode around to all his patients for the purpose of withdrawing his services on the plea of illness. But he still keeps his office open, and today I had the opportunity of witnessing his reception and treatment of the many sufferers who came to him for aid. I think he was conscious of my presence, though an attempt had been made to conceal it. For the listening look never left his face from the moment he entered the room, and once he rose and passed quickly from wall to wall, groping with outstretched hands into every nook and corner and barely escaping contact with the curtain behind which I was hidden. But if he suspected my presence, he showed no displeasure at it, wishing perhaps for a witness to his skill in the treatment of disease.

"And truly I never beheld a finer manifestation of practical insight in cases of a more or less baffling nature than I beheld in him today. He is certainly a most wonderful physician, and I feel bound to record that his mind is as clear for business as if no shadow had fallen upon it.

"Dr. Zabriskie loves his wife, but in a way that tortures both himself and her. If she is gone from the house he is wretched, and yet when she returns he often forbears to speak to her, or if he does speak, it is with a constraint that hurts her more than his silence. I was present when she came in today. Her step, which had been eager on the stairway, flagged as she approached the room, and he naturally noted the change and gave his own interpretation to it. His face, which had been very pale, flushed suddenly, and nervous trembling seized him, which he sought in vain to hide. But by the time her tall and beautiful figure stood in the doorway he was his usual self again in all but the expression of his eyes, which stared straight before him in agony of longing only to be observed in those who have once seen.

" 'Where have you been, Helen?' he asked, as, contrary to his wont, he moved to meet her.

" 'To my mother's, to Arnold & Constable's, and to the hospital, as you requested,' was her quick answer, made without faltering or embarrassment.

"He stepped still nearer and took her hand, and as he did so my physician's eye noted how his finger lay over her pulse in seeming unconsciousness.

" 'Nowhere else?' he queried.

"She smiled the saddest kind of smile and shook her head; then, remembering that he could not see this movement, she cried in a wistful tone:

" 'Nowhere else, Constant; I was too anxious to get back.'

"I expected him to drop her hand at this, but he did not; and his finger still rested on her pulse.

" 'And whom did you see while you were gone?' he continued.

"She told him, naming over several names.

" 'You must have enjoyed yourself,' was his cold comment, as he let go her hand and turned away. But his manner showed relief, and I could not but sympathize with the pitiable situation of a man who found himself forced to means like these for probing the heart of his young wife.

"Yet when I turned toward her I realized her position was but little happier than his. Tears are no strangers to her eyes, but those that welled up at this moment seemed to possess a bitterness that promised but little peace for her future. Yet she quickly dried them and busied herself with ministrations for his comfort.

"If I am any judge of woman, Helen Zabriskie is superior to most of her sex. That her husband mistrusts her is evident, but whether this is the result of the stand she has taken in his regard, or only a manifestation of dementia, I have as yet been unable to determine. I dread to leave them alone together, and yet when I presume to suggest that she should be on her guard in her interviews with him, she smiles very placidly and tells me that nothing would give her greater joy than to see him lift his hand against her, for that would argue that he is not accountable for his deeds or for his assertions.

"Yet it would be a grief to see her injured by this passionate and unhappy man.

"You have said that you wanted all the details I could give; so I feel bound to say that Dr. Zabriskie tries to be considerate of his wife, though he often fails in the attempt. When she offers herself as his guide or assists him in his mail or performs any of the many acts of kindness by which she continually manifests her sense of his affliction, he thanks her with courtesy and often with kindness; yet I know she would willingly exchange all his set phrases for one fond embrace or impulsive smile of affection. That he is not in the full possession of his faculties would be too much to say, and yet upon what other hypothesis can we account for the inconsistencies of his conduct?

"I have before me two visions of mental suffering. At noon I passed the office door, and, looking within, saw the figure of Dr. Zabriskie seated in his great chair, lost in thought or deep in those memories which make an abyss in one's consciousness. His hands, which were clenched, rested upon the arms of his chair, and in one of them I detected a woman's glove, which I had no difficulty in recognizing as one of the pair worn by his wife this morning. He held it as a tiger might hold his prey or as a miser his gold, but his set features and sightless eyes betrayed that a conflict of emotions was raging within him, among which tenderness had but little share.

"Though alive, as he usually is, to every sound, he was too absorbed at this moment to notice my presence, though I had taken no pains to approach quietly. I therefore stood for a full minute watching him, till an irresistible sense of shame of thus spying upon a blind man in his moments of secret anguish seized upon me and I turned away. But not before I saw his features relax in a storm of passionate feeling, as he rained kisses after kisses on the senseless kid he had so long held in his motionless grasp. Yet when an hour later he entered the dining room on his wife's arm, there was nothing in his manner to show that he had in any way changed in his attitude towards her.

"The other picture was more tragic still. I have no business with Mrs. Zabriskie's affairs; but as I passed upstairs to my room an hour ago, I caught a fleeting vision of her tall form, with the arms thrown up over her head in a paroxysm of feeling which made her as oblivious to my presence as her husband had been several hours before. Were the words that escaped her lips, 'Thank God we have no children!' or was this exclamation suggested to me by the passion and unrestrained impulse of her action?"

* * * * * *

Side by side with these lines, I, Ebenezer Gryce, placed the following extracts from my own diary:

"Watched the Zabriskie mansion for five hours this morning, from the second story window of an adjoining hotel. Saw the doctor when he drove away on his round of visits and saw him when he returned. A colored man accompanied him.

"Today I followed Mrs. Zabriskie. I had a motive for this, the nature of which I think it wisest not to divulge. She went first to a house in Washington Place, where I am told her mother lives. Here she stayed for some time, after which she drove down to Canal Street, where she did some shopping, and later stopped at the hospital, into which I took the liberty of following her. She seemed to know many there and passed from cot to cot with a smile in which I alone discerned the sadness of a broken heart. When she left, I left also, without having learned anything beyond the fact that Mrs. Zabriskie is one who does her duty in sorrow as in happiness. A rare and trustworthy woman I should say, and yet her husband does not trust her. Why?

"I have spent this day in accumulating details in regard to Dr. and Mrs. Zabriskie's life previous to the death of Mr. Hasbrouck. I learned from sources it would be unwise to quote just here that Mrs. Zabriskie had not lacked enemies ready to charge her with coquetry; that while she had never sacrificed her dignity in public, more than one person had been heard to declare that Dr. Zabriskie was fortunate in being blind, since the sight of his wife's beauty would have but poorly compensated him for the pain he would have suffered in seeing how that beauty was admired.

"That all gossip is more or less tinged with exaggeration I have no doubt; yet when a name is mentioned in connection with such stories, there is usually some truth at the bottom of them. And a name is mentioned in this case, though I do not think it worth my while to repeat it here; and loth as I am to recognize the fact, it is a name that carries with it doubts that might easily account for the husband's jealousy. True, I have found no one who dares to hint that she still continues to attract attention or to bestow smiles in any direction save where they legally belong. For since a certain memorable night which we all know, neither Dr. Zabriskie nor his wife have been seen save in their own domestic circle, and it is not into such scenes that this serpent, of which I have spoken, ever intrudes, nor is it in places of sorrow or suffering that his smile shines or his fascinations flourish.

"And so one portion of my theory is proved to be sound. Dr. Zabriskie is jealous of his wife: whether with good cause or bad I am not prepared to decide; for her present attitude, clouded as it is by the tragedy in which she and her husband are both involved, must differ very much from that which she held when her life was unshadowed by doubt and her admirers could be counted by the score.

"I have just found out where Harry is. As he is in service some miles up the river, I shall have to be absent from my post for several hours, but I consider the game well worth the candle.

"Light at last. I have seen Harry, and, by means known only to the police, have succeeded in making him talk. His story is substantially this: That on the night so often mentioned he packed his master's portmanteau at eight o'clock and at ten called a carriage and rode with the doctor to the Twenty-ninth Street station. He was told to buy tickets for Poughkeepsie, where his master had been in consultation, and, having done this, hurried back to join his master on the platform. They had walked together as far as the cars, and Dr. Zabriskie was just stepping on to the train when a man pushed himself hurriedly between them and whispered something into his master's ear, which caused him to fall back and lose his footing. Dr. Zabriskie's body slid half under the car, but he was withdrawn before any harm was done, though the cars gave a lurch at the moment, which must have frightened him exceedingly, for his face was white when he rose to his feet, and when Harry offered to assist him again on to the train, he refused to go and said he would return home and not attempt to ride to Poughkeepsie that night.

"The gentleman, whom Harry now saw to be Mr. Stanton, an intimate friend of Dr. Zabriskie, smiled very queerly at this, and taking the doctor's arm led him away to a carriage. Harry naturally followed them, but the doctor, hearing his steps, turned and bade him, in a very peremptory tone, to take the omnibus home, and then, as if on second thought, told him to go to Poughkeepsie in his stead and explain to the people there that he was too shaken up by his misstep to do his duty and that he would be with them next morning. This seemed strange to Harry, but he had no reasons for disobeying his master's orders and so rode to Poughkeepsie. But the doctor did not follow him the next day; on the contrary, he telegraphed for him to return and when he got back dismissed him with a month's wages. This ended Harry's connection with the Zabriskie family.

"A simple story bearing out what the wife has already told us; but it furnishes a link which may prove invaluable. Mr. Stanton, whose first name is Theodore, knows the reason why Dr. Zabriskie returned home on the night of the seventeenth of July, 1851. Mr. Stanton, consequently, I must see, and this shall be my business tomorrow.

"Checkmate! Theodore Stanton is not in this country. Though this points him out as the man from whom Dr. Zabriskie bought the pistol, it does not facilitate my work, which is becoming more and more difficult.

"Mr. Stanton's whereabouts are not even known to his most intimate friends. He sailed from this country most unexpectedly on the eighteenth of July a year ago, which was the day after the murder of Mr. Hasbrouck. It looks like a flight, especially as he has failed to maintain open communication even with his relatives. Was he the man who shot Mr. Hasbrouck? No; but he was the man who put the pistol in Dr. Zabriskie's hand that night, and, whether he did this with purpose or not, was evidently so alarmed at the catastrophe which followed that he took the first outgoing steamer to Europe. So far, all is clear, but there are mysteries yet to be solved, which will require my utmost tact. What if I should seek out the gentleman with whose name that of Mrs. Zabriskie has been linked and see if I can in any way connect him with Mr. Stanton or the events of that night?

"Eureka! I have discovered that Mr. Stanton cherished a mortal hatred for the gentleman above mentioned. It was a covert feeling, but no less deadly on that account; and while it never led him into any extravagances, it was of force sufficient to account for many a secret misfortune which happened to that gentleman. Now, if I can prove he was the Mephistopheles who whispered insinuations into the ear of our blind Faust, I may strike a fact that will lead me out of this maze.

"But how can I approach secrets so delicate without compromising the woman I feel bound to respect, if only for the devoted love she manifests for her unhappy husband!

"I shall have to appeal to Joe Smithers. This is something which I always hate to do, but as long as he will take money, and as long as he is fertile in resources for obtaining the truth from people I am myself unable to reach, so long must I make use of his cupidity and his genius. He is an honorable fellow in one way and never retails as gossip what he acquires for our use. How will he proceed in this case, and by what tactics will he gain the very delicate information which we need? I own that I am curious to see.

"I shall really have to put down at length the incidents of this night. I always knew that Joe Smithers was invaluable to the police, but I really did not know he possessed talents of so high an order.

He wrote me this morning that he had succeeded in getting Mr. T——'s promise to spend the evening with him and advised me that, if I desired to be present also, his own servant would not be at home and that an opener of bottles would be required.

"As I was very anxious to see Mr. T—— with my own eyes, I accepted the invitation to play the spy upon a spy and went at the proper hour to Mr. Smithers' rooms, which are in the University Building. I found them picturesque in the extreme. Piles of books stacked here and there to the ceiling made nooks and corners which could be quite shut off by a couple of old pictures that were set into movable frames that swung out or in at the whim or convenience of the owner.

"As I liked the dark shadows cast by these pictures, I pulled them both out and made such other arrangements as appeared likely to facilitate the purpose I had in view; then I sat down and waited for the two gentlemen who were expected to come in together.

"They arrived almost immediately, whereupon I rose and played my part with all necessary discretion. While ridding Mr. T—— of his overcoat, I stole a look at his face. It is not a handsome one, but it boasts of a gay, devil-may-care expression which doubtless makes it dangerous to many women, while his manners are especially attractive and his voice the richest and most persuasive that I have ever heard. I contrasted him, almost against my will, with Dr. Zabriskie and decided that with most women the former's undoubted fascinations of speech and bearing would outweigh the latter's great beauty and mental endowments; but I doubted if they would with her.

"The conversation which immediately began was brilliant but desultory, for Mr. Smithers, with an airy lightness for which he is remarkable, introduced topic after topic, perhaps for the purpose of showing off Mr. T——'s versatility and perhaps for the deeper and more sinister purpose of shaking the kaleidoscope of talk so thoroughly that the real topic which we were met to discuss should not make an undue impression on the mind of his guest.

"Meanwhile one, two, three bottles passed, and I saw Joe Smithers' eye grow calmer and that of Mr. T—— more brilliant and more uncertain. As the last bottle showed signs of failing, Joe cast me a meaning glance, and the real business of the evening began.

331

"I shall not attempt to relate the half dozen failures which Joe made in endeavoring to elicit the facts we were in search of, without arousing the suspicion of his visitor. I am only going to relate the successful attempt. They had been talking now for some two hours, and I, who had long before been waved from their immediate presence, was hiding my curiosity and growing excitement behind one of the pictures, when suddenly I heard Joe say:

" 'He has the most remarkable memory I ever met. He can tell to a day when any notable event occurred.'

" 'Pshaw!' answered his companion, who, by-the-bye, was known to pride himself upon his own memory for dates, 'I can state where I went and what I did on every day in the year. That may not embrace what you call "notable events," but the memory required is all the more remarkable, is it not?'

" 'Pooh!' was his friend's provoking reply, 'you are bluffing, Ben; I will never believe that.'

"Mr. T——, who had passed by this time into that state of intoxication which makes persistence in an assertion a duty as well as a pleasure, threw back his head and, as the wreaths of smoke rose in airy spirals from his lips, reiterated his statement and offered to submit to any test of his vaunted powers which the other might dictate.

" 'You have a diary'—began Joe.

" 'Which is at home,' completed the other.

" 'Will you allow me to refer to it tomorrow, if I am suspicious of the accuracy of your recollections?'

" 'Undoubtedly,' returned the other.

" 'Very well, then, I will wager you a cool fifty that you cannot tell where you were between the hours of ten and eleven on a certain night which I will name.'

" 'Done!' cried the other, bringing out his pocketbook and laying it on the table before him.

"Joe followed his example and then summoned me.

" 'Write a date down here,' he commanded, pushing a piece of paper towards me, with a look as keen as the flash of a blade. 'Any date, man,' he added, as I appeared to hesitate in the embarrassment I thought natural under the circumstances. 'Put down day, month, and year, only don't go too far back; no farther than two years.'

"Smiling with the air of a flunkey admitted to the sports of his superiors, I wrote a line and laid it before Mr. Smithers, who at once pushed it with a careless gesture towards his companion. You can, of course, guess the date I made use of: July 17, 1851. Mr. T——, who evidently looked upon this matter as mere play, flushed scarlet as he read these words and for one instant looked as if he had rather flee our presence than answer Joe Smithers' nonchalant glance of inquiry.

" 'I have given my word and will keep it,' he said at last, but with a look in my direction that sent me reluctantly back to my retreat. 'I don't suppose you want names,' he went on, 'that is, if anything I have to tell is of a delicate nature?'

" 'Oh, no,' answered the other, 'only facts and places.' "

" 'I don't think places are necessary either,' he returned. 'I will tell you what I did and that must serve you. I did not promise to give number and street.'

" 'Well, well,' Joe exclaimed; 'earn your fifty, that is all. Show that you remember where you were on the night of'—and with an admirable show of indifference he pretended to consult the paper between them—'the seventeenth of July, 1851, and I shall be satisfied.'

" 'I was at the club for one thing,' said Mr. T——; 'then I went to see a lady friend, where I stayed till eleven. She wore a blue muslin—What is that?'

"I had betrayed myself by a quick movement which sent a glass tumbler to the floor. Helen Zabriskie had worn a blue muslin on that same night. I had noted it when I stood on the balcony watching her and her husband.

" 'That noise?' It was Joe who was speaking. 'You don't know Reuben as well as I do or you wouldn't ask. It is his practise, I am sorry to say, to accentuate his pleasure in draining my bottles by dropping a glass at every third one.'

"Mr. T—— went on.

" 'She was a married woman and I thought she loved me; but—and this is the greatest proof I can offer you that I am giving you a true account of that night—she had not had the slightest idea of the extent of my passion and only consented to see me at all because she thought, poor thing, that a word from her would set me straight and rid her of attentions that were fast becoming obnoxious. A sorry figure for a fellow to cut who has not been without his triumphs; but you caught me on the most detestable date in my calendar, and—'

"There is where he stopped being interesting, so I will not waste time by quoting further. And now what reply shall I make when Joe Smithers asks me double his usual price, as he will be sure to do, next time? Has he not earned an advance? I really think so.

"I have spent the whole day in weaving together the facts I have gleaned and the suspicions I have formed into a consecutive whole likely to present my theory in a favorable light to my superiors. But just as I thought myself in shape to meet their inquiries, I received an immediate summons into their presence, where I was given a duty to perform of so extraordinary and unexpected a nature that it effectually drove from my mind all my own plans for the elucidation of the Zabriskie mystery.

"This was nothing more nor less than to take charge of a party of people who were going to the Jersey heights for the purpose of testing Dr. Zabriskie's skill with a pistol."

III

The cause of this sudden move was soon explained to me. Mrs. Zabriskie, anxious to have an end put to the present condition of affairs, had begged for a more rigid examination into her husband's state. This being accorded, a strict and impartial inquiry had taken place, with a result not unlike that which followed the first one. Three out of his four interrogators judged him insane and could not be moved from their opinion, though opposed by the verdict of the young expert who had been living in the house with him. Dr. Zabriskie seemed to read their thoughts, and, showing extreme agitation, begged as before for an opportunity to prove his sanity by showing his skill in shooting. This time a disposition was evinced to grant his request, which Mrs. Zabriskie no sooner perceived than she added her supplications to his that the question might be thus settled.

A pistol was accordingly brought; but at sight of it her courage failed, and she changed her plea to an entreaty that the experiment should be postponed till the next day and should then take place in the woods away from the sight and hearing of needless spectators.

Though it would have been much wiser to have ended the matter there and then, the superintendent was prevailed upon to listen to her entreaties, and thus it was that I came to be a spectator, if not a participator, in the final scene of this most somber drama.

There are some events which impress the human mind so deeply that their memory mingles with all after-experiences. Though I have made it a rule to forget as soon as possible the tragic episodes into which I am constantly plunged, there is one scene in my life which will not depart at my will; and that is the sight which met my eyes from the bow of the small boat in which Dr. Zabriskie and his wife were rowed over to Jersey on that memorable afternoon.

Though it was by no means late in the day, the sun was already sinking, and the bright red glare which filled the heavens and shone full upon the faces of the half dozen persons before me added much to the tragic nature of the scene, though we were far from comprehending its full significance.

The doctor sat with his wife in the stern, and it was upon their faces my glance was fixed. The glare shone luridly on his sightless eyeballs, and as I noticed his unwinking lids I realized as never before what it was to be blind in the midst of sunshine. Her eyes, on the contrary, were lowered, but there was a look of hopeless misery in her colorless face which made her appearance infinitely pathetic, and I felt confident that if he could only have seen her, he would not have maintained the cold and unresponsive manner which chilled the words on her lips and made all advance on her part impossible.

On the seat in front of them sat the inspector and a doctor, and from some quarter, possibly from under the inspector's coat, there came the monotonous ticking of a small clock, which, I had been told, was to serve as a target for the blind man's aim.

This ticking was all I heard, though the noise and bustle of a great traffic were pressing upon us on every side. And I am sure it was all she heard, as, with hand pressed to her heart and eyes fixed on the opposite shore, she waited for the event which was to determine whether the man she loved was a criminal or only a being afflicted of God and worthy of her unceasing care and devotion.

As the sun cast its last scarlet gleam over the water, the boat grounded, and it fell to my lot to assist Mrs. Zabriskie up the bank. As I did so, I allowed myself to say: "I am your friend, Mrs. Zabriskie," and was astonished to see her tremble and turn toward me with a look like that of a frightened child.

But there was always this characteristic blending in her countenance of the childlike and the severe, such as may so often be seen in the faces of nuns, and beyond an added pang of pity for this beautiful but afflicted woman, I let the moment pass without giving it the weight it perhaps demanded.

"The doctor and his wife had a long talk last night," was whispered in my ear as we wound our way along into the woods. I turned and perceived at my side the expert physician, portions of whose diary I have already quoted. He had come by another boat.

"But it did not seem to heal whatever breach lies between them," he proceeded. Then in a quick, curious tone, he asked: "Do you believe this attempt on his part is likely to prove anything but a farce?"

"I believe he will shatter the clock to pieces with his first shot," I answered and could say no more, for we had already reached the ground which had been selected for this trial at arms, and the various members of the party were being placed in their several positions.

The doctor, to whom light and darkness were alike, stood with his face towards the western glow, and at his side were grouped the inspector and the two physicians. On the arm of one of the latter hung Dr. Zabriskie's overcoat, which he had taken off as soon as he had reached the field.

Mrs. Zabriskie stood at the other end of the opening, near a tall stump, upon which it had been decided that the clock should be placed when the moment came for the doctor to show his skill. She had been accorded the privilege of setting the clock on this stump, and I saw it shining in her hand as she paused for a moment to glance back at the circle of gentlemen who were awaiting her movements. The hands of the clock stood at five minutes to five, though I scarcely noted the fact at the time, for her eyes were on mine, and as she passed me she spoke:

"If he is not himself, he cannot be trusted. Watch him carefully and see that he does no mischief to himself or others. Be at his right hand and stop him if he does not handle his pistol properly."

I promised, and she passed on, setting the clock upon the stump and immediately drawing back to a suitable distance at the right, where she stood, wrapped in her long, dark cloak, quite alone. Her face shone ghastly white, even in its environment of snow-covered boughs which surrounded her, and, noting this, I wished the minutes fewer between the present moment and the hour of five, at which he was to draw the trigger.

"Dr. Zabriskie," quoted the inspector, "we have endeavored to make this trial a perfectly fair one. You are to have one shot at a small clock which has been placed within a suitable distance and which you are expected to hit, guided only by the sound which it will make in striking the hour of five. Are you satisfied with the arrangement?"

"Perfectly. Where is my wife?"

"On the other side of the field, some ten paces from the stump upon which the clock is fixed."

He bowed, and his face showed satisfaction.

"May I expect the clock to strike soon?"

"In less than five minutes," was the answer.

"Then let me have the pistol; I wish to become acquainted with its size and weight."

We glanced at each other, then across at her.

She made a gesture; it was one of acquiescence.

Immediately the inspector placed the weapon in the blind man's hand. It was at once apparent that the doctor understood the instrument, and my last doubt vanished as to the truth of all he had told us.

"Thank God I am blind this hour and cannot see her," fell unconsciously from his lips; then, before the echo of these words had left my ears, he raised his voice and observed calmly enough, considering that he was about to prove himself a criminal in order to save himself from being thought a madman.

"Let no one move. I must have my ears free for catching the first stroke of the clock." And he raised the pistol before him.

There was a moment of torturing suspense and deep, unbroken silence. My eyes were on him, and so I did not watch the clock, but suddenly I was moved by some irresistible impulse to note how Mrs. Zabriskie was bearing herself at this critical moment, and, casting a hurried glance in her direction, I perceived her tall figure swaying from side to side, as if under an intolerable strain of feeling. Her eyes were on the clock, the hands of which seemed to creep with snail-like pace along the dial, when unexpectedly, and a full minute before the minute hand had reached the stroke of five, I caught a movement on her part, saw the flash of something round and white show for an instant against the darkness of her cloak, and was about to shriek warning to the doctor, when the shrill, quick stroke of a clock rang out on the frosty air, followed by the ping and flash of a pistol.

A sound of shattered glass, followed by a suppressed cry, told us that the bullet had struck the mark, but before we could move, or rid our eyes of the smoke which the wind had blown into our faces, there came another sound which made our hair stand on end and sent the blood back in terror to our hearts. Another clock was striking, the clock which we now perceived was still standing upright on the stump where Mrs. Zabriskie had placed it.

Whence came the clock, then, which had struck before the time and had been shattered for its pains? One quick look told us. On the ground, ten paces at the right, lay Helen Zabriskie, a broken clock at her side, and in her breast a bullet which was fast sapping the life from her sweet eyes.

We had to tell him, there was such pleading in her looks; and never shall I forget the scream that rang from his lips as he realized the truth. Breaking from our midst, he rushed forward and fell at her feet as if guided by some supernatural instinct.

"Helen," he shrieked; "what is this? Were not my hands dyed deep enough in blood that you should make me answerable for your life also?"

Her eyes were closed, but she opened them. Looking long and steadily at his agonized face, she faltered forth:

"It is not you who have killed me; it is your crime. Had you been innocent of Mr. Hasbrouck's death, your bullet would never have found my heart. Did you think I could survive the proof that you had killed that good man?"

"I—I did it unwittingly. I—"

"Hush!" she commanded, with an awful look, which, happily, he could not see. "I had another motive. I wished to prove to you, even at the cost of my life, that I loved you, had always loved you, and not—"

It was now his turn to silence her. His hand crept over her lips, and his despairing face turned itself blindly towards us.

"Go!" he cried; "leave us! Let me take a last farewell of my dying wife, without listeners or spectators."

Consulting the eye of the physician who stood beside me, and seeing no hope in it, I fell slowly back. The others followed, and the doctor was left alone with his wife. From the distant position we took, we saw her arms creep round his neck, saw her head fall confidingly on his breast, then silence settled upon them and upon all nature, the gathering twilight deepening, till the last glow disappeared from the heavens above and from the circle of leafless trees which enclosed this tragedy from the outside world.

But at last there came a stir, and Dr. Zabriskie, rising before us, with the dead body of his wife held closely to his breast, confronted us with a countenance so rapturous that he looked like a man transfigured.

"I will carry her to the boat," said he. "Not another hand shall touch her. She was my true wife, my true wife!" And he towered into an attitude of such dignity and passion that for a moment he took on heroic proportions and we forgot that he had just proved himself to have committed a cold-blooded and ghastly crime.

*   *   *   *   *   *

The stars were shining when we again took our seats in the boat; and if the scene of our crossing to Jersey was impressive, what shall be said of that of our return?

The doctor, as before, sat in the stern, an awesome figure, upon which the moon shone with a white radiance that seemed to lift his face out of the surrounding darkness and set it, like an image of frozen horror, before our eyes. Against his breast he held the form of his dead wife, and now and then I saw him stoop as if he were listening for some tokens of life at her set lips. Then he would lift himself again, with hopelessness stamped upon his features, only to lean forward in renewed hope that was again destined to disappointment.

The inspector and the accompanying physician had taken seats at the bow, and unto me had been assigned the special duty of watching over the doctor. This I did from a low seat in front of him. I was therefore so close that I heard his laboring breath, and, though my heart was full of awe and compassion, I could not prevent myself from bending towards him and saying these words:

"Dr. Zabriskie, the mystery of your crime is no longer a mystery to me. Listen and see if I do not understand your temptation and how you, a conscientious and God-fearing man, came to slay your innocent neighbor.

"A friend of yours, or so he called himself, had for a long time filled your ears with tales tending to make you suspicious of your wife and jealous of a certain man whom I will not name. You knew that your friend had a grudge against this man and so for many months turned a deaf ear to his insinuations. But finally some change which you detected in your wife's bearing or conversation roused your own suspicions, and you began to doubt if all was false that came to your ears and to curse your blindness, which in a measure rendered you helpless. The jealous fever grew and had risen to a high point, when one night—a memorable night—this friend met you just as you were leaving town and with cruel craft whispered in your ear that the man you hated was even then with your wife and that if you would return at once to your home you would find him in her company.

"The demon that lurks at the heart of all men, good or bad, thereupon took complete possession of you, and you answered this false friend by saying that you would not return without a pistol. Whereupon he offered to take you to his house and give you his. You consented, and, getting rid of your servant by sending him to Poughkeepsie with your excuses, you entered a coach with your friend.

"You say you bought the pistol, and perhaps you did, but, however that may be, you left his house with it in your pocket and, declining companionship, walked home, arriving at the Colonnade a little before midnight.

"Ordinarily you have no difficulty in recognizing your own doorstep. But, being in a heated frame of mind, you walked faster than usual and so passed your own house and stopped at that of Mr. Hasbrouck, one door beyond. As the entrances of these houses are all alike, there was but one way in which you could have made yourself sure that you had reached your own dwelling, and that was by feeling for the doctor's sign at the side of the door. But you never thought of that. Absorbed in dreams of vengeance, your sole impulse was to enter by the quickest means possible. Taking out your night-key, you thrust it into the lock. It fitted, but it took strength to turn it, so much strength that the key was bent and twisted by the effort. But this incident, which would have attracted your attention at another time, was lost upon you at this moment. An entrance had been effected, and you were in too excited a frame of mind to notice at what cost or to detect the small differences apparent in the atmosphere and furnishings of the two houses—trifles which would have arrested your attention under other circumstances and made you pause before the upper floor had been reached.

"It was while going up the stairs that you took out your pistol so that by the time you arrived at the front-room door you held it ready cocked and drawn in your hand. For, being blind, you feared escape on the part of your victim and so waited for nothing but the sound of a man's voice before firing. When, therefore, the unfortunate Mr. Hasbrouck, roused by this sudden intrusion, advanced with an exclamation of astonishment, you pulled the trigger, killing him on the spot. It must have been immediately upon his fall that you recognized some word he uttered, or from some contact you may have had with your surroundings, that you were in the wrong house and had killed the wrong man; for you cried out, in evident remorse, 'God what have I done!' and fled without approaching your victim.

"Descending the stairs, you rushed from the house, closing the front door behind you and regaining your own without being seen. But here you found yourself baffled in your attempted escape by two things. First, by the pistol you still held in your hand, and secondly, by the fact that the key upon which you depended for entering your own door was so twisted out of shape that you knew it would be useless for you to attempt to use it. What did you do in this emergency? You have already told us, though the story seemed so improbable at the time, you found nobody to believe it but myself. The pistol you flung far away from you down the pavement, from which, by one of those rare chances which sometimes happen in this world, it was presently picked up by some late passer-by of more or less doubtful character. The door offered less of an obstacle than you anticipated;

341

for when you turned to it again you found it, if I am not greatly mistaken, ajar, left so, as we have reason to believe, by one who had gone out of it but a few minutes before in a state which left him but little master of his actions. It was this fact which provided you with an answer when you were asked how you succeeded in getting into Mr. Hasbrouck's house after the family had retired for the night.

"Astonished at the coincidence, but hailing with gladness the deliverance which it offered, you went in and ascended at once into your wife's presence; and it was from her lips, and not from those of Mrs. Hasbrouck, that the cry arose which startled the neighborhood and prepared men's minds for the tragic words which were shouted a moment later from the next house.

"But she who uttered the scream knew of no tragedy save that which was taking place in her own breast. She had just repulsed a dastardly suitor, and, seeing you enter so unexpectedly in a state of unaccountable horror and agitation, was naturally stricken with dismay and thought she saw your ghost or what was worse, a possible avenger; while you, having failed to kill the man you sought and having killed a man you esteemed, let no surprise on her part lure you into any dangerous self-betrayal. You strove instead to soothe her, and even attempted to explain the excitement under which you labored, by an account of your narrow escape at the station, till the sudden alarm from next door distracted her attention and sent both your thoughts and hers in a different direction. Not till conscience had fully awakened and the horror of your act had had time to tell upon your sensitive nature, did you breathe forth those vague confessions, which, not being supported by the only explanations which would have made them credible, led her as well as the police to consider you affected in your mind. Your pride as a man and your consideration for her as a woman kept you silent, but did not keep the worm from preying upon your heart.

"Am I not correct in my surmises, Dr. Zabriskie, and is not this the true explanation of your crime?"

With a strange look, he lifted up his face.

"Hush!" said he; "you will awaken her. See how peacefully she sleeps! I should not like to have her awakened now, she is so tired, and I—I have not watched over her as I should."

Appalled at his gesture, his look, his tone, I drew back, and for a few minutes no sound was to be heard but the steady dip-dip of the oars and the lap-lap of the waters against the boat. Then there came a quick uprising, the swaying before me of something dark and tall and threatening, and before I could speak or move or even stretch forth my hands to stay him, the seat before me was empty and darkness had filled the place where but an instant previous he had sat, a fearsome figure, erect and rigid as a sphinx.

What little moonlight there was served to show us a few rising bubbles, marking the spot where the unfortunate man had sunk with his much-loved burden. We could not save him. As the widening circles fled farther and farther out, the tide drifted us away, and we lost the spot which had seen the termination of one of earth's saddest tragedies.

The bodies were never recovered. The police reserved to themselves the right of withholding from the public the real facts which made this catastrophe an awful remembrance to those who witnessed it. A verdict of accidental death by drowning answered all purposes and saved the memory of the unfortunate pair from such calumny as might have otherwise assailed it. It was the least we could do for two beings whom circumstances had so greatly afflicted.

STUDY NOTES

1. Comment on whether the clearest and fullest portrayal of character in "The Doctor, His Wife, and the Clock" is of the sleuth, a practice that often appears in detective stories.

2. Supporting somewhat the criticism sometimes offered that Anna Katharine Green's characterizations are often artificial, show that in this story the main method of character delineation is subjective.

3. Explain why this story is more interesting for plot than for characterization.

4. Give reasons for classifying Ebenezer Gryce as a detective of the keenly intellectual and deductive type.

5. Point out the activities of Gryce in his inductive investigation of Dr. Zabriskie's crime.

6. What evidence does the story present that the ability of the police who seek to solve the mystery of Hasbrouck's murder is inferior to that of Gryce?

7. Mention whatever foreshadowing of the solution you can discover.

343

8. Through what physical features and overt actions do the emotions of Dr. and Mrs. Zabriskie express themselves?

9. Justify your position as to whether the motive of Dr. Zabriskie and his method in the committing of the murder are probable.

10. Point out the use of suspense and surprise in this story.

11. State the purposes of the dialogue and whether it seems natural and generally effective.

12. List the chief deductions revealed in the detective's explanation to the criminal himself.

WAIT FOR ME DOWNSTAIRS [1]
(1940)

CORNELL WOOLRICH

SHE WAS always the last one out, even on the nights I came around to pick her up—that was another thing that burned me up. Not with her of course, but with her job there. Well, she was on the last leg of it now, it would be over with pretty soon. We weren't going to be one of those couples where the wife kept on working after the marriage. She'd already told them she was leaving anyway, so it was all settled. I didn't blame her for hanging on to the very end. The couple of extra weeks pay would come in handy for a lot of little this-ems and that-ems that a girl about to settle down always likes to buy herself (knowing she's going to have a tough time getting them afterwards). But what got me was, why did she always have to be the last one out?

I picketed the doorway, while the cave-dwellers streamed out all around me. Everyone but her. Back and forth and back and forth; all I needed was a "Don't Patronize" sign and a spiel. Finally I even saw the slave-driver she worked for come out, but still no her. He passed by without knowing me, but even if he had he wouldn't have given me any sunny smiles.

And then finally she came—and the whole world faded out around us and we were just alone on the crowded sidewalk. I've heard it called love.

She was very good to look at, which was why I'd waited until I was twenty-five and met her. Here's how she went: first a lot of gold all beaten up into a froth and poured over her head and allowed to set there in crinkly little curls. Then a pair of eyes that—I don't know how to say it. You were in danger of drowning if you looked into them too deep, but, boy, was drowning a pleasure. Yes, blue. And then a mouth with real lines. Not one of those things all smeared over with red jam.

She had about everything just right, and believe me I was going to throw away the sales-slip and not return the merchandise once it got up to my house.

For trimmings, a dark-blue skirt and a short little jacket that flared out from her shoulders, and a kind of cockeyed tam o'shanter. And a package. I didn't like the looks of that package.

I told her so the minute I stepped up and took off my hat, while she was still looking down the other way for me. "What's that?"

She said: "Oh, Kenny, been waiting long? I hurried up all I could. This? Oh, just a package. I promised His Nibs I'd leave it at a flat on Martine Street on my way home."

"But you're not going home. I've got two ducats for 'Heavens-abustin,' and I was gonna take you to Rafft's for dinner first; I even brought a clean collar to work with me this morning. Now this is going to cut down our time for eating to a shadow—"

She tucked her free hand under my arm to pacify me. "It won't take any time at all, it's right on our way. And we can cut out the fruit cup or something."

"Aw, but you always look so classy eating fruitcup," I mourned.

But she went right ahead; evidently the matter had already been all settled between us without my knowing about it. "Wait a minute, let me see if I've got the address straight. Apartment 4F, 415 Martine Street. That's it."

I was still grouching about it, but she already had me under control. "What are you supposed to do, double as an errand-girl, too?" But by that time we were halfway there, so what was the use of kicking any more about it.

"Let's talk about us," she said. "Have you been counting the days?"

"All day. Thirteen left."

"And a half. Don't forget the half, if it's to be a noon-wedding." She tipped her shoulders together. "I don't like that thirteen by itself. I'll be glad when it's tomorrow, and only twelve left."

"Gee you're cute," I beamed admiringly. "The more I know you, the cuter you get."

"I bet you wont say that a year from now. I bet you'll be calling me your old lady then."

"This is it," I said.

"That's right, 415." She backed up, and me with her. "I was sailing right on past it. See what an effect you have on me?"

It was the kind of building that still was a notch above a tenement, but it had stopped being up-to-date about 1918. We went in the outer vestibule together, which had three steps going up and then a pair of inner glass doors, to hold you up until you said who you were.

"All right, turn it over to the hallman or whoever it is and let's be on our way."

She got on that conscientious look that anything connected with her job always seemed to bring on. "Oh no, I'm supposed to take it right up personally and get a receipt. Besides, there doesn't seem to be any hallman . . ."

She was going to do it her way anyway, I could see that, so there was no use arguing. She was bent over scanning the name-plates in the brass letter-boxes set into the marble trim. "What'd I say that name was again?"

"I dunno, Muller or something," I said sulkily.

"That's it. What would I do without you?" She flashed me a smile for a bribe to stay in good humor, then went ahead scanning. "Here it is. 4F. The name-card's fallen out of the slit and gotten lost, no wonder I couldn't find it." She poked the button next to it. "You wait downstairs here for me," she said. "I won't take a minute."

"Make it as fast as you can, will you? We're losing all this good time out of being together."

She took a quick step back toward me. "Here," she said, "let this hold you until I come down again." And that mouth I told you about, went right up smack against mine—where it belonged. "And if you're very good, you may get a chaser to that when I come down again."

Meanwhile the inner vestibule-door catch was being sprung for her with a sound like crickets with sore throats. She pushed it open, went inside. It swung shut again, cutting us off from one another. But I could still see her through it for a moment longer, standing in there by the elevator-bank waiting to go up. She looked good even from the back. When the car came down for her, she didn't forget to turn around and flash me another heartbreaker across her shoulder, before she stepped in and set the control-button for the floor she wanted. It was self-service, nobody else in it.

The door closed after her, and I couldn't see her any more. I could see the little red light that told the car was in use, gleaming for a few minutes after that, and then that went out too. And there wasn't anything left of her.

I lit a cigarette and leaned against the right-hand wall waiting. Then my shoulder got tired and I leaned against the left-hand wall. Then my both shoulders got tired and I just stood up by myself in the middle.

I've never timed a cigarette. I suppose they take around five minutes. This one seemed to take longer, but then look who I was waiting for. I punched it out with my foot without bothering to throw it out through the door; I didn't live there after all.

I thought: "Nice and fast. I mighta known it." I thought: "What's she doing, staying to tea up there?"

I counted my change, just to give myself something to do. I took off my hat and looked it over, like I'd never seen it before.

Things happened. Nothing much, little things that were to last so long. The postman came into the vestibule, shoved letters in here and there. 4F didn't get any. He shifted his girth straps and went out again. A stout lady in a not-very-genuine fur coat came in, one arm full of bundles, and hauling a yowling little kid by the other. She looked to see if there was any mail first. Then she looked for her key, and it took a lot of juggling. Then she looked at me, kind of supercilious. If a look can be translated into a single word, hers said: "Loafer!" Meanwhile the kid was beefing away. He had adenoids or something, and you couldn't tell if he was talking English or choking to death. She seemed to be able to tell the difference though. She said: "Now Dwight, I don't want to hear another word. If pot cheese is good enough for your father, pot cheese is good enough for you. If you don't hush up, I'll give you to this man here."

I thought: "Oh no you won't, not with a set of dishes thrown in!"

After they'd gone in, more waiting started in. I started to trace patterns with my feet, circles, diagonals, Maltese crosses. After I'd covered about a block-and-a-half that way, I stopped to rest again. I started to talk to myself, under my breath. "Must be out of pencils up there, to sign the receipt with, and she's waiting while they whittle out a new one! We'll be in time for the intermission at the show—"

I lit another cigarette. That act, slight as it was, put the finishing-touch to my self-control. I no sooner finished doing it than I hit the opposite wall with it. "What the hell is this anyway?" It wasn't under my breath any more, it was a full-toned yap. I stepped over, picked out 4F, and nearly sent the button through to the other side of the wall.

I didn't want to go in, of course. I just wanted to tip her off I was still alive down here. Aging fast, but still in fairly usable shape. She'd know who it was when she heard that blast. So when they released the catch on the door, I intended staying right outside where I was.

But they didn't. They were either ignoring the ring or they hadn't heard it. I gave it a second flattening. Again the catch on the door remained undisturbed. I knew the bell wasn't out of order, because I'd seen her give just a peck at it and the door-catch had been released for her. This time I gave it a triple-header. Two short ones and a long one, that went on for weeks. So long that my thumb joint got all white down to my wrist before I let go.

No acknowledgment. Dead to the world up there.

I did the instinctive thing, even though it was quite useless in the present case. Backed out into the street, as far as the outer rim of the sidewalk, and scanned the face of the building. There was just a checkerboard pattern of lighted squares and black ones. I couldn't tell which windows belonged to 4F, and even if I could have it wouldn't have done me any good unless I intended yelling her name up from the open sidewalk—and I didn't yet.

But being all the way out there cost me a chance to get in free, and lost me some more valuable time in the bargain. A man came out, the first person who had emerged from inside since I'd been waiting around, but before I could get in there and push through in his wake, the door had clicked shut again.

He was a scrawny-looking little runt, reminded you of an old-clothes-man on his night off. He went on out without even looking at me, and I tackled the 4F bell some more, gave it practically the whole Morse Code.

I wasn't frightened yet, just sizzling and completely baffled. The only thing I could figure, far-fetched as it was, was that the bell-apparatus had been on its last gasp when she rang it, and had given

349

up the ghost immediately afterwards. Otherwise why didn't they hear it, the kind of punishment I was giving it?

Then the first trickle of fright did creep in, like a dribble of cold water down your back when you're perspiring. I thought: "Maybe there's some guy up there trying to get funny with her, that's why the bell isn't answered. After all, things like that do happen in a big city all the time. I better get up there fast and find out what this is!"

I punched a neighboring bell at random, just to get past the door, and when the catch had been released for me, I streaked into the elevator, which the last guy had left down, and gave it the 4-button.

It seemed to me to set a new record for slowness in getting up there, but maybe that was just the state of mind I was in. When it finally did and I barged out, I made a false turn down the hall first, then when I came up against 4B and C and so on, turned and went back the other way.

It was at the far end of the hall, at the back. The bell I'd rung was evidently on some other floor, for none of the doors on this one opened to see who it was. I went close against it and listened. There were no sounds of a scuffle and I couldn't hear her saying "Unhand me, you brute!" so I calmed down by that much. But not all the way.

I couldn't hear anything at all. It was stone-silent in there. And yet these flat-doors weren't soundproof, because I could hear somebody's radio filtering through one at the other end of the hall clear as day.

I rang the bell and waited. I could hear it ring inside, from where I was. I'd say: "Will you ask that young lady that brought a package up here whether she's coming down tonight or tomorrow?" No, that sounded too dictatorial. I'd say: "Is the young lady ready to leave now?" I knew I'd feel slightly foolish, like you always do when you make a mountain out of a molehill.

Meanwhile, it hadn't opened. I pushed the bell again, and again I could hear the battery sing out on the inside. I rapped with my knuckles. Then I rang a third time. Then I rattled the knob (as though that would attract their attention, if ringing the bell hadn't!). Then I pounded with the heel of my hand. Then I alternated all three, the whole thing became a maelstrom of frenzied action. I think I even kicked. Without getting the results I was after—admittance.

Other doors began to open cautiously down the line, attracted by the noise I was making. But by that time I had turned and bolted down the stairs, without waiting for the paralytic elevator, to find the janitor. Fright wasn't just a cold trickle any more, it was an icy torrent gushing through me full-force.

I got down into the basement and found him without too much trouble. He was eating his meal or something on a red-checkered tablecloth, but I had no time to assimilate details. A glimpse of a napkin tucked in collarwise was about all that registered. "Come up with me quick, will you?" I panted, pulling him by the arm. "Bring your passkey, I want you to open one of those flats!"

"What's matter, something wrong?"

"I don't like the looks of it. My girl took a package up—I've been waiting for her over twenty minutes and she never came down again. They won't answer the bell—"

He seemed to take forever. First he stood up, then he finished swallowing, then he wiped his mouth, then he got a big ring of keys, then finally he followed me. As an afterthought he peeled off the napkin and threw it behind him at the table, but missed it. He even wanted to wait for the elevator. "No, no, no," I groaned, steering him to the stairs.

"Which one is it?"

"It's on the fourth floor, I'll show you!" Then when we got up there, "Here—right here."

When he saw which door I was pushing him to, he suddenly stopped. "That one? No, now wait a minute, young fellow, it couldn't be. Not that one."

"Don't try to tell me!" I heaved exasperatedly. "I say it is!"

"And don't you try to tell me! I say it couldn't be!"

"Why?"

"I'll show you why," he said heatedly. He went ahead up to it, put his passkey in, threw the door open, and flattened himself to let me get a good look past him.

I needed more than just one. It was one of those things that register on the eye but don't make sense to the brain. The light from the hall filtered in to make a threadbare half-moon, but to

351

make sure I wasn't missing any of it, he snapped a switch inside the door and a dim, left-over bulb somewhere further back went on flickeringly. You could see why it had been left in—it wasn't worth taking out. It threw a watery light around, not much better than a candle. But enough to see by.

"Now! You see why?"

The place was empty as a barn. Unfurnished, uninhabited, whatever you want to call it. Just bare walls, ceiling, and floor-boards. You could see where the carpet used to go: they were lighter in a big square patch in the middle than around the outside. You could see where a picture used to go, many moons ago; there was a patch of gray wool-dust adhering like fiber to the wall. You could even see where the telephone used to go; the wiring still led in along the baseboard, then reared up to waist-level like a pothook and ended in nothing.

The air alibied for its emptiness. It was stale, as though the windows hadn't been opened for months. Stale and dusty and sluggish.

"So you see? Mister, this place ain't been rented for six months." He was getting ready to close the door, as though that ended it; pulling it around behind his back, I could see it coming toward me, the "4F" stencilled on it in tarnished gold-paint seemed to swell up, got bigger and bigger until it loomed before me a yard high.

"No!" I croaked, and planted the flat of my hand against it and swept it back, out of his backhand grasp. "She came in here, I tell you!"

I went in a step or two, called her name into the emptiness. "Steffie! Steffie!"

He stayed pat on the rational, everyday plane of things as they ought to be, while I rapidly sank down below him onto a plane of shadows and terror. Like two loading platforms going in opposite directions, we were already miles apart, cut off from each other. "Now, what're you doing that for? Use your head. How can she be in here, when the place is empty?"

"I saw her ring the bell and I saw the door open for her."

"You saw *this door?*" He was obdurately incredulous.

"The downstairs door. I saw the catch released for her, after she rang this bell."

"Oh, that's different. You must have seen her ring some other bell, and you thought it was this one; then somebody else opened the building-door for her. How could anyone answer from here? Six months the people've been out of here."

I didn't hear a word. "Lemme look! Bring more lights!"

He shrugged, sighed, decided to humor me. "Wait, I get a bulb from the hall." He brought one in, screwed it into an empty socket in the room beyond the first. That did for practically the whole place. It was just two rooms, with the usual appendages: bath and kitchenette.

"How is it the current's still on, if it's vacant?"

"It's on the house-meter, included in the rent. It stays on when they leave."

There was a fire-escape outside one pair of windows, but they were latched on the inside and you couldn't see the seams of the two halves any more through the coating of dust that had formed over them. I looked for and located the battery that gave juice to the downstairs doorbell. It had a big pouch of a cobweb hanging from it, like a thin-skinned hornet's nest. I opened a closet and peered into it. A wire coat-hanger that had been teetering off-balance for heaven knows how long swung off the rod and fell down with a clash.

He kept saying: "Now listen, be sensible. What are you, a child?"

I didn't care how it looked, I only knew how it felt. "Steffie," I said. I didn't call it any more, just said it. I went up close to him. He was something human, at least. I said, "What'll I do?" I speared my fingers through my hair, and lost my new hat, and let it lie.

He wasn't much help. He was still on that other, logical plane, and I had left it long ago. He tried to suggest we'd had a quarrel and she'd given me the slip; he tried to suggest I go to her home, I might find her there waiting for me.

"She didn't come *out* again, damn you!" I flared tormentedly. "If I'd been down at the corner— But I was right at the front door! What about the back way—is there a back way out?"

"Not a back way, a delivery-entrance, but that goes through the basement, right past my quarters. No one came down there, I was sitting there eating my supper the whole time."

And another good reason was, the stairs from the upper floor came down on one side of the elevator, in the front hall. Then they continued on down to the basement on the *other* side of it. To get down to there anyone would have to pass in front of the elevator, for its entire width. I'd been right out there on the other side of the glass vestibule-door, and no one had. So I didn't have to take his word for it. I had my own senses.

"Is there a Muller in the house anywhere at all?"

"No, no one by that name. We never had anyone by that name in the whole twelve years I been working here."

"Someone may have gotten in here and been lurking in the place when she came up—"

"It was locked, how could anyone? You saw me open it with the pass-key."

"Come on, we're going to ask the rest of the tenants on this floor if they heard anything, saw her at all."

We made the rounds of the entire five flats. 4E came to the door in the person of a hatchet-faced elderly woman, who looked like she had a good nose—or ear—for the neighbors' activities. It was the adjoining flat to 4F, and it was our best bet. I knew if this one failed us, there wasn't much to hope for from the others.

"Did you hear anything next-door to you within the past half-hour?" I asked her.

"How could I, it's empty," she said tartly.

"I know, but *did you hear anything*—like anyone walking around in there, the door opening or closing, voices, or—" I couldn't finish it. I was afraid to say "a scream." Afraid she'd say yes.

"Didn't hear a pin drop," she said, and slammed the door. Then she opened it again. "Yes I did, too. Heard the doorbell, the downstairs one, ringing away in there like fifty. With the place empty like it is, it sounded worse than a fire-alarm."

"That was me," I said, turning away disheartenedly.

As I'd expected after that, none of the others were any good either. No one had seen her, no one had heard anything out of the way.

I felt like someone up to his neck in a quicksand, and going down deeper every minute. "The one underneath," I said, yanking him toward the stairs. "3F! If there was anything to be heard, they'd get

354

it quicker through their ceiling than these others would through their walls."

He went down to the floor below with me and we rang. They didn't open. "Must be out, I guess," he muttered. He took his passkey, opened the door, called their name. They were out all right, no one answered. We'd drawn another blank.

He decided he'd strung along with me just about far enough—on what after all must have seemed to him to be a wild goose chase. "Well," he said, slapping his sides and turning up his palms expressively. Meaning, "Now why don't you go home like a good guy and leave me alone?"

I wasn't having any. It was like asking you to leave your right arm behind you, chopped off at the shoulder. "You go up and stick there by that empty flat. I'm going out and get a cop." It sounds firm enough on paper, it came out plenty shaky and sick. I bounded down the stairs. In the vestibule I stopped short, punched that same 4F bell. His voice sounded hollowly through the interviewer after a minute. "Yuss?"

"It's me. The bell works all right up there, does it?"

"Sure."

"Okay, stay there. I'll be right back." I didn't know what good that had done. I went out bareheaded.

The one I brought back with me wasn't anything to rave about on the score of native intelligence. It was no time to be choosy. All he kept saying all the way back to the house was "All right, take it easy." He was on the janitor's plane, and immediately I had two of them against me instead of one.

"You saw her go in, did ye?"

I controlled myself with an effort. "Yes."

"But you don't know for sure which floor she got off at?"

"She rang 4F, so I know she got off at the fourth—"

"Wait a minute, you didn't *see* her, did ye?"

"No, I didn't see her."

"That's all I wanted to know. You can't say for sure she went into this flat, and the man here says it's been locked up for months."

He rang every bell in every flat of the building and questioned the occupants. No one had seen such a girl. The pot-cheese lady with the little boy remembered having seen me, that was the closest he got to anything. And one other flat, on the fifth, reported a ring at their bell with no follow-up.

I quickly explained I'd done that, to gain admittance to the building.

Three out of the twenty-four occupancies in the building were out; 1B, 3C and 3F. He didn't pass them by either. Had the janitor passkey their doors and examined the premises. Not a trace of her anywhere.

That about ended his contribution. According to his lights he'd done a thorough job, I suppose. "All right," he said. "I'll phone it in for you, that's the most I can do."

God knows how he expressed it over the wire. A single plainclothesman was dropped off at the door a few minutes later, came in to where the three of us were grouped waiting in the inner lobby. He looked me over like he was measuring me for a new suit of clothes. He didn't say anything.

"Hello, Gilman," the cop said. "This young fellow says he brought a girl here, and she disappeared in there." Putting the burden of the proof on me, I noticed. "I ain't been able to find anyone that saw her with him," he added helpfully.

"Let's see the place," the dick said.

We all went up there again. He looked around. Better than I had, maybe, but just as unproductively. He paid particular attention to the windows. Every one of the six, two regular-size apiece for the two main rooms, one small one each for the bath and kitchenette, was latched on the inside. There was a thick veneer of dust all around the frames and in the finger-grips. You couldn't have grabbed them any place to hoist them without it showing. And it didn't. He studied the keyhole.

He finally turned to me and gave me the axe. "There's nothing to show that she—or anyone else—ever came in here, bud."

"She rang the bell of this flat, and someone released the door-catch for her from up here." I was about as steady as jello in a high wind about it. I was even beginning to think I could see a ghost in the corner.

"We're going to check on that right now," he said crisply. "There's already one false ring accounted for, attributable to you. What we want is to find out if there was a second one registered, anywhere in the building."

We made the rounds again, all twenty-four flats. Again the fifth-floor flat reported my spiked ring—and that was all. No one else had experienced any, for the past twenty-four hours or more. And the fifth-floor party had only gotten the one, not two.

That should have been a point in my favor: she hadn't rung any of the other flats and been admitted from them, therefore she must have rung 4F and been admitted from there—as I claimed. Instead he seemed to twist it around to my discredit: she hadn't rung any of the other flats and been admitted from them, and since there could have been no one in 4F to hear her ring and admit her from there, she hadn't rung any bell at all, she hadn't been admitted at all, she hadn't been with me at all. I was a wack. Which gave me a good push in the direction of being one, in itself.

I was in bad shape by now. I started to speak staccato. "Say listen, don't do this to me, will you? You all make it sound like she didn't come here with me at all."

He gave me more of the axe. "That's what it does sound like to us."

I turned northeast, east, east-by-south, like a compass on a binge. Then I turned back to him again. "Look." I took the show-tickets out of my pocket, held them toward him with a shaky wrist. "I was going to take her to a show tonight—"

He waved them aside. "We're going to build this thing from the ground up first and see what we've got. You say her name is Stephanie Riska." I didn't like that "you say." "Address?"

"120 Farragut."

"What'd she look like?"

I should have known better than to start in on that. It brought her before me too plainly. I got as far as "She comes up to here next to me—" Then I stopped again.

The cop and janitor looked at me curiously, like they'd never seen a guy cry before. I tried to turn my head the other way, but they'd already seen the leak.

The dick seemed to be jotting down notes, but he squeezed out a grudging "Don't let it get you," between his eye-tooth and second molar while he went ahead doing it.

357

I said: "I'm not scared because she's gone. I'm scared because she's gone in such a fairy-tale way. I can't get a grip on it. Like when they sprinkle a pinch of magic powder and make them disappear in thin air. It's got me all loose in the joints, and my guts are rattling against my backbone, and I believe in ghosts all over again."

My spiritual symptoms didn't cut any ice with him. He went right ahead with the business at hand. "And you met her at 6:15 outside the Bailey-Goodwin Building, you say, with a package to be delivered here. Who'd she work for?"

"A press-clipping service called the Green Star; it's a one-man organization, operated by a guy named Hessen. He just rented one dinky little rear room, on the ground floor of the Bailey-Goodwin Building."

"What's that?"

"I don't know myself. She tried to explain it to me once. They keep a list of clients' names, and then they sift through the papers, follow them up. Any time one of the names appears, in connection with any social activity or any kind of mention at all, they clip the item out, and when they've got enough of them to make a little batch, they send them to the client, ready for mounting in a scrapbook. The price for the service is about five bucks a hundred, or something like that."

"How is there any coin in that?" he wanted to know.

"I don't know myself, but she was getting twenty-two a week."

"All right. Now let's do a little checking." He took me back with him to where she worked, first of all. The building was dead, of course, except one or two offices, doing night-work on the upper floors. He got the night-watchman, showed his credentials, and had him open up the little one-room office and let us in.

I'd never been in the place myself until now. I'd always waited for her outside at the street-entrance at closing time. I don't think it was even intended for an office in the first place; it was more like a chunk of left-over storage-space. It didn't even have a window at all, just an elongated vent up near the ceiling, with a blank shaft-wall about two feet away from it.

There was a flat-topped desk taking up one side, his I guess, with a phone on it and a wire paper-basket and nothing else. And a smaller-size "desk," this time a real table and not a desk at all, with nothing on it at all. The rest was just filing cabinets. Oh yeah, and a coat-rack. He must have been getting it for a song.

"What a telphone-booth," remarked the dick.

He looked in the filing cabinets; they were just alphabetized names, with a scattering of newspaper-clippings distributed among them. Some of the names they didn't have any clippings for, and some of the letters they didn't even have any clients for—and I don't mean only X.

"There's about a hundred bucks' worth of clippings in the whole kitty," Gilman said, "at your own estimate of what the charge was." He didn't follow up with what he meant by that, and I was too worried about her to pay any attention to his off-side remarks. The only thing that meant anything to me was, there was nothing around the place to show him that she had ever worked here or even been here in her life. Nothing personalized, I mean. The single drawer of the little table just had a pair of shears for clipping and a pot of paste for mounting, and a stack of little salmon-colored paper mounts.

The night-watchman couldn't corroborate me, because the place was always locked up by the time he came on-shift. And the elevator-runners that worked the building in the daytime wouldn't have been able to either, I knew, even if they'd been on hand, because this hole-in-the-wall was on a branch-off of the main entrance-corridor, she didn't have to pass the cars on her way in from or out to the street, so they'd probably never seen her the whole time she'd worked here.

The last thing he did, after he'd gotten Hessen's name and address, which was readily available in the place itself, was to open a penknife and cut a notch from the under-side of the small table. At least, it looked like he was doing that from what I could see, and he kept his back to me and didn't offer any explanation. He thumbed me at the door and said, "Now we'll go out there and hear what he has to say." His tone held more of an eventual threat in it toward me than toward her employer though, I couldn't help noticing.

It was a bungalow-type place on the outskirts, and without being exactly a mansion, it wasn't low-cost housing. You walked up flat stones to get to the door, and it had dwarf Japanese fir-trees dotted all around it.

"Know him?" he said while we were waiting.

"By sight," I swallowed. I had a feeling of that quicksand I'd been bogging into ever since she'd left me in the lobby at Martine Street, being up to my eyes now and getting ready to close over the top of my head. This dick mayn't have taken sides yet, but that was the most you could say; he certainly wasn't on my side.

A guy with a thin fuzz on his head, who looked like he belonged to some unhealthy nationality nobody ever heard of before, opened the door, stepped in to announce us, came back and showed us in, all in fast time.

A typewriter was clicking away busily somewhere near at hand, and I thought it was him first, her boss, but it wasn't. He was smoking a porcelain-bowled pipe and reading a book under a lamp. Instead of closing the book, he just put his finger down on the last word he'd read to keep his place, so he could go right ahead as soon as this was over with. He was tall and lean, with good features, and dark hair cut so short it just about came out of his scalp and then stopped.

Gilman said: "Did you ever see this young fellow before?"

He eyed me. He had a crease under one eye; it wasn't a scar so much as an indentation from digging in some kind of a rimless glass. "No-o," he said with a slow benevolence. A ghost of a smile pulled at his mouth. "What's he done?"

"Know anyone named Muller, at 415 Martine Street?" There hadn't been any Muller in the filing cabinets at the office.

"No-o, I don't know anyone by that name there or anywhere else. I think we have a Miller, a Mrs. Elsie Miller, on our list, who all the time divorces and marries. Will that do?" He sighed tolerantly. "She owes us twenty-nine dollars."

"Then you didn't send a package over to Muller, Apartment 4F, 415 Martine Street, at 6:15 this evening?"

"No," he said again, as evenly as the other two times. I started forward spasmodically. Gilman braked me with a cut of his hand. "I'm sure I didn't. But wait, it is easy enough to confirm that." He raised his voice slightly, without being boorish about it. And right there in front of me, right there in the room with me, he called—

"Stephanie. Stephanie Riska, would you mind coming in here a moment?"

The clicking of the typewriter broke off short and a chair scraped in the next room. "Steffie," I said huskily, and swallowed past agony, and the sun came up around me and it wasn't night any more, and the bad dream was over.

"My assistant happens to be right here at the house tonight; I had some dictation to give her and she is transcribing it. We usually mail out clippings however, only when there is an urgent request do I send them around by personal messen——"

"Yes sir?" a velvety contralto said from the doorway.

I missed some of the rest of it. The lights took a half-turn to the right, streaking tracks across the ceiling after them like comet-tails, before they came to a stop and stood still again. Gilman reached over and pulled me up short by the coatsleeve, as though I'd been flopping around loose in my shoes or something.

She was saying, "No, I don't believe I do," in answer to something he had asked her, and looking straight over at me. She was a brunette of an exotic foreign type, and she came up as high as me, and the sun had gone out again and it was night all over again.

"That isn't Steffie!" I bayed. "He's calling somebody else by her name!"

The pupils of Hessen's eyes never even deflected toward me. He arched his brows at Gilman. "That is the only young lady I have working for me."

Gilman was holding me back with sort of a half-nelson. Or half a half-nelson. The brunette appeared slightly agitated by my outburst, no more. She hovered there uncertainly in the doorway, as though not knowing whether to come in or go out.

"How long have you been working for Mr. Hessen?" Gilman asked her.

"Since October of last year. About eight months now."

"And your name is Stephanie Riska?"

She smiled rebukingly, as if at the gratuitousness of such a question. "Yes, of course." She decided to come a little further forward into the room. But she evidently felt she needed some moral support to do so. She'd brought a small black handbag with her, tucked under her arm, when she left the typewriter. She opened it, so that the

361

flap stood up toward Gilman and me, and plumbed in it for something. The two big gold-metal initials were so easy to read, even upside-down; they were thick, bold Roman capitals, S. R. The bag looked worn, as though she'd had it a long time. I could sense, rather than see, Gilman's mind's eye turned accusingly toward me: "What about it now?" though his physical ones were fastened on the bag.

She got what she was looking for out of it, and she got more than she was looking for. She brought up a common ordinary stick of chewing gum in tin-foil, but she also accidentally brought up an envelope with it, which slipped through her fingers to the floor. She was very adroitly awkward, to coin a phrase.

Gilman didn't exactly dive for it, but he·managed to get his fingers on it a half-inch ahead of hers. "Mind?" he said. I read the address on it with glazed eyes, over his shoulder. It had been postmarked and sent through the mail. "Miss Stephanie Riska, 120 Farragut Street." He stripped the contents out of it and read the single sheet of notepaper. Then he gravely handed it back. Again I could feel his mind's eye on me.

She had broken the stick of chewing gum in half, put part between her lips, and the rest she was preparing to wrap up in tin-foil again for some other time. She evidently didn't like to chew too much at a time.

Gilman absently thumbed a vest-pocket as though he would have liked some too. She noticed that. "May I offer you some?" she said gravely.

"I wish you would, my mouth's kind of dry." He put the second half-piece in his own trap. "And you didn't deliver a package for Mr. Hessen at 415 Martine Street this evening?" he said around it.

"No, sir, I did not. I'm afraid I don't even know where Martine Street is."

That about concluded the formalities. And we were suddenly outside again, him and me, alone. In the dark. It was dark for me, anyway. All he said when we got back in the car was: "This 'girl' of yours, what kind of gum did she habitually chew, wintergreen or licorice or what have you?"

What could I tell him but the truth? "She didn't use gum, she detested the habit."

He just looked at me. Then he took the nugget he'd mooched

from the brunette out of his mouth, and he took a little piece of paper out of his pocket that held another dab in it, and he compared them—by scent. "I scraped this off that desk in the office, and it's the same as what she gave me just now. Tutti-frutti. Not a very common flavor in chewing gum. She belongs in that office, she parked her gum there. She had a letter addressed to herself in her handbag, and the initials on the outside checked. What's your racket, kid? Are you a pushover for mental observation? Or are you working off a grudge against this guy? Or did you do something to some little blonde blue-eyed number and are you trying to pass the buck in this way before we even found out about it?"

It was like a ton of bricks had landed all over my dome. I held my head with both hands to keep it in one piece and leaned way over toward the floor and said, "My God!"

He got me by the slack of the collar and snapped me back so viciously it's a wonder my neck didn't break.

"Things like this don't happen," I groaned. "They can't. One minute all mine, the next she isn't anywhere. And no one'll believe me."

"You haven't produced a single person all evening long that actually laid eyes on this 'blonde girl' of yours," he said hard as flint. "Nowhere, d'you understand?"

"Where'd I get the name from then, the address?"

He looked at me when I said that. "I'll give you one more spin for your money. You stand or fall by the place she lived." He leaned forward and he said "120 Farragut" to the driver. Then he kept eyeing me like he was waiting for me to break down and admit it was a hoax or I'd done something to her myself, whoever she was.

Once he said, "Remember, this girl at his place had a letter, three days old, addressed to *her*, giving this same address we're heading for now. If you still want to go through with it . . ."

"I took her home there," I said.

"Parents?"

"No, it's a rooming-house. She was from Harrisburg. But the landlady—He—" Then I went, "O-oh," and let my head loll limply back against the back of the seat. I'd just remembered he'd recommended the place to her.

He was merciless, noticed everything. "D'ye still want to make

363

it there—or d'ye want to make it Headquarters? And the tougher you are with me, the tougher I'm going to be with you, buddy." And his fist knotted up and his eyes iced over.

It was a case of self-preservation now. We were only minutes away. "Listen. Y'gotta listen to me. She took me up one night, just for a minute, to lend me a magazine she had in the room. Y'gotta listen to this, for heaven's sake. Sticking in the mirror of the dresser she's got a litho of the Holy Mother. On the radiator she's got a rag doll that I won for her at Coney Island." I split open my collar in front trying to bring it all back. "On a little shelf against the wall she's got a gas-ring, with a tube running up to the jet. From the light-fixture to that jet there runs a string, and she'll have stockings hanging from it to dry. Are you listening? Will you remember these things? Don't you see I *couldn't* make all these things up? Don't you see she's *real?*"

"You almost persuade me," he said half under his breath. Which was a funny thing coming from a detective. And then we got there.

We stepped down and went in. "Now if you open your mouth," he said to me, teeth interlocked, "and say one word the whole time we're in here, I'll split your lip so wide open you'll be able to spit without opening your mouth." He sent for the landlady. I'd never seen her before.

"Y'got a girl named Stephanie Riska living in your house?"

"Yep. Fourth-floor front." That was right.

"How long?"

"Riska?" She took a tuck in her cheek. "She's been rooming with me now for six months." That was right too.

"I want to know what she looks like." He took a wicked half-turn in my arm that dammed up the blood.

"Dark hair, sort of dark skin. About as tall as this young fellow you got with you. She talks kind of husky."

"I want to see her room. I'm the police." He had to practically support me all the way up the four flights of stairs.

She threw open a door, gave it the switch. I came back to life enough to open my eyes. On the mirror, no picture. On the radiator, no rag doll. On the shelf no gas-ring, but a row of books. The jet had no tube plugged-in, was soldered-over with lead. No string led from it to the light. No nothing.

"Has she always had it fixed this way?" Gilman asked.

"Always since the first day she's here. She's a real clean roomer, only one thing I got to complain about—— There it is again." She went over to the washstand and removed a little nugget of grayish substance that had plastered to the underside of it. But she smiled indulgently, as though one such peccadillo were permissible.

Gilman took it from her on a scrap of paper, shifted it from left to right across his face. "Tutti-frutti," he said.

"Look out, you better hold your friend!" she exclaimed in sharp alarm.

He swung me so that instead of going down flat, I landed against him and stayed up. "Let him fold," he said to her. "That isn't anything to the falls he's going to be taking five or ten minutes from now." And we started down the stairs again, with two pairs of workable feet between the three of us.

"What'd he do, *murder* her?" she breathed avidly on the way down.

"Not her, but I got a good hunch he murdered someone—and picked the wrong name out of a hat."

She went: "Tsk-tsk-tsk-tsk. He don't *look* like——"

I saw some rheumatic lodger's knotty walking-stick up-ended out of a brass umbrella-stand at the foot of the stairs. As he marched me by, I was on that side, luckily. I let my arm fall behind us instead of in front of us where it had been—he didn't have me handcuffed yet, remember—and the curved handle of the stick caught in my hand, and it came up out of the holder after me.

Then I swung it and beaned him like no dick was ever beaned before. He didn't go down, he just staggered sidewise against the wall and went, "Uff!"

She was bringing up in the rear. She went, "Oh!" and jumped back. I cleared the front steps at a bound. I went, "Steffie! Steffie!" and I beat it away in the dark. I didn't know where I was going and I didn't care, I only knew I had to find her. I came out so fast the driver of the headquarters-car we'd left at the door wasn't expecting me. I'd already flashed around the corner below before his belated "Hey, you!" came ringing after me.

I made for the Martine Street flat. That was instinctive: the place I'd last seen her, calling me back. Either the car didn't start right up after me or I shook it off in my erratic zigzag course through the streets. Anyway I got there still unhindered.

I ganged up on the janitor's bell, my windpipe making noises like a stuffed drainpipe. I choked, "Steffie!" a couple of times to the mute well-remembered vestibule around me. I was more demented than sane by now. Gilman was slowly driving me into the condition he'd already picked for me ahead of time.

The janitor came up with a sweater over his nightshirt. He said, "You again? What is it—didn't you find her yet? What happened to the other fellow that was with you?"

"He sent me back to take another look," I said craftily. "You don't have to come up, just gimme the passkey."

He fell for it, but killed a couple of valuable minutes going down to get it again. But I figured I was safe for the night; that it was my own place, across town, Gilman would make a beeline for.

I let myself in and lit up and started looking blindly all around— for what I didn't know, where a professional detective had been over this ground once already and gotten nothing. The story-book ending, I kept looking for the story-book ending, some magic clue that would pop up and give her back to me. I went around on my hands and knees, casing the cracks between the floorboards; I tested the walls for secret panels (in a $50-a-month flat!); I dug out plaster with my bare nails where there was a hole, thinking I'd find a bullet, but it was only a mouse-hole.

I'd been there about ten minutes when I heard a subtle noise coming up the hall-stairs outside. I straightened to my feet, darted through the door, ran down the hall to the stairs. Gilman was coming up, like thunder 'cross the China Bay,[2] with a cop and the janitor at his heels. It was the fool Janitor's carpet-slippers, which had no heel-grip, that were making more noise than the other two's shoes put together. Gilman had tape on the back of his skull and a gun in his hand. "He's up there now," the janitor was whispering. "I let him in about ten minutes ago; he said you sent him."

I sped up the stairs for the roof, the only way that was open to me now. That gave me away to them, and Gilman spurted forward with a roar. "Come down here, you, I'll break every bone in your body! You won't live to get to Headquarters!" The roof-stairs ended

---

[2] An allusion to Kipling's "Mandalay."

in a skylight-door that I just pushed through, although it should have been latched on the inside. There was about a yard-high partition-wall dividing the roof from the next one over. I tried to clear it too fast, miscalculated, and went down in a mess, tearing a hole in my trouser-knee and skinning my own knee beneath. That leg wouldn't work right for a minute or two after that, numb, and before I could get upright again on it and stumble away, they were out on me. A big splatter of white shot ahead of me on the gravelled roof from one of their torches, and Gilman gave what can only be described as an Iroquois war-whoop and launched himself through space in a flying tackle. He landed crushingly across my back, flattening me a second time.

And then suddenly the rain of blows that I'd expected was held in check, and he lay just inert on top of me, doing nothing. We both saw it at the same time, lying on the roof there a few yards ahead of us, momentarily played up by the cop's switching torch, then lost again. I could recognize it because I'd seen it before. *The package that she'd brought over here tonight.*

"Hold that light steady!" Gilman bellowed, and got off of me. We both got over to it at the same time, enmity forgotten. He picked it up, tore open the brown paper around it, and a sheaf of old newspapers slowly flattened themselves out. With squares and oblongs scissored out here and there. She hadn't been sent over with clippings, but with the valueless remnants of papers after the clippings had already been taken out. It was a dummy package, a decoy, used to send her to her—disappearance.

The rest of it went double-quick—or seemed to. It had built up slow; it unraveled fast.

"Someone did bring a package here tonight, kid," was the way he put it. "And if I give you that much, I'll give you the whole thing on credit alone, no matter what the odds still outstanding against it are. Blonde, really named Stephanie Riska, works for Hessen, lives at 120 Farragut, *never* chews gum, and all the rest of it. Come on. My theory in a pinch would be she was jumped from behind outside the door of that vacant flat before she had a chance to cry out, spirited up over this roof, down through the next house and into a waiting car—while you hugged the vestibule below. Calhoun, call in and have someone get out there fast to Hessen's house, Myrtle Drive, and keep it

367

spotted until we can get out there. I want to take another crack at that office first."

On the way over I gasped, "D'you think they—?"

"Naw, not yet," he reassured me. "Or they would have done it right in the empty flat and let you take the rap." Whether he meant it or not I couldn't tell, so it didn't relieve me much.

The second knot came out in the office. I went over to the little table she'd used, while he turned the filing cabinets inside-out. Again our two discoveries came almost simultaneously. "Look" I breathed. It was stuck in a crack in the floor, hidden by the shadow of the table. A gilt hairpin she must have dropped one time at her work. Such as no brunette like the one Hessen had showed us at his house would have ever used in her life. "Blonde, all right," he grunted, and tipped me to his own find. "I muffed this before, in my hurry: about every third name in this card-index of 'clients' has a foreign mailing-address. Neutral countries, like Switzerland and Holland. Why should they be interested in social items appearing in papers over here? The mere fact that they're not living here shows the items couldn't possibly refer to them personally. If you ask me, the guy's an espionage-agent of some kind, and these 'clippings' are some kind of a code. With a scattering of on-the-level ones interspersed, to cover up. But that's a job for the FBI. I'm only interested in this girl of yours. My lieutenant can notify their local office about the rest of it, if he sees fit.

"The second leg of my theory," he went on, as we beat it out of there fast, "is she found out something, and they figured she was too dangerous to them. Did she say anything to you like that?"

"Not a word. But she had told him she was quitting end of next week to get married."

"Well, then she *didn't* find out anything, but he thought she did, so it amounted to the same thing. He could not afford to let her quit. And did he cover up beautifully, erase her existence! They only slipped up on that package. Maybe some tenant came up on the roof to take down her wash, before they could come back and pick it up, so they had to leave it there, rather than risk being identified later. Come on, we'll stop off at that rooming-house on the way. I want that landlady picked up. She's obviously one of them, since he recommended the girl there as a lodger in the beginning. Changed the whole room around, even to sticking a wad of tutti-frutti gum on the washstand."

"Let's go," I cried.

A second knot came out at the rooming-house, but it was simply a duplicate of the one at her office: confirmation of the color of her hair. "A girl shampoos her hair once in a while," he said to me, and stuck a matchstick down the drain of the washbasin. He spread something on a piece of paper, showed it to me: two unmistakably blonde hairs. "Now why didn't I think of that the first time?" He turned the steel-plated landlady over to a cop to be sent in, and we were on our way again—this time out to the Myrtle Drive house, fast.

There was no sign of the guy he'd sent out ahead of us to keep it cased, and he swore under his breath, while my heart deflated. The place was dark and lifeless, but neither of us was foolish enough to believe they'd gone to bed yet. He took the front door and I took the back, with a gun he furnished me—he was on my side now, don't forget. We blew the locks simultaneously and met in the middle of the hall that ran through the place. In three minutes we were downstairs again. Nothing was disturbed, but the birds had flown; suave Hessen, and the butler, and the pinch-hitting brunette. No incriminating papers, but a very incriminating short-wave set. Incriminating because of the place it was located. It was built into the overhead water-tank of a dummy toilet, not meant to hold water or be used. Gilman made the discovery in the most natural way possible.

"Spy-ring, all right," he grunted, and phoned in then and there from the place itself.

That wasn't getting me back Steffie. I was in such a blue funk that I didn't notice it as soon as I should have; I mean, something had seemed to tickle my nostrils unpleasantly the whole time we were in there. It only registered *after* I came out into the open again with him, and we stood there crestfallen in front of it. Before I could call his attention to it, headlights slashed through the dark and a car drew up in front.

We crouched back, but it was only the spotter that was supposed to have been hung up there before. Gilman rushed him with a roar. "What the hell's the idea? You were supposed to—"

"I tailed 'em!" the guy insisted. "They piled into a car, locked up the house, and lit. I tailed 'em the whole way, those were the only orders I got!"

369

"Where'd they go?"

"Pier 07, North river. They boarded some kind of a fuzzy tramp-steamer, and it shoved off in less than a quarter of an hour later. I tried to reach you at Head—"

"Was there a blonde girl with them?" Gilman rapped out.

"No, just the three that were in the house here when I first made contact; the two men and a dark-haired girl. There was no one else smuggled aboard ahead of them either; I pumped one of the crew—"

Meanwhile, my heart's eight lives had died, and its ninth was wearing thin. "They're out of our reach now," I groaned, "we'll never—"

"Oh, no, they're not," Gilman promised viciously. "They may have cleared the pier; a police-launch can pull them off again at Quarantine." He spilled in the house again, to phone in the alarm.

I went after him; that was when I again noticed that unpleasant tickling. I called his attention to it when he got through on the wire. "Don't it smell as though they've had this place fumigated or some—"

He twitched the end of his nose. Then his face got drab. "That's gasoline!" he snapped. "And when you smell it that heavy—indoors like this—it's not a good sign!" I could tell he was plenty scared all at once—which made me twice as scared as he was. "Bill!" he hollered to the other guy. "Come in here fast and give us a hand! That girl they *didn't* take with them must still be around these premises someplace, and I only hope she isn't—"

He didn't finish it; he didn't have to. He only hoped she wasn't dead yet. I wasn't much good to them, in the sudden mad surge of ferreting they blew into. I saw them dimly, rustling around, through a sick haze.

He and I had been over the house once already—the upper part of it—so they found the right place almost at once. The basement. A hoarse cry from Gilman brought myself and the other guy down there after him. I couldn't go all the way, went into a paralysis half-way down the stairs. She was wedged down out of sight between two trunks, she'd been loosely covered over with sacking. I saw them lifting her up between them, and she carried awfully inert.

"Tell me now," I said, "don't wait until you get her—" I waited for the axe to fall.

"She's alive, kid," Gilman said. "Her chest's straining against the ropes they've got around—" Then he broke off, said to the other guy, "Don't stop to look at her now, hurry up out of here with her! Don't you hear that ticking down around here someplace, don't you know what that gasoline-reek means—?"

I was alive again; I jumped in to help them, and we got her up and out of the cursed place fast. So fast we were almost running with her.

We untied her out by the car. She was half-dead with fright, but they hadn't done anything to her, just muffled her up. The other guy wanted to go back in again and see if they could locate the bomb, but Gilman stopped him. "You'll never make it; it'll blow before you—"

He was right. In the middle of what he was saying, the whole house seemed to lift a half-foot above its foundations, it lit up all lurid inside, there was a roar, and in a matter of minutes flame was mushrooming out of all the lower-story windows.

"An incendiary-bomb," Gilman said. "Turn in a fire-alarm, Bill, that's about all we can do now. He went off someplace to use a phone, and when he came back some time later, he had a mean face. A face I wouldn't have wanted to run up against on a dark night. I thought he'd heard bad news. He had—but not for us. "They got 'em," he said. "Yanked 'em off it just as the tub was clearing the Narrows. They're earmarked for the FBI, but before we turn them over, I wouldn't be surprised if they show wear and tear—She *is* pretty at that, kid."

She was sitting there in the car by now, talking to me and crying a little. I was standing on the outside of it. I was standing up, that was my mistake.

"Well, I gotta go," I heard him say. And then something hit me. It felt like a cement-mixer.

Our roles changed. When my head cleared, she was the one bending over me, crooning sympathetically. "And he said to tell you, no hard feelings, but when anyone socks Dick Gilman on the head with a walking stick, they get socked back even if they're the best of friends. And he said he'd see us both down at Headquarters later in the night, to be sure and get there on time if we don't want to miss the fun."

I was still seeing stars, but I didn't care, I was seeing her too. And now it was only twelve days off, we'd licked the thirteenth.

371

MATTER

STUDY NOTES

1. From whose point of view is "Wait for Me Downstairs" told?
2. Mention the methods by which Woolrich heightens the mystery— makes it seem impossible that Stephanie appeared at Apartment 4F to deliver a package.
3. List the elements by which Woolrich indicates the passing of time, Kenny's impatience when waiting for Stephanie to return from the trip upstairs in an elevator.
4. Point out the inductive investigation in which Kenny engages in his efforts to find Stephanie.
5. Point out the policeman's inductive work when her disappearance is reported to him.
6. Point out the detective's searches to determine whether the woman has really disappeared (before he begins to think that Kenny may be telling him the truth).
7. List the misleading clues that cause Gilman to suspect Kenny unjustly.
8. What clues favorable to Kenny's story does the detective find on his second search of the office where Stephanie has worked, her apartment in the rooming-house, and Hessen's place of residence?
9. Summarize Gilman's chief deductions as stated to Stephanie's lover.
10. Give reasons for classifying Gilman as a detective of the tough and pugnacious type.
11. Point out the use of irony in this story.
12. Show that the style is terse and lurid and homely rather than too highly literary.

COMPARISON EXERCISES

1. Compare "The Doctor, His Wife, and the Clock" and "Wait for Me Downstairs" with reference to the probability of their plots.
2. Compare the two stories for realism in the characterizations.
3. For the clever use of suspense.
4. For quality of diction—the levels of language employed.
5. For the extent to which Poe's detective-story devices are utilized.

WRITING SUGGESTION

Develop a suspense-filled plot, not too gory (placing the strongest tension immediately before the solution), beginning with a mysterious crime and proceeding to the detection of the culprit, having the sleuth investigate by the inductive method which he supports by revealing, near the end of the story, his deductions.

372

ADVENTURE

Introduction to Adventure Stories

AN adventure is a strange or extraordinary experience or a dangerous undertaking (exploration, mutiny, war, or some other exciting situation), an undertaking that requires and reveals courage. Stories dealing with exposure to harm are published in juvenile, adventure, pulp Western-story, and commercial magazines. The adventure type of story is action-packed, filled with an atmosphere of courage in the face of danger, and usually ends with a surprise. The interest in the plot is greater than that in the characters. Plot is particularly important and should move fast all the way to the climax. The action must be dramatic, such as will cause the adventurer difficulty and give his valor opportunity to express itself. Each new main incident should be somewhat more exciting than its predecessor. The use of suspense will help to hold the reader's interest. Often, some sentimental theme imbues the plot. Whatever characters the story may contain, at least a protagonist and an antagonist, must, under present-day standards, be realistic and individual, interesting because lifelike. The style is usually simple and dramatic and sometimes even beautiful.

Adventure magazines have had to win their way to popularity by battling against the feeling of some readers and critics that stories dealing primarily with action for its own sake cannot have high literary quality. Some people have felt that the adventure story, like the fairy tale of cruelty and of bloodshed, should be relegated to oblivion as inartistic and of doubtful ethical value. Another group of readers, however, thinks that the reading of adventure stories is a form of sublimation, lifts a person to a higher cultural plane than that on which a primitive impulse might otherwise keep him. This group believes that the craving for intense struggle, for conflict that might in its cruelty reach even to bloodshed, is natural and that this primi-

373

tive desire can be vicariously and ideally gratified without the inflicting of bodily harm in real life. According to these readers, no sound psychological basis exists for declining to read an adventure story on the ground that the ethical and literary quality are necessarily low. Adventure fiction has held a popular position despite the somewhat skeptical attitudes that some critics have entertained. And some of the writers of adventure stories have proved that the literary style can be high grade.

Near the end of the first quarter of the nineteenth century, Washington Irving created a group of adventure stories, most of which appeared in *Tales of a Traveller*. "The Adventure of Sam, the Black Fisherman" vividly presents a Negro fisherman's fright and curiosity when observing some men bury an object that he supposed was a human body. "Governor Manco and the Soldier," in *The Alhambra*, recounts a strikingly strange experience, a soldier's visit to an enchanted mountain and viewing military forces and supplies and treasures of Boabdil, the last king of Granada. "The Painter's Adventure" deals with real danger, the kidnapping of an artist by robbers who thought he was an Italian prince. Irving's adventure stories often contain touches of humor. They are rich in atmosphere. Both their substance and method are glamorous. Many of them, such as "My Aunt's Adventure" and "The Painter's Adventure," impressively individualize the characters. The style is classical and graceful.

A little past the middle of the century, Harriet Prescott Spofford was writing a few romantic, richly imaginative, and sentimental adventure stories. "In a Cellar," the story of the recovery of a stolen diamond, is French in background and contains some brilliant, florid descriptions. "Circumstance" is chiefly romantic but has also a realistic appeal. This story, like the earlier one, employs glowing description, a style containing many superlatives. The plots of her narratives, whether of adventure or of other subject matter, are somewhat improbable, but her writing possesses such merits as consciousness and a fine sense of the dramatic. She enjoyed a period of immense popularity.

In the early twentieth century, two of America's prominent writers of adventure stories were Richard Harding Davis and Jack London. Those by Davis are somewhat melodramatic. Many of them concern his lawbreaking clubman character, Van Bibber. Davis's adventure narratives are more important for their manner of telling than for their subject matter. They are vivid and facile but somewhat lacking in lastingly impressive individualized characterization. Davis enjoyed tremendous popularity in his day; and some of his tales of adventure are still read, especially by the young. Much of London's best writing deals with man's struggles against nature. In partly romantic and partly realistic stories of harsh life in the Klondike region, London has pictured this conflict. Romantic in theme and scene and in imagination, these narratives contain much realistic detail. Written in a distinctive, forceful style, sometimes poetic, they rise to dramatic climaxes.

More recently, Walt Coburn and Paul Annixter have been prominent adventure-story writers. Coburn has published in pulp magazines cowboy stories, somewhat of the O. Henry type, that have commanded top rates because of high quality. They are packed with fast action, have dramatic climaxes, often end in surprises. Summers has called Coburn "the dean of Western story writers." [1] Annixter has been represented in commercial magazines by numerous brief fictions of deadly dangerous adventure. In some cases the conflict is between wild animals; in other cases, between man and brute beast. "Dragon Rider" tells of a man's killing an alligator. In "Orchids and Crocodiles" a man rescues his companion from a crocodile while fighting off other crocodiles. In "Kadiak" a hunter saves himself from an Alaskan bear. Annixter's stories have varied wild and remote settings and they narrate exciting outdoor action in a pleasing rhythmical style.

Some other writers have recently made excellent contributions to the short-length literature of adventure. Though Howard Bloomfield's stories tend more often toward character study than the recounting of a danger-laden enterprise, "The Trap" places the hero in ample and exciting difficulty from which escape is effected only through the harassed man's ingenuity. Besides narrating action imbued with peril, this story exemplifies effective characterization.

[1] Richard Summers, *Craft of the Short Story*, New York: Rinehart and Company, 1948, p. 498.

CIRCUMSTANCE [1]
(1860)
HARRIET PRESCOTT SPOFFORD

SHE had remained, during all that day, with a sick neighbor— those eastern wilds of Maine in that epoch frequently making neighbors and miles synonymous—and so busy had she been with care and sympathy that she did not at first observe the approaching night. But finally the level rays, reddening the snow, threw their gleam upon the wall, and, hastily donning cloak and hood, she bade her friends farewell and sallied forth on her return. Home lay some three miles distant, across a copse, a meadow, and a piece of woods— the woods being a fringe on the skirts of the great forests that stretch far away into the North. That home was one of a dozen log-houses lying a few furlongs apart from each other, with their half-cleared demesnes separating them at the rear from a wilderness untrodden save by stealthy native or deadly panther tribes.

She was in a nowise exalted frame of spirit—on the contrary, rather depressed by the pain she had witnessed and the fatigue she had endured; but in certain temperaments such a condition throws open the mental pores, so to speak, and renders one receptive of every influence. Through the little copse she walked slowly, with her cloak folded about her, lingering to imbibe the sense of shelter, the sunset filtered in purple through the mist of woven spray and twig, the companionship of growth not sufficiently dense to band against her the sweet home-feeling of a young and tender wintry wood. It was therefore just on the edge of the evening that she emerged from the place and began to cross the meadow-land. At one hand lay the forest to which her path wound; at the other the evening star hung over a tide of failing orange that slowly slipped down the earth's broad side to sadden other hemispheres with sweet regret. Walking rapidly now, and with her eyes wide-open, she distinctly saw in the air before her what was not there a moment ago, a winding-sheet— cold, white, and ghastly, waved by the likeness of four wan hands— that rose with a long inflation and fell in rigid folds, while a voice, shaping itself from the hollowness above, spectral and melancholy, sighed—"The Lord have mercy on the people! The Lord have mercy

[1] First published in *The Atlantic* (May, 1860) ; reprinted in *The Amber Gods and Other Stories* (1863).

on the people!" Three times the sheet with its corpse-covering outline waved beneath the pale hands, and the voice, awful in its solemn
and mysterious depth, sighed, "The Lord have mercy on the people!"
Then all was gone, the place was clear again, the gray sky was ob-
structed by no deathly blot; she looked about her, shook her shoulders decidedly, and, pulling on her hood, went forward once more.

She might have been a little frightened by such an apparition, if
she had led a life of less reality than frontier settlers are apt to lead;
but dealing with hard fact does not engender a flimsy habit of mind,
and this woman was too sincere and earnest in her character, and
too happy in her situation, to be thrown by antagonism merely upon
superstitious fancies and chimeras of the second-sight. She did not
even believe herself subject to an hallucination, but smiled simply,
a little vexed that her thought could have framed such a glamour
from the day's occurrences, and not sorry to lift the bough of the
warder of the woods and enter and disappear in their sombre path.
If she had been imaginative, she would have hesitated at her first
step into a region whose dangers were not visionary; but I suppose
that the thought of a little child at home would conquer that pro-
pensity in the most habituated. So, biting a bit of spicy birch, she
went along. Now and then she came to a gap where the trees had
been partially felled, and here she found that the lingering twilight
was explained by that peculiar and perhaps electric film which sometimes sheathes the sky in diffused light for very many hours before
a brilliant aurora. Suddenly, a swift shadow, like the fabulous flying-
dragon, writhed through the air before her, and she felt herself instantly seized and borne aloft. It was that wild beast—the most savage and serpentine and subtle and fearless of our latitudes—known
by hunters as the Indian Devil,[2] and he held her in his clutches on
the broad floor of a swinging fir-bough. His long sharp claws were
caught in her clothing, he worried them sagaciously a little, then,
finding that ineffectual to free them, he commenced licking her bare
white arm with his rasping tongue and pouring over her the wide
streams of his hot, fetid breath. So quick had this flashing action been
that the woman had had no time for alarm; moreover, she was not
of the screaming kind: but now, as she felt him endeavoring to dis-
entangle his claws, and the horrid sense of her fate smote her, and

---

[2] The cougar; also known as panther or mountain lion.

she saw instictively the fierce plunge of those weapons, the long strips of living flesh torn from her bones, the agony, the quivering disgust, itself a worse agony—while by her side, and holding her in his great lithe embrace, the monster crouched, his white tusks whetting and gnashing, his eyes glaring through all the darkness like balls of red fire—a shriek, that rang in every forest hollow, that startled every winter-housed thing, that stirred and woke the least needle of the tasselled pines, tore through her lips. A moment afterward, the beast left the arm, once white, now crimson, and looked up alertly.

She did not think at this instant to call upon God. She called upon her husband. It seemed to her that she had but one friend in the world; that was he; and again the cry, loud, clear, prolonged, echoed through the woods. It was not the shriek that disturbed the creature at his relish; he was not born in the woods to be scared of an owl, you know; what then? It must have been the echo, most musical, most resonant, repeated and yet repeated, dying with long sighs of sweet sound, vibrated from rock to river and back again from depth to depth of cave and cliff. Her thought flew after it; she knew, that, even if her husband heard it, he yet could not reach her in time; she saw that while the beast listened he would not gnaw—and this she *felt* directly, when the rough, sharp, and multiplied stings of his tongue retouched her arm. Again her lips opened by instinct, but the sound that issued thence came by reason. She had heard that music charmed wild beasts—just this point between life and death intensified every faculty—and when she opened her lips the third time, it was not for shrieking, but for singing.

A little thread of melody stole out, a rill of tremulous motion; it was the cradlesong with which she rocked her baby—how could she sing that? And then she remembered the baby sleeping rosily on the long settee before the fire—the father cleaning his gun, with one foot on the green wooden rundle—the merry light from the chimney dancing out and through the room, on the rafters of the ceiling with their tassels of onions and herbs, on the log walls painted with lichens and festooned with apples, on the king's-arm slung across the shelf with the old pirate's-cutlass, on the snow-pile of the bed, and on the great brass clock—dancing, too, and lingering on the baby, with his fringed gentian eyes, his chubby fists clenched on the pillow, and his fine breezy hair fanning with the motion of his father's foot. All this struck her in one, and made a sob of her breath, and she ceased.

Immediately the long red tongue was thrust forth again. Before it touched, a song sprang to her lips, a wild sea-song, such as some sailor might be singing far out on trackless blue water that night, the shrouds whistling with frost and the sheets glued in ice—a song with the wind in its burden and the spray in its chorus. The monster raised his head and flared the fiery eyeballs upon her, then fretted the imprisoned claws a moment and was quiet; only the breath like the vapor from some hell-pit still swathed her. Her voice, at first faint and fearful, gradually lost its quaver, grew under her control and subject to her modulation; it rose on long swells, it fell in subtile cadences, now and then its tones pealed out like bells from distant belfries on fresh sonorous mornings. She sung the song through, and, wondering lest his name of Indian Devil were not his true name, and if he would not detect her, she repeated it. Once or twice now, indeed, the beast stirred uneasily, turned, and made the bough sway at his movement. As she ended, he snapped his jaws together, and tore away the fettered member, curling it under him with a snarl— when she burst into the gayest reel that ever answered a fiddle-bow. How many a time she had heard her husband play it on the homely fiddle made by himself from birch and cherry-wood! how many a time she had seen it danced on the floor of their one room, to the patter of wooden clogs and the rustle of homespun petticoat! how many a time she had danced it herself!—and did she not remember once, as they joined clasps for right-hands-round how it had lent its gay, bright measure to her life? And here she was singing it alone, in the forest, at midnight, to a wild beast! As she sent her voice trilling up and down its quick oscillations between joy and pain, the creature who grasped her uncurled his paw and scratched the bark from the bough; she must vary the spell; and her voice spun leaping along the projecting points of tune of a hornpipe. Still singing, she felt herself twisted about with a low growl and a lifting of the red lip from the glittering teeth; she broke the hornpipe's thread, and commenced unravelling a lighter, livelier thing, an Irish jig. Up and down and round about her voice flew, the beast threw back his head so that the diabolical face fronted hers, and the torrent of his breath pre-

379

pared her for his feast as the anaconda slimes his prey. Frantically she darted from tune to tune; his restless movements followed her. She tired herself with dancing and vivid national airs, growing feverish and singing spasmodically as she felt her horrid tomb yawning wider. Touching in this manner all the slogan and keen clan cries, the beast moved again, but only to lay the disengaged paw across her with heavy satisfaction. She did not dare to pause; through the clear cold air, the frosty starlight, she sang. If there were yet any tremor in the tone, it was not fear—she had learned the secret of sound at last; nor could it be chill—far too high a fervor throbbed her pulses; it was nothing but the thought of the log-house and of what might be passing within it. She fancied the baby stirring in his sleep and moving his pretty lips—her husband rising and opening the door, looking out after her, and wondering at her absence. She fancied the light pouring through the chink and then shut in again with all the safety and comfort and joy, her husband taking down the fiddle and playing lightly with his head inclined, playing while she sang, while she sang for her life to an Indian Devil. Then she knew he was fumbling for and finding some shining fragment and scoring it down the yellowing hair, and unconsciously her voice forsook the wild war-tunes and drifted into the half-gay, half-melancholy "Rosin the Bow."

Suddenly she woke pierced with a pang, and the daggered tooth penetrating her flesh—dreaming of safety, she had ceased singing and lost it. The beast had regained the use of all his limbs, and now, standing and raising his back, bristling and foaming, with sounds that would have been like hisses but for their deep and fearful sonority, he withdrew step by step toward the trunk of the tree, still with his flaming balls upon her. She was all at once free, on one end of the bough, twenty feet from the ground. She did not measure the distance, but rose to drop herself down, careless of any death, so that it were not this. Instantly, as if he scanned her thoughts, the creature bounded forward with a yell and caught her again in his dreadful hold. It might be that he was not greatly famished; for, as she suddenly flung up her voice again, he settled himself composedly on the bough, still clasping her with invincible pressure to his rough, ravenous breast, and listening in a fascination to the sad, strange U-la-lu that now moaned forth in loud, hollow tones above him. He half closed his eyes, and sleepily reopened and shut them again.

What rending pains were close at hand! Death! and what a death! worse than any other that is to be named! Water, be it cold or warm, that which buoys up blue ice-fields, or which bathes tropical coasts with currents of balmy bliss, is yet a gentle conqueror, kisses as it kills, and draws you down gently through darkening fathoms to its heart. Death at the sword is the festival of trumpet and bugle and banner, with glory ringing out around you and distant hearts thrilling through yours. No gnawing disease can bring such hideous end as this; for that is a fiend bred of your own flesh, and this—is it a fiend, this living lump of appetites? What dread comes with the thought of perishing in flames! but fire, let it leap and hiss never so hotly, is something too remote, too alien, to inspire us with such loathly horror as a wild beast; if it have a life, that life is too utterly beyond our comprehension. Fire is not half ourselves; as it devours, arouses neither hatred nor disgust; is not to be known by the strength of our lower natures let loose; does not drip our blood into our faces from foaming chaps, nor mouth nor snarl above us with vitality. Let us be ended by fire, and we are ashes, for the winds to bear, the leaves to cover; let us be ended by wild beasts, and the base, cursed thing howls with us forever through the forest. All this she felt as she charmed him, and what force it lent to her song God knows. If her voice should fail! If the damp and cold should give her any fatal hoarseness! If all the silent powers of the forest did not conspire to help her! The dark, hollow night rose indifferently over her; the wide, cold air breathed rudely past her, lifted her wet hair and blew it down again; the great boughs swung with a ponderous strength, now and then clashed their iron lengths together and shook off a sparkle of icy spears or some long-lain weight of snow from their heavy shadows. The green depths were utterly cold and silent and stern. These beautiful haunts that all the summer were hers and rejoiced to share with her their bounty, these heavens that had yielded their largess, these stems that had thrust their blossoms into her hands, all these friends of three moons ago forgot her now and knew her no longer.

Feeling her desolation, wild, melancholy, forsaken songs rose thereon from that frightful aerie—weeping, wailing tunes, that sob among the people from age to age, and overflow with otherwise unexpressed sadness—all rude, mournful ballads—old tearful strains,

381

that Shakespeare heard the vagrants sing, and that rise and fall like the wind and tide—sailor-songs, to be heard only in lone mid-watches beneath the moon and stars—ghastly rhyming romances, such as that famous one of the "Lady Margaret," when

> "She slipped on her gown of green
> A piece below the knee—
> And 'twas all a long, cold winter's night
> A dead corse followed she."

Still the beast lay with closed eyes, yet never relaxing his grasp. Once a half-whine of enjoyment escaped him—he fawned his fearful head upon her; once he scored her cheek with his tongue: savage caresses that hurt like wounds. How weary she was! and yet how terribly awake! How fuller and fuller of dismay grew the knowledge that she was only prolonging her anguish and playing with death! How appalling the thought that with her voice ceased her existence! Yet she could not sing forever; her throat was dry and hard; her very breath was a pain; her mouth was hotter than any desert-worn pilgrim's—if she could but drop upon her burning tongue one atom of the ice that glittered about her!—but both of her arms were pinioned in the giant's vice. She remembered the winding-sheet, and for the first time in her life shivered with spiritual fear. Was it hers? She asked herself, as she sang, what sins she had committed, what life she had led, to find her punishment so soon and in these pangs—and then she sought eagerly for some reason why her husband was not up and abroad to find her. He failed her—her one sole hope in life; and without being aware of it, her voice forsook the songs of suffering and sorrow for old Covenanting hymns—hymns with which her mother had lulled her, which the class-leader pitched in the chimney-corners—grand and sweet Methodist hymns, brimming with melody and with all fantastic involutions of tune to suit that ecstatic worship—hymns full of the beauty of holiness, steadfast, relying, sanctified by the salvation they had lent to those in worse extremity than hers—for they had found themselves in the grasp of hell, while she was but in the jaws of death. Out of this strange music, peculiar to one character of faith, and than which there is none more beautiful in its degree nor owning a more potent sway of sound, her voice soared into the glorified chants of churches. What to her was death by cold or famine or wild beasts? "Though He slay me, yet will I trust in Him," she sang. High and clear through the frore fair night, the level moonbeams splintering in the wood, the scarce glints of stars in the shadowy roof of branches, these sacred anthems rose— rose as a hope from despair, as some snowy spray of flower-bells from blackest mould. Was she not in God's hands? Did not the world swing at His will? If this were in His great plan of providence, was it not best, and should she not accept it?

"He is the Lord our God; His judgments are in all the earth."

Oh, sublime faith of our fathers, where utter self-sacrifice alone was true love, the fragrance of whose unrequired subjection was pleasant as that of golden censers swung in purple-vapored chancels!

Never ceasing in the rhythm of her thoughts, articulated in music as they thronged, the memory of her first communion flashed over her. Again she was in that distant place on that sweet spring morning. Again the congregation rustled out, and the few remained, and she trembled to find herself among them. How well she remembered the devout, quiet faces, too accustomed to the sacred feast to glow with their inner joy! how well the snowy linen at the altar, the silver vessels slowly and silently shifting! and as the cup approached and passed, how the sense of delicious perfume stole in and heightened the transport of her prayer, and she had seemed, looking up through the windows where the sky soared blue in constant freshness, to feel all heaven's balms dripping from the portals, and to scent the lilies of eternal peace! Perhaps another would not have felt so much ecstasy as satisfaction on that occasion; but it is a true, if a later disciple, who has said, "The Lord bestoweth his blessings there, where he findeth the vessels empty."—"And does it need the walls of a church to renew my communion?" she asked. "Does not every moment stand a temple four-square to God? And in that morning, with its buoyant sunlight, was I any dearer to the Heart of the World than now?" "My beloved is mine, and I am his," she sang over and over again, with all varied inflection and profuse tune. How gently all the winter-wrapt things bent toward her then! into what relation with her had they grown! how this common dependence was the spell of their intimacy! how at one with Nature had she become! how all the night and the silence and the forest seemed to hold its breath, and to send its soul up to God in her singing! It was no longer despondency, that singing. It was neither prayer nor petition. She had left

383

imploring, "How long wilt thou forget me, O Lord?" "Lighten mine eyes, lest I sleep the sleep of death!" "For in death there is no remembrance of thee"—with countless other such fragments of supplication. She cried rather, "Yea, though I walk through the valley of the shadow of death, I will fear no evil: for thou art with me; thy rod and thy staff, they comfort me"—and lingered, and repeated, and sang again, "I shall be satisfied, when I awake, with thy likeness."

Then she thought of the Great Deliverance, when he drew her up out of many waters, and the flashing old psalm pealed forth triumphantly:

> "The Lord descended from above,
>   and bow'd the heavens hie:
> And underneath his feet he cast
>   the darknesse of the skie.
> On cherubs and on cherubins
>   full royally he road:
> And on the wings of all the winds
>   came flying all abroad."

She forgot how recently, and with what a strange pity for her own shapeless form that was to be, she had quaintly sung—

> "Oh, lovely appearance of death!
>   What sight upon earth is so fair?
> Not all the gay pageants that breathe
>   Can with a dead body compare!"

She remembered instead—"In thy presence is fulness of joy; at thy right hand there are pleasures forevermore"; and, "God will redeem my soul from the power of the grave: for he shall receive me"; "He will swallow up death in victory." Not once now did she say, "Lord, how long will thou look on? Rescue my soul from their destructions, my darling from the lions"—for she knew that "the young lions roar after their prey and seek their meat from God." "O Lord, thou preservest man and beast!" she said.

She had no comfort or consolation in this season, such as sustained the Christian martyrs in the amphitheatre. She was not dying for her faith; there were no palms in heaven for her to wave; but how many a time had she declared—"I had rather be a doorkeeper in the house of my God, than to dwell in the tents of wickedness!" And as the broad rays here and there broke through the dense covert of shade and lay in rivers of lustre on crystal sheathing and frozen fretting of trunk and limb and on the great spaces of refraction, they builded up visibly that house, the shining city on the hill, and singing, "Beautiful for situation, the joy of the whole earth, is Mount Zion, on the sides of the North, the city of the Great King," her vision climbed to that higher picture where the angel shows the dazzling thing, the holy Jerusalem descending out of heaven from God, with its splendid battlements and gates of pearls, and its foundations, the eleventh a jacinth, the twelfth an amethyst—with its great white throne, and the rainbow round about it, in sight like unto an emerald—"And there shall be no night there, for the Lord God giveth them light," she sang.

What whisper of dawn now rustled through the wilderness? How the night was passing! And still the beast crouched upon the bough, changing only the posture of his head, that again he might command her with those charmed eyes—half their fire was gone; she could almost have released herself from his custody; yet, had she stirred, no one knows what malevolent instinct might have dominated anew. But of that she did not dream; long ago stripped of any expectation, she was experiencing in her divine rapture how mystically true it is that "he that dwelleth in the secret place of the Most High shall abide under the shadow of the Almighty."

Slow clarion cries now wound from the distance as the cocks caught the intelligence of day and re-echoed it faintly from farm to farm—sleepy sentinels of night, sounding the foe's invasion, and translating that dim intuition to ringing notes of warning. Still she chanted on. A remote crash of brushwood told of some other beast on his depredations, or some night-belated traveller groping his way through the narrow path. Still she chanted on. The far, faint echoes of the chanticleers died into distance—the crashing of the branches grew nearer. No wild beast that, but a man's step—a man's form in the moonlight, stalwart and strong—on one arm slept a little child, in the other hand he held his gun. Still she chanted on.

Perhaps, when her husband last looked forth, he was half ashamed to find what a fear he felt for her. He knew she would never leave the child so long but for some direst need—and yet he may have

385

laughed at himself, as he lifted and wrapped it with awkward care, and, loading his gun and strapping on his horn, opened the door again and closed it behind him, going out and plunging into the darkness and dangers of the forest. He was more singularly alarmed than he would have been willing to acknowledge; as he had sat with his bow hovering over the strings, he had half believed to hear her voice mingling gayly with the instrument, till he paused and listened if she were not about to lift the latch and enter. As he drew nearer the heart of the forest, that intimation of melody seemed to grow more actual, to take body and breath, to come and go on long swells and ebbs of the night-breeze, to increase with tune and words, till a strange, shrill singing grew ever clearer, and, as he stepped into an open space of moonbeams, far up in the branches, rocked by the wind, and singing, "How beautiful upon the mountains are the feet of him that bringeth good tidings, that publisheth peace," he saw his wife—his wife—but, great God in heaven! how? Some mad exclamation escaped him, but without diverting her. The child knew the singing voice, though never heard before in that unearthly key, and turned toward it through the veiling dreams. With a celerity almost instantaneous, it lay, in the twinkling of an eye, on the ground at the father's feet, while his gun was raised to his shoulder and levelled at the monster covering his wife with shaggy form and flaming gaze —his wife so ghastly white, so rigid, so stained with blood, her eyes so fixedly bent above, and her lips, that had indurated into the chiselled pallor of marble, parted only with that flood of solemn song.

I do not know if it were the mother-instinct that for a moment lowered her eyes—those eyes, so lately riveted on heaven, now suddenly seeing all life-long bliss possible. A thrill of joy pierced and shivered through her like a weapon, her voice trembled in its course, her glance lost its steady strength, fever-flushes chased each other over her face, yet she never once ceased chanting. She was quite aware, that, if her husband shot now, the ball must pierce her body before reaching any vital part of the beast—and yet better that death, by his hand, than the other. But this her husband also knew, and he remained motionless, just covering the creature with the sight. He dared not fire, lest some wound not mortal should break the spell exercised by her voice, and the beast, enraged with pain, should rend her in atoms; moreover, the light was too uncertain for his aim. So he waited. Now and then he examined his gun to see if the damp were injuring its charge, now and then he wiped the great drops from his forehead. Again the cocks crowed with the passing hour— the last time they were heard on that night. Cheerful home sound then, how full of safety and all comfort and rest it seemed! what sweet morning incidents of sparkling fire and sunshine, of gay household bustle, shining dresser, and cooing baby, of steaming cattle in the yard, and brimming milk-pails at the door! what pleasant voices! what laughter! what security! and here—

Now, as she sang on in the slow, endless, infinite moments, the fervent vision of God's peace was gone. Just as the grave had lost its sting, she was snatched back again into the arms of earthly hope. In vain she tried to sing, "There remaineth a rest for the people of God"—her eyes trembled on her husband's, and she could think only of him, and of the child, and of happiness that yet might be, but with what a dreadful gulf of doubt between! She shuddered now in the suspense; all calm forsook her; she was tortured with dissolving heats or frozen with icy blasts; her face contracted, growing small and pinched; her voice was hoarse and sharp—every tone cut like a knife—the notes became heavy to lift—withheld by some hostile pressure—impossible. One gasp, a convulsive effort, and there was silence—she had lost her voice.

The beast made a sluggish movement—stretched and fawned like one awaking—then, as if he would have yet more of the enchantment, stirred her slightly with his muzzle. As he did so, a sidelong hint of the man standing below with the raised gun smote him; he sprung round furiously, and, seizing his prey, was about to leap into some unknown airy den of the topmost branches now waving to the slow dawn. The late moon had rounded through the sky so that her gleam at last fell full upon the bough with fairy frosting; the wintry morning light did not yet penetrate the gloom. The woman, suspended in mid-air an instant, cast only one agonized glance beneath— but across and through it, ere the lids could fall, shot a withering sheet of flame—a rifle-crack, half heard, was lost in the terrible yell of desperation that bounded after it and filled her ears with savage echoes, and in the wide arc of some eternal descent she was falling— but the beast fell under her.

I think that the moment following must have been too sacred for

387

us, and perhaps the three have no special interest again till they issue from the shadows of the wilderness upon the white hills that skirt their home. The father carries the child hushed again into slumber, the mother follows with no such feeble step as might be anticipated— and as they slowly climb the steep under the clear gray sky and the paling morning star, she stops to gather a spray of the red-rose berries or a feathery tuft of dead grasses for the chimney-piece of the log-house, or a handful of brown ones for the child's play—and of these quiet, happy folk you would scarcely dream how lately they had stolen from under the banner and encampment of the great King Death. The husband proceeds a step or two in advance; the wife lingers over a singular foot-print in the snow, stoops and examines it, then looks up with a hurried word. Her husband stands alone on the hill, his arms folded across the babe, his gun fallen— stands defined against the pallid sky like a bronze. What is there in their home, lying below and yellowing in the light, to fix him with such a stare? She springs to his side. There is no home there. The log-house, the barns, the neighboring farms, the fences, are all blotted out and mingled in one smoking ruin. Desolation and death were indeed there, and beneficence and life in the forest. Tomahawk and scalping-knife, descending during that night, had left behind them only this work of their accomplished hatred and one subtle foot-print in the snow.

For the rest—the world was all before them, where to choose.

STUDY NOTES

1. Inasmuch as critics have sometimes mentioned that Mrs. Spofford's plots are somewhat improbable, comment on the improbability of the action in "Circumstance."

2. Though the characterization in this story is rather slight, point out the method or methods by which the personality of the woman captured by the beast is revealed.

3. Indicate the appropriateness of the vision of the winding-sheet to the mood the woman was already in and the effect of the vision upon her.

4. What contribution does the vision make to the development of the plot of the story?

5. Mention the activities of the wild beast, the Indian Devil, that were threatening to the woman and that endangered her life.

6. List the types of song that she sang while charming the beast through all the night and explain why she varied the types.

7. Enumerate her fancies concerning the activities that might be occurring in her home and point out the significance of her having such fancies.

8. State the gist of the woman's philosophizing concerning the horror of death produced by a wild beast's claws.

9. Cite instances of the use of suspense during the long hours of the night when the woman was alone with the beast and shortly before her husband slew the animal.

10. With what surprise does the story end and does any connection seem to exist between the surprise and the title "Circumstance"?

11. Point out the romantic elements of the story.

12. Also such of its realistic elements as you can find.

MATTER

THE TRAP [1]
(1947)

HOWARD BLOOMFIELD

T HE way that Armstrong Destin tried to put George Turner
overboard was simple, and yet it held a trick, a touch of drama.
The trick was misdirection: a focusing of the eye on one spot, and
not letting the right hand know what the left hand is doing.

The old Nassau sloop wallowed along with a broad arrow of foam
at the bow and a gay bubble and froth sweeping out under the fat
stern, because the trade wind could make any boat move, even though
the boat waved foul grasses from its bottom like this sloop of Destin's. George Turner felt himself living in the middle of a color film
and, at times, during the past two days, he had closed his eyes and
opened them again, convincing himself of a vividness that was a
blow on the eyeballs. The foam was so white, the sky so blue; and
the dozens of sandy keys were golden chips on a sea of jade satin.
And some of the keys wore dark green tufts of vegetation, though
empty of human life—the Bahamas hold scores and hundreds of
such tiny low islands, useless but pretty.

This was old stuff to Destin, but to George Turner it was adventure. Turner was a slight, wiry man, with brown face and brown
hair, and brown eyes behind his glasses. His face gave an occasional
pleased twitch, and his eyes blinked like an owl's. He kept thinking
that pirate ships had sailed these waters, and it was easy to picture
one here, prowling boldly, full of fighting men who were not at all
like himself, men more like Destin.

The sun was beginning to set, and here it was a bigger red ball
than elsewhere, and a red-and-gold cloud was a brighter and longer
banner.

"Damned beautiful," said George Turner, jerking his fishing rod
at the sunset. "And a good moon to come. We can go on sailing,
huh?"

"Sure," said Destin. "Get us there sooner." Destin was taking him
to a place where they could look down through clear water and see
the ribs of an old wreck and the shape of a cannon.

Destin got up from the tiller, planted one foot across it to steer by, and stretched and yawned lazily. He was a bigger man than Turner, but the difference was more striking than that. He was a strong male animal, even if he seemed a sort of gentleman on the surface. Aside from the long knife scar down his forearm, it was plain to see that Destin had been in dangers and tight places and had fought his own fights and made his own laws.

As Destin put his right hand over his yawning mouth, a gleam in his ring caught his eye. The ring was a heavy band of gold, with a green stone that was square and large. Destin held out his hand, turning it, letting the light strike into the stone.

"You ever notice this ring?" he asked George Turner. "It was found in an old wreck. I got the ring off a dead man, down in Port-au-Prince. I took it for a souvenir. Look at this engraving—I think it's Spanish."

While Turner stepped to him, Destin made his hand into a fist and remarked, "Not a bad brass knuckle, if a man ever needs one." He relaxed the fist and spread out his fingers. Turner gazed down at the worn, indistinct chasing either side of the stone.

"The man I took the ring from tried to kill me, when I wasn't expecting a thing," said Destin. "Do you notice, right next to the stone—"

Then George Turner was staggering, reeling, on the very edge of the stern, flailing his fishing rod for balance. The unexpected shove by Destin's left hand would have sent him overboard at once, except that he had tensed a little to hear Destin's story of killing the man; except that earlier that day a barracuda had staggered him by its savage strike, so that Turner had since kept himself braced when he held the rod.

In his wild gyration he saw that Destin's fist was cocked again, and behind it Destin's face was astonishingly savage. Turner smashed the heavy deep-sea reel on his rod against that face for he had succeeded in swaying inward on the boat. Then Destin wrenched the rod down, but Turner, on his feet again, whipped a fish knife from the sheath at his belt. It opened a red streak on Destin's arm, and Destin turned and jumped down into the cabin.

Turner gasped, trying to realize what had happened. It had been only a few bewildering seconds since he was staring at Destin's ring, and now Destin was bleeding in the cabin. Turner stood in paralysis of fright, and then he thought of the revolver on a shelf below, and of Destin's hand snatching up the gun.

Turner raced forward in a panic to get off the boat, to dive and swim madly away. The sloop, its tiller free, was rounding into the wind, the sails shaking and banging. But it could come under control again in a minute, and follow and overtake him like a porpoise charging upon a fish. He slashed the main halyard. The big leg-of-mutton sail came down like a snowslide, a rotten topping lift broke, the boom was a thick club smiting the cabin roof. Destin was just coming up out of the hatchway when the boom struck his shoulder and knocked him below.

Turner slashed the jib halyard. The jib, on its slanting head stay, came down in a gentler folding fall.

The mainsail lay all over the hatchway like a great canvas rug, and the rug heaved up over a crawling form. George Turner delayed his departure one instant more, to run back and snatch the fishing rod. He swung the heavy reel down on the moving bulge and the bulge backed into the cabin.

Then Turner in his fear went overboard. The water closed around him in a cool safe bath and swept some of his fright away. A strange crashing sound had entered his ears when he dove, because the cork helmet was still on his head, held by a strap under his chin. He had his glasses, too, hooked over his ears.

He swam furiously at first, and instinct told him to go upwind, because the sloop would be drifting away down the wind. When he looked back, the sloop was only a hundred yards away, a dark bulk. Though the night would not come for a while, the boat was dark because it lay against the red stain of sunset, in reddening water. Destin was not yet on deck.

Turner sprinted again. A slow ground swell heaved and fell, like a leisurely breathing of the sea. A man would be hidden in the hollow, and Turner tried to stay there, but he could not swim quite fast enough, and so he went under in a dead man's float when he felt himself being lifted, and began to swim again when he was lowered. Out of breath, he trod water for another look. Destin was on deck, walking and turning slowly, no doubt searching the water. Farther away than Turner had expected, until he thought again of the downward drift of the boat. The red was turning leaden on the water, and dulling in the sky.

Turner remembered the dinghy lashed upside down on deck, and he wished he were in it. There had been time—it seemed now—to get it overboard. Turner was bitter that he had not thought there was time. He could not even remember if he had thought of the dinghy at all; and the bitterness engulfed him and made him feel heavy and tired in the water. It was too late now to think of all the things he should have done. But Destin would not be treading out here in a thickening gloom. If it had happened to Destin, Destin would still be on the sloop, and the only man alive.

Turner wondered if Destin would come after him in the dinghy. Unless he came soon and fast, he would risk losing the sloop in the night. Unless—Turner's brain kept making quick snaps at the situation, like the snaps of a cornered dog—unless Destin should hang up a lantern first, so he could find the sloop again. Destin couldn't come after him in the sloop without a job of rigging first, because the severed halyards had whipped aloft and run out of the blocks.

Thinking of that, the immediate fear of Destin went out of George Turner. He swam along slowly on his back, keeping his feet toward the dull maroon in the west. That color faded so rapidly, while stars came out in a slow sprinkle, that he picked a star to keep him straight on his course to nowhere.

The water was comfortably warm. Turner remembered reading once of a man who floated in the Gulf Stream for a week and was saved—true, he was unconscious and supported by a life preserver. But Turner thought he had at least a few hours ahead of him. The human body was ninety-eight per cent—was it more?—water, and flotation was only a matter of ounces. He floated quite easily so long as he lay on his back as if in a loose strait jacket, but if he tried to turn the water gushed into his nose and mouth.

The pith helmet that was now under the back of his head seemed to help a bit, though it might slowly become a soggy thing. Already he imagined that a part of the brim flapped loosely against his neck as each push of his hands moved him onward a little more. He removed his waterproof wrist watch, his belt and the sheath that had held the knife, but these were motions that sunk his face and left him out of breath.

393

MATTER

He was dressed only in shirt and shorts and sandals. He thought of stuffing the helmet inside his shirt, but it gave him a weak comfort under his head, as if his head were really lying on something. And perhaps the sandals helped a bit, being of a composition cork sole. But a man could float, without helmet or sandals. A man had a few ounces of buoyancy in himself.

Turner tried to think reasonably about it. Life was a few ounces that would rather float; Death was a few ounces that would rather sink. He was in a big, warm swimming pool. He was lying on a kind of fluid couch, pushing himself along it by his hands, and covered all over but for his eyes and nose and mouth. But a swimming pool has sides and ends, and a ladder for climbing out, and a swimming pool holds no sharks and barracuda. He tried not to think about that, because it was a frantic thought. But it was very difficult not to wonder what might be moving below him, surveying him, as he inched along in this great black space with his eyes fixed on a star.

So Turner was immensely lonely. He imagined he heard friends wondering aloud what had become of him. He saw an office in Pittsburgh where soot fell on papers ready for him to sign, where familiar faces of men and women turned to one another and talked about him, not knowing that a man named Destin had dissolved a partnership with abrupt violence. Turner was utterly shaken—he had liked to be with Destin, had secretly admired Destin's strength and his adventurous life. Now Turner was only two eyes and two nostrils in a black liquid world because he had put funds with Destin in a beef-cattle venture on a large island near Nassau—a plausible-looking experiment, a joint account with some cautious safeguards. Cautions against everything except one big thing that had never occurred to Turner: that he should suddenly be dead and it would all belong to Destin. The familiar faces wouldn't know about that, or that Destin had suggested this quiet side trip to see a wreck that might hold a treasure.

George Turner thought the night grew a little brighter, and trod water to stare eastward where the moon rose full. He searched the horizon for an island he thought might be there, and saw nothing but the silver path of the moon across the water. He then sobbed suddenly, and wanted to scream and claw at the water and go down, swallow water and fill his lungs and have the thing over—and told himself to go on pushing with his hands, and that all these islands were very low.

A new and startling sound came through the water that so quietly lapped and patted around his face. It was a slashing noise, like canvas being ripped, of something coming toward him very fast, and Turner went rigid, though trembling violently. In his rigidity his feet sank down until he was almost upright, and then, the slashing coming very close to him, he screamed and beat his arms and legs and tried to climb out of the water. He fought himself into exhaustion, and then saw the moonlight glisten on the shining black hides of a school of porpoise leaping and diving past him.

After that Turner was very tired. He rested on his back, his hands moving as if they belonged to someone else, his eyes on the star and his head toward the low moon, until he heard another sound ahead of him. There was a gurgling, rather rhythmical and musical sound. He trod water to look, and found his feet standing on sand.

Through a lapping froth he went ashore on the island, which was one of the three he had seen within several miles while he slashed the halyards; and this was undoubtedly the one to the eastward.

The island was about three quarters of a mile long, and half as wide, and a broad rim of sandy beach ran all around it. Turner followed the beach, walking to get warm— the breeze chill on his wet skin—until he came to his own footprints again. So low was the island that, under the bright moon, he could see across it from beach to beach. In the middle were tufts of wiry grass and one low clump of bushes. That might shade a man who crawled into it; that might make a hideaway, if a man could hide at the end of a track of footprints. Some sea birds went up with crazy screams as Turner walked among nests. Here was food, when a man began to starve. The thicket was thorny, and he went back to the beach. He lay on the warm sand and pulled it over him like a blanket.

Along the windward beach stretched a snake of sea grasses and kelp. Turner heaved up out of the sand and prowled carefully. A heavy timber of ship's deadwood, studded with rusted spikes, lay rooted in the beach. Here and there was some odd useless thing, dropped off a steamer long ago and perhaps hundreds of miles away. An electric light bulb. Three rum bottles. A little vial that had held someone's tonic, or vitamin pills. Turner snatched up four coconuts and shook each at his ear, hoping to hear a liquid thud inside. Each was light, empty, dry as an old skull, and he flung it down.

Something round and big crawled out of the sea, moved patiently up the beach, and began to settle into the sand. A sea turtle, feeling the pressure of eggs. A man could eat, now and then, on this island. He could roof over some bushes with seaweed. Likely he could get a fire for cooking, with water in a curved shoulder of a bottle to make a burning glass. He might even unravel a fishing line out of his clothes. He could get himself some scraps of food. But there wasn't any water.

Turner broke a bottle on a spike and began to dig near the bushes. Below the sand was a crumbling coral rock that became harder, then too hard. He imagined dampness in the bottom of the hole. He decided it was only cooler than the surface sand.

Turner began to arrange seaweed into letters ten paces long on the beach. Sea draped its grasses in slow twists along the sand. The angular lines of H E L P would show better than S O S from the air. Someday someone in a plane would go over; perhaps a sportsman, making a wide swing, then circling and staring at a big word H E L P. Turner began another message for the man who came down to investigate, if the man came too late. In small letters he traced out *Armstrong Destin killed George Turner,* and began to build up the letters with shells, into ridges. But now the moon was dropping low, and the night turned darker. He lay down to wait for daylight.

When the sun came up, Destin's sails were a fluttering white tent two miles away. The sloop was anchored off a sandy key. The little white dinghy moved to the beach. It was hard for Turner to follow the dinghy at that distance, and Destin he could hardly see at all—a small black mark on the sand. The dinghy moved off the beach. The sloop began to sail. Destin was looking over the few near-by islands before he sailed away, rowing in and glancing about for footprints. And now he sailed toward Turner's island.

Turner fell on the sand and beat it with his fists. He poured out hoarse curses at the boat. A man might try to hide. But it would be at the end of a plain trail. Turner stared at the sloop, the fat curve of sail, the white curl round the bow, with wincing eyes. He was a thin brown animal with a leg caught in a trap of sand, watching the hunter come. He sat down in the middle of the island and pushed up a sand wall around him, like a breastwork. It was a fort but with no defense. His pith helmet and his face were fixed still above it as he watched the sloop grow, the jib coming distinct from the mainsail, the figure of Destin standing up. The sloop held food and water. Turner remembered just where they were: the canned goods, the crate of fruit, the big galvanized tank beneath the deck. The cigarettes, the bottles of rum. They were all only a quarter of a mile away when Destin dropped the sails. The anchor made a brief white splash.

The dinghy trailed behind the sloop. Destin jumped down into it and began to row, turned his head, and pulled the oars harder. Destin knew. Turner watched the powerful back and arms move with the blades, and when the head did not turn again, Turner knew that Destin was very sure of himself. Destin would speak to him quite calmly. Destin might say, "Sorry, old man. You've only managed to string the thing out." He would be calm and steady with the pistol.

String the thing out. But if he strung it out, he would die of thirst. All that Destin really had to do was to sit on his boat and let him die. Turner saw that he must try to be calm and conserve his strength. He had an emptiness in his stomach that wasn't really hunger, and he hadn't yet so very much thirst. The day was brightening beautifully, the sea sparkling, the breeze cool, the sky very blue and the clouds very white above him and Destin.

Turner slipped out of the back of his sand pit, and on the far beach filled a bottle with sea water. The splash over his hands and wrists, the water round his ankles, made him more conscious of the dryness in his throat. He went in a crouch along the beach until the clump of bushes was between him and the dinghy. Into the dry hole he had dug, he emptied the bottle. The water stood still for a moment, and then began to seep away. Turner filled the bottle again on the beach, and crawled back into his pit.

He sat up and looked over the top at Destin, who was now pulling the dinghy up on the sand.

"Destin!" he called.

Destin looked toward him briefly, without reply. He had seen the big word on the sand. He walked around it deliberately and

397

cast a slow look round the sky. Evidently he came to the smaller message that Turner had started, for his feet made some measured kicks and sent up spurts of sand. Then with wide sweeps of his legs he went through the letters H E L P, driving the letters out of shape. Taking the revolver out of his trousers, he walked toward Turner. He called, "Good morning!"

Turner was not much exposed in his sand pit, only his head up, a glint of sunlight on his glasses, and his legs were tense under him. A hundred yards and no closer, he thought—about the length of a football field. He got up and began to walk away from Destin. He carried the bottle of sea water like a precious thing. Destin fired. Then they were both running.

Turner thought he could hold his own with Destin in running, though he was much less of a man in every other way. But he was lighter, and in Pittsburgh he had liked to play tennis. He saw some flicks in the sand ahead, and counted the shots until there were six. He looked back, and Destin was not so close as he had been. The distance had opened very definitely. Destin stopped, taking a box from his pocket, and reloaded.

Destin sat down. Turner was quite out of breath himself, and so he lay on the sand, pulling a heap up under his shoulders for a head rest, to relax as comfortably as he could. A hundred yards was a very long revolver shot. It called for luck, even if the target stood still.

There had been a box of cartridges beside the gun on the shelf, and a box held twenty-five. Two or three had been fired at a shark. Perhaps there was another box.

Destin had a white bandage on his arm. Turner could not be sure at the distance, but he thought there was a red streak across his face, the nose swollen, where the reel had struck. Destin's broad shoulders heaved slowly as he rested, watching Turner. Turner held the bottle at his mouth, and did not swallow. Even the motion made his throat drier. Destin stood up to glare at him with both hands on hips, and then looked at the clump of bushes, as the only likely place for water.

When Destin walked away, Turner ran toward the dinghy. The attempt was hopeless, as Destin had kept himself closer to the boat. But it made Destin sprint for an instant, and fire another shot. Destin pushed the dinghy out and rowed along the beach, and Turner walked beside him, though across a wide reach of sand. Turner saw now that he might make it difficult for Destin to go far from his boat. At least he could give Destin a problem to solve.

Destin saw the problem, too, when he pulled in to the beach abreast of the low thicket. Turner watched him from a hundred yards away. Destin chased him up the beach, shot three times, and one of the bullets made a hiss. Then Destin walked toward the bushes. Turner ran back toward the dinghy. Destin ran back, too.

The thicket was at least two hundred yards from the beach. Destin took the oars from the boat, and started again. And Turner's heart leaped, hoping that Destin would rely on having the oars. He slipped toward the dinghy as Destin left it, thinking he could push it ahead of him by swimming, get into it and paddle with his hands. Destin came back on a run, but clumsily, because it was difficult to run with the oars, and fired a long shot.

Turner thought that Destin must be very angry. Destin sat near the boat a while. Then he shoved it off, and rowed toward his sloop.

Lifting the bottle again, Turner walked to the thicket. He stopped at the hole he had dug. He might have felt some elation at baffling Destin, but now he felt only an aching thirst. He had thought that Destin might examine the hole, feel some dampness, and wonder. But Destin could not approach the place. Turner poured the water over his face and chest, and noticed that Destin had stopped rowing. He shoved the bottle down into the dry hole, and then walked with it toward some sea-bird nests.

Eggs held moisture. A score of birds wheeled and screamed and dived at Turner, who carried a dozen eggs to his sand pit in his helmet.

He cracked two together, finding one liquid, and swallowed it, with fingers closed over his nose. But he retched; the egg came up. Then he remembered the mound, the scuffed place, the turtle had left. He dug with his hands. The leathery skin of eggs broke in his teeth with a relieving wet salve. He covered the place carefully and marked it with a shell. He stuffed wiry grass into his mouth, and it made a tough chewing gum.

Turner lay in the edge of the water. A man could not evaporate so much water when he was immersed, and perhaps he would absorb a little. The constant lapping and bubbling was maddening.

After a time he went back to the wreckage of his word. The sand was very hot, and it was fortunate he had his sandals. The heat soared round him in shimmering bands. On the sloop Destin was undoubtedly eating, drinking and having a smoke, training his binoculars on Turner. When Turner had raked the seaweed all into ridges again, and the letters were sharp on bare sand, when he had walked around it in final perusal, Destin rowed ashore.

Turner watched over the rim of his sand pit while Destin struck a match. The seaweed was mostly very dry, though some was still green. But there was plenty more of it, rolling in the edge of the water. The seaweed burned. But it sent up a thickening smudge, like a windrow of hay flaming and smoldering, trailing off the key like steamer smoke. Destin did not like that. He kicked the fire apart, flung sand on it, and kicked a path through the remaining letters.

"Are you here again?" called Turner. "Then let's play another set."

He seemed very calm, waiting for Destin. But the calm was a weakness, a dizziness of heat and thirst. He let Destin come almost too close, or the shot was lucky. It tossed sand up into Turner's face. It buried in the low sand wall just in front of his chest, and Turner jumped up and ran.

Two other shots passed him. When he glanced back, Destin was hammering after him, his face dark, running at a strong, ruthless gait, driving his legs with a will power that was ready to run his heart out. Turner couldn't leave him, though he had panic in his body. The distance closed a little. It was very hard to run in sand, sinking to the ankles, gulping air that was too hot to ease the lungs. He was almost ready to fling himself down when another shot sounded. He turned his head. Destin had stopped. Destin aimed at him, emptied the revolver, sat down to rock his head and body slowly, to open his mouth like a fish.

Turner was relieved that Destin sat for such a long while before he tried to approach again. Turner tilted the mockery of a bottle, stood up with an appearance of lightness, and walked away. Destin left the beach to Turner. Destin took the center of the ring, and the center was too small for them both. He kept Turner moving round the rim—Turner taking two and three steps to his one—trying to pin him in one spot against the sea. There was little running, except when Turner had to make quick spurts to hold his distance. Turner's head and eyeballs ached, and at times his legs stumbled; but whenever there was an appearance of a chance, or whenever Destin wanted to rest, he moved doggedly toward the boat. Once Destin roared in rage, and at last he went to the shore and sat on the stern of the dinghy.

Turner lay in the water once more, rolling his burned face under, filling his mouth and blowing it out, and soaking some coolness into his skin. The water bottle was hot. He immersed it to cool. He could get through today. He had had luck against Destin, but tomorrow he could not escape. Tomorrow he would be too weak; he would collapse on the burning sand.

Destin slid the dinghy to sea. Turner sat up and felt the temperature of his bottle, and put it to his mouth.

"Turner!" shouted Destin. "See you tomorrow!"

Turner called back, "Sweet dreams!"

What was the ruse for tonight? he wondered. Would Destin come ashore, trying to catch him asleep. Would he risk leaving the dinghy on the moonlit beach while he searched? Turner considered whether he should himself try to swim out, whether he had the strength—a fly crawling to a spider. Destin would get himself a little drunk tonight, and scowl at the moon and the island. Only one thing was certain. Destin dared not leave.

The sun had not yet gone down. Turner looked around the empty sky, and began to restore his word on the beach.

At daybreak Destin rowed in to the seaweed printing. He kicked out the bellies of the letters once more, but with a difference in his motions this time, not swinging his arms with the violence of his kicks, but keeping a hand behind his back in concealment from the sand pit. Then he made his steps casually slow, as if a long day were ahead and there was no need for haste. The hand remained behind him in a careless way, while he walked toward the defenseless breastwork. Once he stopped to yawn.

Turner saw that the slow approach had taken Destin a little closer to the sand pit than usual.

Turner saw this, from a comfortable distance, when he emerged from the sand and raised himself through the seaweed in the end of one leg of the letter H.

MATTER

Turner saw Destin kneel and aim at the helmet, with the glint of spectacles beneath it, and fire. Destin had lashed some kind of stock to the revolver, that nestled snugly like a rifle butt into his shoulder, and evidently greatly increased the accuracy of his aim. For the helmet, the glasses rolled down out of sight. Turner supposed that there was a hole right through the skull-dry coconut.

The dinghy was only a few steps away, and as Turner pushed it out he saw that Destin was running, in triumph at last, to the sand pit.

An uncontrollable shivering ran over Turner as he rowed. But he wasn't cold—each grain of sand and fleck of seaweed touched a nerve end in his burned skin. But this was from the hours of waiting.

The water in the sloop's tank was warm, yet it had a deliciousness, an ecstatic seep of life in his parched throat. Turner reminded himself not to drink too much at once. He went on deck to raise the jib, because that was the easy sail. The jib would move the boat sufficiently until he had eaten and drunk enough strength into himself to hoist the mainsail. The windlass was heavy enough work for now, and he did not trouble to bring the anchor all the way up. The sloop began to move.

Turner would conscientiously report Destin at the first chance, he decided, though it might be a few days, and the government could send out a plane to rescue him and let him explain. And if Destin grew too impatient with his thirst, then—Turner's trembling ceased of a sudden—Destin had a gun.

Turner drank another glass of water, sipping each wonderful drop, and sucked the juices out of a sapodilla plum, and presently looked at the island through the binoculars. He regretted his glasses, but the binoculars focused clearly.

The plane would be able to find Destin, because Destin had an armful of seaweed and was restoring the big word H E L P on the beach.

STUDY NOTES

1. What methods does Bloomfield employ in "The Trap" for portraying the character of Armstrong Destin?

2. What methods does he employ for delineating the character of George Turner?

3. Indicate Destin's motive for trying to shove Turner off the sloop.

ADVENTURE

4. Show that Turner's adventures were fraught with peril by naming the dangers he faced when swimming in the sea and after reaching the island.

5. Detail Turner's efforts to relieve his thirst.

6. By what ruse did he escape from Destin and the island?

7. Point out the suspense that appears in the account of Destin's firing at Turner with a revolver.

8. Point out the suspense in the account of Turner's struggle with thirst and heat.

9. Show that realism marks the description of the setting of the story.

10. Show that realism appears in the characterizations of Destin and Turner.

11. Show that the fast-moving action rises to a dramatic and satisfying climax.

12. Summarize the qualities of Bloomfield's literary style that you discover in this story.

COMPARISON EXERCISES

1. Contrast "Circumstance" and "The Trap" with respect to their use of realism.

2. Compare the two stories for their employment of suspense.

3. Compare these stories for their emphasis upon the ingenuity of the character beset with danger.

4. Compare these stories for the rapidity and dramatic quality of the actions narrated.

5. Which story has the more effective characterization, judged by standards of today?

WRITING SUGGESTION

Write a short story that places the hero or the heroine in a series of dangerous and thrilling experiences, rising to a dramatic climax but avoiding melodrama.

SHORT BIOGRAPHIES

WASHINGTON IRVING (1783-1859)

Irving's life began in New York City in the last year of the American Revolution, when that metropolis had a population of about twenty thousand. His parents through respect for the American commander in chief named their eleventh child Washington. The boy grew up, observing with keen interest the characters, manners, and scenes of the Hudson River valley, a region that the matured Washington Irving glamorized in some of the stories of his *Sketch Book*. It was during a seventeen-year sojourn in Europe (1815-1831) that he wrote most of his best-remembered books. He went to England in 1815 to work in behalf of a hardware firm, P. Irving and Company. When that company became bankrupt in 1818, he resorted to writing to gain a livelihood, producing during his unexpectedly long sojourn *The Sketch Book* (1820), *Bracebridge Hall* (1822), *Tales of a Traveller* (1824), and *The Alhambra* (1832). Besides these volumes of short stories he wrote a few other books during these years. *The Sketch Book* caused him to be regarded in England as the greatest literary genius of the New World. Between the close of his ministry to Spain, 1846, and the end of his life, he wrote as a labor of love his five-volume work, *The Life of George Washington*. His fame rests chiefly on his writings concerning Dutch New York and rural England, in *The Sketch Book,* and those concerning old Moorish Spain, in *The Alhambra*.

CHARLES TENNEY JACKSON (1874-   )

Both his novels and his short stories reflect Jackson's love of the outdoors. His stories may be even richer than his novels in revealing his love for animals and for nature. Having been born in St. Louis, Missouri, and having lived there for ten years, the boy, Charles Tenney Jackson, moved from place to place rather frequently, as his father, an Army colonel, went under military orders from one tour of duty to another. From about ten to twenty years of age, the youth had an opportunity to learn much about such aspects of life as particularly appeal to a naturalist. From 1884 to 1888 he lived on a ranch in the Platte River valley, near Aurora, Nebraska. From 1888 to 1893 his home was in Tracy, Iowa, and during these years he hunted, fished, and roamed the Des Moines River woodlands. Later, 1911 to 1919, he lived at New Orleans, gaining the knowledge of the Gulf region reflected in his short story, "The Horse of Hurricane

405

Reef." Much of his education he received from communing with nature. Formal learning he obtained from the Madison, Wisconsin, high school, 1893 to 1896, and from the University of Wisconsin, 1896-97. He also spent two periods in service in the United States Army: during the Spanish-American War, 1897-1900, and during the First World War, 1917. To his sister, nee Ida May Jackson and later Mrs. Charles F. Burgess, who worked for the Milwaukee *Sentinel,* and to his maternal grandfather, Major Horace Tenney, who was once editor of the Chicago *Post,* Jackson has expressed indebtedness for his interest in writing as a career. Jackson wrote some stories that have received high rating, and "The Horse of Hurricane Reef" has appeared in several anthologies. He made his home in Miami from 1930 to 1946 and still resides in Florida.

MARY E. WILKINS FREEMAN (1862-1930)

As a writer, Mrs. Freeman was highly original, perhaps partly because of receiving little formal schooling. As a child, she was in too poor health to obtain much formal education but did attend the Mount Holyoke Female Seminary, predecessor of the Mount Holyoke College, in 1870-71, and a school in Brattleboro, Vermont, in 1873. She read widely, especially the English and Russian novelists. In her native Randolph, Massachusetts, she lived, except for ten years in Brattleboro, until her marriage to Dr. Charles M. Freeman in 1902, after which she and her husband resided in Metuchen, New Jersey. Her first published story for adults, "A Shadow Family," appeared in a Boston newspaper but no copy of the text exists. Her earliest adult story that has survived, "Two Old Lovers," was published in *Harper's Bazar* (March 31, 1883). Her period of book publication began in 1886 with *The Adventures of Ann,* a collection of stories for children, and ended in 1927 with *The Best Stories of Mary E. Wilkins,* selected and edited by Henry Wysham Lanier. Her writings are extensive, including, besides her short narratives, a play, two books of poetry, and a dozen novels. The titles of her short-story volumes for adults reach to twenty-two: *A Humble Romance* (1887), *A New England Nun* (1891), *The Pot of Gold* (1892), *Young Lucretia* (1892), *Comfort Pease and Her Gold Ring* (1895), *The People of Our Neighborhood* (1898), *Silence* (1898), *The Jamesons* (1899), *Evelina's Garden* (1899), *In Colonial Times* (1899), *The Love of Parson Lord* (1900), *Understudies* (1901), *Six Trees* (1903), *The Wind in the Rosebush* (1903), *The Givers* (1904), *The Fair Lavinia* (1907), *The Winning Lady* (1909), *The Green Door* (1910), *The Yates Pride* (1912), *The Copy Cat* (1914), *Edgewater People* (1918), and *The Best Stories* (1927). *A New England Nun* established her reputation as a story writer. Among the honors that Mrs.

406

Freeman received were the Howells medal, bestowed in 1925 by the American Academy of Arts and Letters for excellent work in fiction, and election to membership in the National Institute of Arts and Letters in 1926. By and large, her shorter narratives are superior to her novels. In her stories she wrote objectively and grimly of the frustrating life of the simple New England village, such life as she knew in eastern Massachusetts in her early days. Her stories are concise, smooth, varied, forceful, and sometimes elusively humorous. The characters possess moral dignity, notwithstanding their undernourishment, lack of sufficient suitable clothing, and arduous toil. Her stories are the more to be admired because she broke with the sentimentality popular in much of the fiction of her day.

WALTER DUMAUX EDMONDS (1903-   )

With little exception the region of which Walter D. Edmonds writes is upper New York State. Having been born on a farm near Boonville, New York, he grew up on that farm and in New York City, where his father practiced law. In his boyhood Walter took great delight in hearing the farmers of his native region tell stories. His pre-college formal training was received in the Cutler School of New York City, the St. Paul's School of Concord, New Hampshire, and the Choate School of Wallingford, Connecticut. He was a member of the board of editors of the *Choate Literary Magazine*. At Harvard, where he graduated in 1926 with the Bachelor of Arts degree, his major study was English and he gave much time to the editorship of the *Harvard Advocate*. He was inspired by a composition course, English 12, taught by Professor Charles T. Copeland, to write short stories. His first story published outside of school or college magazines, "The End of the Tow-Path," *Scribner's* (July, 1926), was written for that composition course. He is comparable to Washington Irving for creating historical fiction dealing with New York State. The Erie Canal region—the Mohawk valley and its hinterland—the part of the state in which Edmonds has spent his life, has served as the setting for nearly all his novels and short stories. He has published ten novels, exclusive of his books for boys. His first novel, *Rome Haul* (1929), was later dramatized with the title, *The Farmer Takes a Wife*. His most popular novel, *Drums Along the Mohawk* (1936), has been filmed, also *Rome Haul* and *Chad Hanna* (1940). His first juvenile book, *The Matchlock Guns*, received in 1942 the Newbery medal for being the most distinguished American book for children published in 1941. His second book for boys or young readers, *Tom Whipple* (1942), is the story of a resourceful and courageous Yankee boy. His third book for youthful readers, *Two Logs Crossing* (1943), is an adaptation of his short story,

BIOGRAPHIES

"Judge," giving a more detailed treatment of John Haskell's two trapping expeditions than appeared in the earlier version. Though primarily a novelist, Edmonds has published two volumes of short stories, interesting for both their settings and their characterizations: *Mostly Canallers* (1934) and *Young Ames* (1942). Some of the stories treat of the pioneering period, others of contemporary life. The style is direct, vigorous, and polished. Edmonds' work has been represented in the O'Brien and O. Henry collections.

BRET HARTE (1836-1902)

Francis Bret Harte was born in Albany, New York, and during the first nine years of his life, until his father's death, his home was in at least five other cities, Philadelphia; Providence; Lowell, Massachusetts; Brooklyn; and New York City. The boy read widely, especially in the writings of Dickens and Irving. From 1854 to 1871 he resided in California, becoming well acquainted with the Far West of the Gold Rush period and most of his successful short stories dealt with that region and time. From 1858 to 1860 he was the assistant editor of the newspaper, *The Northern Californian,* in a town which was a mining supply-base (then called *Union,* now *Arcata).* Later he served as editor of *The Golden Era* and *The Overland Monthly,* both of San Francisco. In the latter magazine he published some of his short stories. During the year, July 1871 to June 1872, he filled a $10,000 contract with the *Atlantic Monthly,* publishing several stories and poems. His most admirably productive years lay between 1868, when he became editor of the *Overland,* and 1871, when he returned from San Francisco to New York City. The stories of that period are striking for their application of old methods (those of Irving and Dickens) to new materials. After two consulships, one at Crefeld, Prussia, 1878 to 1880, the other at Glasgow, 1880 to 1885, he made his home in London until his death. His outstanding literary contribution was in the field of the short story, in which he published about two dozen volumes. *The Luck of Roaring Camp and Other Sketches* (1870) proved to be his most popular collection. He established the local color vogue in a number of excellent stories that are still read for their sentiment, their humor, and their pathos, as well as their regionalism.

O. HENRY (1862-1910)

Born in Greensboro, North Carolina, William Sydney Porter (pen name: O. Henry) spent his first twenty years in the city of his birth. At fifteen he quit school to work as a clerk in the drug store of his uncle, Clark Porter, in Greensboro, where he continued for five years. Then he went to Texas because of his health (tuberculosis, the disease of which he finally died, was already threatening) and lived two years on a ranch, obtaining a knowledge of cowboy life that he utilized later in some of his stories, for example, in the volumes, *Heart of the West* (1907), and *Roads of Destiny* (1909). Early in 1884 he moved to Austin, where he spent two years mainly in three employments: bookkeeper for a real estate company, assistant compiling draftsman for the Texas General Land Office and teller in the First National Bank. In 1887 he published some humorous sketches in the *Detroit Free Press*. In 1895 he went to Houston and while there wrote a humorous column for the *Houston Daily Post*. When in 1896 he was summoned to Austin to stand trial on a charge of having embezzled funds from the bank where he had worked, unnerved by the prospect, he boarded a train for New Orleans and visited Honduras, South America, and Mexico, before returning to Austin early in 1897 upon learning that his wife was ill. At the trial he was convicted (though his guilt may have been only technical, inasmuch as the bank is alleged to have been very loosely managed) and sentenced to a five-year term. During his imprisonment he published twelve short stories. Upon his release (1901) he went to Pittsburgh, where he stayed about a year writing stories. In 1902 he moved to New York City where he lived the remainder of his life, except for brief periods at Asheville, North Carolina. He found New York City with its variety and picturesquesness a prolific source of short story materials and here he achieved real fame. He was America's most popular short story writer during the first two decades of the twentieth century. His main type of narrative, the kind that has a sharply unexpected ending, enjoys less vogue today than in his lifetime. Nevertheless, his work is still entertaining. "A Municipal Report" was first published in *Hampton's Magazine* (November, 1909).

NATHANIEL HAWTHORNE (1804-1864)

In his writings Hawthorne interpreted seventeenth century Puritanism and its effects upon the consciences of New Englanders. He wrote of the Puritan traditions indigenous to the Salem and the Massachusetts where families of the Hathorne name had long resided. Nathaniel was born in Salem, the descendant of a long line of Puritan ancestors. One of his great-great-grandfathers had been a judge during the Salem witchcraft trials. In his native Salem Nathaniel spent most of his boyhood prior to entering Bowdoin College, Brunswick, Maine, at seventeen. While at Bowdoin, he was an excellent student of English composition. He formed at the college warm and lasting friendships with Henry W. Longfellow, Franklin Pierce, and Horatio Bridge. After graduating from Bowdoin,

Hawthorne returned to Salem, where he served a twelve years' apprenticeship (1825 to 1837) learning his art and sometimes contributing tales to Samuel Griswold Goodrich's Boston annual, *The Token,* and to some newspapers and magazines. From 1829 to 1841 he was employed at the Boston Custom House. From 1842 to 1852 he made his homes at various times in Concord, Salem, Lenox, and West Newton, all in Massachusetts. From 1852 to his death he maintained his American residence at Concord in a home that is known as The Wayside. Several of those years, however, he was in England or in Europe. In 1837 he published his first volume of short stories, *Twice-Told Tales.* In 1842 the second series of *Twice-Told Tales* appeared, containing the eighteen tales from the first series and twenty-one others. Besides the *Twice-Told Tales,* Hawthorne's books of short stories for general readers are *Mosses from an Old Manse* (1846), *The Snow Image and Other Twice-Told Tales* (1851), *The Dolliver Romance and Other Pieces* (1876), and *Fanshawe and Other Sketches* (1876). The main types of tale that Hawthorne wrote are the character sketch, the philosophical sketch, the historical tale, and the allegorical tale. The last-named is his predominant type. His literary style is clear, graceful, symbolic, and richly imaginative. Notwithstanding the Puritanism that still lingered in his New England, he made the short story a popular form of art in his native region.

WILBUR DANIEL STEELE (1886-   )

Wilbur Daniel Steele began life in the same North Carolina city, Greensboro, in which O. Henry had been born. Steele's first school attendance was in a kindergarten in Berlin, with a niece of Friedrich Froebel as his teacher, when his father was in Germany as a graduate student. His schooling continued in Denver, where his father had become a professor in the University of Denver. In that city, Wilbur attended grammar school, high school, and the university, graduating with the Bachelor of Arts degree in 1907. He next studied art in the Museum of Fine Arts, Boston, 1907-8. He also studied art in the Académie Julien, Paris, 1908-9, and in the Art Students League, New York City, 1909-10. He served as naval correspondent during the First World War. In 1932 his alma mater conferred on him the honorary degree, Doctor of Letters. His writings include a few dramas, *The Terrible Woman and Other One Act Plays* (1925) ; a novelette, *Undertow* (1930) ; seven novels; and six volumes of collected short stories. He is known chiefly for his character novels and psychological stories, more favorably for his shorter narratives than for the longer ones. *Land's End* (1918) contains cleverly written and dramatic stories of the New England coast. *The Shame Dance* (1923)

is a volume of vivid stories that combine romantic and realistic elements
and that end with surprises. *Urkey Island* (1926) is a collection of
somber or tragic tales of village life on an imaginary island, a fishing
community, near the New England coast. *The Man Who Saw Through
Heaven* (1927) presents a dozen narratives, all rather striking for their
implications. *Tower of Sand* (1929) brings together eight of the author's
most popular short fictions. And *The Best Stories of Wilbur Daniel Steele*
(1946) contains two dozen ingenious, robust, superbly told stories that
end in violence and tragedy. Some of his most popular stories won either
cash prizes or decisions from the O. Henry Memorial Award Committee.
"For They Know Not What They Do" received the second prize in 1919.
"The Man Who Saw Through Heaven" tied with another story for first
place in 1925. "Bubbles" achieved the highest award in 1926. And
"Can't Cross Jordan by Myself" won the top decision in 1931. Steele's
stories are rich in drama and power of suggestion. Their style is smooth,
facile, concise, and vigorous. They can hardly fail to impress the reader
with the excellence of Steele's craftsmanship.

EDGAR ALLAN POE (1809-1849)

Poe was keenly intellectual, highly sensitive, idealistic, original, and
aesthetic. In an age when literature was dominantly didactic, his interest
in the three fields in which he wrote, poetry, criticism, and the short story,
was in art for art's sake. Poe was born in Boston, the son of a man who
had been reared in Baltimore and of an actress who was a native of
London, England. When his mother died Poe was orphaned at a little
less than three years of age. His father had already either died or deserted
the family. The boy was taken into the home of Mr. and Mrs. John Allan,
of Richmond, for rearing, without being legally adopted. When Poe was
six, his foster parents took him to England for what proved to be a
five-year stay abroad. During this period, Poe attended some of the schools
of England and Scotland. After the return to America, he received some
private tutoring and attended William Burke's academy in Richmond. In
1826 he studied in the University of Virginia, showing excellent ability
in mastering Latin and French. Mr. Allan withdrew the young man from
the university because of gambling debts that Poe had contracted. Poe
enlisted in the Army in 1827 and served with distinction for nearly two
years, receiving an honorable discharge. He entered the West Point
Military Academy in 1830 and remained there less than a year until dismissed by court-martial for neglect of duties. He had wanted to resign
but such a step Mr. Allan refused to permit. From 1831 to 1835 he lived
in the home of an aunt in Baltimore. During this time he began to

publish short stories. It was during his six-year Philadelphia residence (1838-44) that he published his first story collection, *Tales of the Grotesque and Arabesque* (1839). After 1844 he made his home in New York City and suburban Fordham. In 1845 he published his second collection of stories, *Tales: By Edgar A. Poe*. He held several editorial positions, staff-member and editor of the *Southern Literary Messenger* (1835-37), editor of *Burton's Gentleman's Magazine* (1839-40), literary editor of *Graham's Magazine* (1841-42), literary critic for the *New York Evening Mirror* (1844-45), and editor of the *Broadway Journal* (1845-46). About half of his short stories appeared in his two volumes of tales and the other half in magazines, newspapers, and annuals. His stories belong to several classes. Perhaps, his least successful type was that which attempted to be humorous and his most successful types were those dealing with mystery and detection or with horror and death. He was the creator of the detective story. His influence on the American short story has been heavy, largely because he formulated the technique by which he thought tales should be written. His stories are good examples of the application of that technique. They are unified and compact. Many story writers have acknowledged him their master.

AUGUST DERLETH (1909-   )

Biographer, poet, novelist, writer of short stories and miscellaneous prose is August Derleth. The number of volumes that he has published as author, editor, and coeditor, more than sixty, is about one and a half times the years he has lived. He was born in Sauk City, Wisconsin, and in the schools of that village obtained his elementary and secondary education. In 1930 he received the Bachelor of Arts degree from the University of Wisconsin. His writings have been appearing in print since 1926. In 1933 he was placed on O'Brien's Roll of Honor for the short story, "Five Alone." He served as director and clerk of the Sauk City Board of Education from 1937 to 1943. And this tremendously energetic man has participated in various social and civic projects of his home community. For his creative writing he was in 1938 appointed to a John Simon Guggenheim Memorial Fellowship. Since 1939 he has been director of the Arkham House, Publishers, and since 1941 an editor of the *Capital Times*, Madison. From 1940 to 1943 he was a special lecturer in the university of his state, teaching a course in American regional literature. And much of his writing is regional in the best sense, frequently sounding the universal note. His chief writing project has been the Sac Prairie Saga, planned, while he was a student in the university, to contain about fifty volumes of the history of Sac Prairie (the typical Wisconsin village), covering the period from about 1830 to 1950. Twenty have been published: seven novels, three story collections, three volumes of miscellaneous prose, and seven books of poetry. Besides the Saga, the works of which he is the author include two biographies, nine Judge Peck mystery novels, a few other novels, four poetic volumes, a few books of miscellaneous prose, and five collections of stories. He has also edited about a dozen books, chiefly weird stories and science-fiction tales. The three volumes of stories that belong to the Saga are *Place of Hawks* (1935), *Country Growth* (1940), and *Sac Prairie People* (1945). Two of the remaining five, *In Re: Sherlock Holmes—The Adventures of Solar Pons* (1945) and *The Memoirs of Solar Pons* (1951) are pastiches of Doyle's Sherlock Holmes stories. The other three contain tales of the supernatural: *Someone in the Dark* (1941), *Something Near* (1945), and *Not Long for This World* (1948). Derleth's short stories are both artistic and emotional, ranging in mood from the comic to the tragic. "The Sheraton Mirror" first appeared in the *Weird Tales* magazine (September, 1932) and was collected in *Someone in the Dark*.

EDWARD EVERETT HALE (1822-1909)

Many-sided was the life of Edward Everett Hale. Born in Boston, the fourth of eight children, he lived to be eighty-seven. In his useful life, he was a lecturer, a teacher, a pastor, an editor, and an author. He prepared for college by studying in a dame school and in the Boston Latin School. He entered Harvard in 1835 and was graduated four years later. At Harvard, he showed particular interest in English composition and in the classics. After leaving Harvard, he studied theology under private tutoring. In 1842 he began preaching. In 1846 he became the minister of the Church of the Unity, in Worcester, and held this position until he was made pastor of the South Congregational Church, Boston, in 1856. From 1856 to 1901 he served as active minister of the South Congregational Church and from the latter year to his death was pastor emeritus. From 1903 to 1909 he was chaplain of the United States Senate. The most popular of his published works are his five volumes of short stories: *If, Yes, and Perhaps* (1868), *His Level Best* (1873), *Crusoe in New York* (1880), *Susan's Escort* (1897), and *The Brick Moon* (1899). His two stories that seem destined to live longest, "The Man Without a Country," written on Mackinac Island in Michigan, and "My Double and How He Undid Me," were first published in the *Atlantic*. Both are skilfully written and realistic. The first-named is patriotic; the latter, satirical and whimsical. In their realism or verisimilitude, his stories were influenced by Defoe. They are Hale's most permanent contributions to literature.

BIOGRAPHIES

WILLIAM HAZLETT UPSON (1891-   )

Upson was born in Glen Ridge, New Jersey (at the time of his birth, however, the birthplace was a part of Bloomfield). He attended grade school and high school in Glen Ridge. In 1910 he enrolled in the New York State College of Agriculture, Cornell University, and was graduated four years later with the Bachelor of Science degree. After leaving the college, he worked on five farms, near Rush and near North Rose, New York, and near Leesburg, Charlottesville, and Colman Falls, Virginia, until he entered military service. He was admitted to an officer's training camp at Fort Myer, Virginia, in 1917, and, after three months of training, he enlisted in the Army, being placed in the Thirteenth Field Artillery. Upon release from the Army in 1919, he entered employment with the Holt Manufacturing Company, working for a few months in the shop and then in the field as a traveling service mechanic, demonstrating, delivering, and repairing tractors. In 1922 he underwent a serious operation and during the convalescence (about a year), began to write short stories. In 1923 he resumed work with the company and remained about another year, composing stories in the nighttime, but finally left the position to devote himself to a writing career. Since 1924 he has resided at Middlebury, Vermont. Though he has published a humorous one-act play and a few semi-autobiographic articles, he has written chiefly short stories. Of his nine volumes of stories, two treat of the First World War: *The Piano Movers* (1927) and *Me and Henry and the Artillery* (1928); two, of the Second World War, also of tractors: *Keep 'Em Crawling, Earthworms at War* (1943) and *Botts in War, Botts in Peace* (1944); and the remaining five contain stories about tractors: *Alexander Botts—Earthworm Tractors* (1929), *Earthworms in Europe* (1931), *Earthworms Through the Ages* (1947), *Hello, Mr. Henderson* (1949), and *No Rest for Botts; Earthworms Make the World Go Round* (1951). Nearly all his stories deal with either tractors or war. His writing has been consistently humorous. Occasionally he has touched a story with irony. He created Botts, a self-assured, audacious, persistent, and verbose super-salesman of tractors, who first appeared in the story, "I'm a Natural-born Salesman" (1927). "I'm in a Hurry," a humorous tractor story, was first published in *Collier's* (1925).

HENRY CUYLER BUNNER (1855-1896)

H. C. Bunner was born in Oswego, New York. His parents moved to New York City while he was a small child, and there he obtained his schooling. He studied in a private school but was not financially able to attend college. He served his journalistic apprenticeship by working for

414

a weekly magazine, *The Arcadian* (1873-77). He spent approximately half of his forty-one years (1877-96) as a member of the staff, first as assistant editor and later as editor-in-chief, of *Puck,* the earliest humorous magazine established in America. In 1887, one year after he married, he moved to Nutley, New Jersey, and made that city his home the remainder of his life. Much of his poetry and his fiction has its setting in New York City. His short stories probably rank second in popularity to his graceful and charming social poems. His first volume of stories, *In Partnership: Studies in Story-Telling* (1884), was written in collaboration with Brander Matthews. Interesting for its ability to reproduce a foreign writer's style (Maupassant's) in stories that are given American characters and settings is the volume, *Made in France: French Tales Retold with a United States Twist* (1893). His most popular book of tales is *Short Sixes: Stories to be Read While the Candle Burns* (1890). These tales belong to the type of writing now known as short short stories. Bunner's stories are clever, spirited, original, witty, and artistic. They contain humor, pathos, and their author's broad sympathy for his fellow men. The spirit of humanitarianism, of love for all the world, reflected in his writings has been an important cause of their popularity.

ALLAN SEAGER (1906-   )

A native of Adrian, Michigan, Allan Seager moved to Memphis, Tennessee, at age eleven and there remained until 1925. After graduation from high school in Memphis, he entered the University of Michigan, where he obtained the Bachelor of Arts degree in 1930. That year he was appointed a Rhodes Scholar to Oriel College, Oxford, receiving the Bachelor of Arts in 1933 and from the same university the Master of Arts in 1948. He served as one of the editors of the *Vanity Fair* magazine a year and a half, 1934-35. Since 1935, except for one year at Bennington College, 1944-45, he has taught English in the University of Michigan, as Teaching Fellow to 1938, then Instructor to 1943, Assistant Professor to 1947, and Associate Professor since 1947. His study of languages, his editorship, his travels in Europe and South America, and his teaching of a course in literature and one in short-story writing at the University of Michigan have helped qualify him for creating novels and stories. He has published a book of biographies, *They Worked for a Better World* (1939); two novels, *Equinox* (1943) and *The Inheritance* (1948); and a volume of short stories, *The Old Man of the Mountain* (1950). In 1947 he won a $5,000 first prize in a short-story contest conducted by *Good Housekeeping.* He has published about fifty stories in magazines, some of which have appeared in the O'Brien, Foley, and O. Henry collections. His stories show marked variation of theme; simple, lyrical phrasing; vivid, lifelike characterization; and realistic depiction of setting. Irony sometimes appears in both his novels and shorter fictions and may be noted, for example, in his story, "The Conqueror." His work has been translated into French, German, Spanish, Italian, and Portuguese.

THOMAS BAILEY ALDRICH (1836-1907)

Aldrich, born in Portsmouth, New Hampshire, spent his boyhood there, except for periods in New York City, New Orleans, and several other places. In 1849 his father died. Thomas Bailey was, therefore, not able to enter Harvard, as he had wished, but was obliged to work to support the family. From 1852 to 1865 he lived in New York City. During the first three of these years he was a clerk in an uncle's counting-house. Between 1855 and the close of the Civil War he held staff positions on five New York magazines and newspapers: literary critic for the *Evening Mirror* (1855), assistant editor of the *Home Journal* (1855-59), associate editor of the *Saturday Press* (1858-60), war correspondent for the *Tribune* in the early part of the war, and managing editor of the *Illustrated News* (1863). Within the New York period, he published several volumes of poetry and his first collection of short stories, *Out of His Head, a Romance* (1862). From 1865 to his death his home was in Boston. Within these years he held two editorships, that of *Every Saturday* (1866-74) and that of the *Atlantic Monthly* (1881-90). In this period he also published a blank-verse tragedy, a few novels, some books of poetry, a few books of essays and sketches, and five more volumes of short stories: *Marjorie Daw and Other People* (1873), *A Midnight Fantasy and The Little Violinist* (1877), *Marjorie Daw and Other Stories* (1885), *Two Bites at a Cherry with Other Tales* (1894), and *A Sea Turn and Other Matters* (1902). His extensive travels, to England and Europe and Africa and around the world, occurred mainly between his two Boston editorships and after he left his position with the *Atlantic*. Except for his poetry, Aldrich's literary fame rests chiefly on his short stories. His autobiographical novel, *The Story of a Bad Boy* (1870), reminiscent of the boyhood days in Portsmouth, is a delightful juvenile classic. This novel and the *Marjorie Daw* volume of 1873 seem to be his most successful prose works. His writings are impressive for their craftsmanship: their condensation, unique atmosphere, and in some cases surprise endings. "Marjorie Daw" is an artistic and charming story, famous for the surprise at the end.

416

BIOGRAPHIES

HENRY SYDNOR HARRISON (1880-1930)

Henry Sydnor Harrison was born in Sewanee, Tennessee, when his father, Dr. Caskie Harrison, was a professor of classical languages at the University of the South. In 1885 Dr. Harrison moved his family to Brooklyn, New York, where he had opened his own private Brooklyn Latin School two years before. Henry began attending his father's school the year the family moved and there he did the study which fitted him for entrance into Columbia University. He graduated from the university in 1900. From 1902 to 1908 he conducted for the *Richmond Times-Dispatch* a column entitled, "Rhymes for the Day." From 1908 until 1910 he was the chief editorial writer for this newspaper. Later (1929), he contributed articles to the *Richmond News-Leader*. In 1910 he moved from Richmond, where he had resided since 1902, to Charleston, West Virginia, to make authorship his sole occupation. After the publication of three or four novels and a few short stories, his plans to devote himself solely to writing were interrupted by a stay in France, March to July, 1915, driving an ambulance as a member of the American Ambulance Service, and by a period in Washington, D. C., 1917 to 1919, as a cable editor, during the First World War. From 1919 until death he made his home in New York City. His novels include seven volumes: *Captivating Mary Carstairs* (1910), *Queed* (1911), *V. V.'s Eyes* (1913), *Angela's Business* (1915), *Saint Teresa* (1922), *Andrew Bride of Paris* (1925), and *The Good Hope* (1931). In the novels are urbane style, excellent plot construction, and masterful character delineation. The combined listings of Firkins's *Index to Short Stories* and of the *Readers' Guide to Periodical Literature* mention fourteen titles of stories by Harrison. "Miss Hinch" is his story that has most frequently appeared in anthologies. Its setting, plot, and characterization are all skilfully handled. It cleverly sustains the suspense and closes with a dramatic surprise.

ANNA KATHARINE GREEN (1846-1935)

Partly because of her early appearance as a writer of detective fiction, nearly a decade before Sir Arthur Conan Doyle began writing his Sherlock Holmes stories, Anna Katharine Green holds an important place in American literature. She was born in Brooklyn, New York. From her father, an attorney, she obtained much knowledge of criminal law, a useful background for creating detective novels and detective short stories. In 1867 she graduated from the Ripley Female College, Poultney, Vermont, with the Bachelor of Arts degree. In 1884 she married Charles Rohlfs, a furniture designer. She and her family made their home in Buffalo. Even before her marriage she had begun to write detective fiction and she continued to publish novels and stories until near 1920. She created the two detectives, Ebenezer Gryce and Violet Strange. It was in a best-seller novel, *The Leavenworth Case* (1878), that Gryce first appeared; and he continued to appear in other books, including *The Doctor, His Wife, and the Clock* (1895), *That Affair Next Door* (1897), *Lost Man's Lane* (1898), and *One of My Sons* (1901). Among Mrs. Rohlfs's most popular mystery novels, besides the four already named, are *Hand and Ring* (1883), *Behind Closed Doors* (1888), *The Forsaken Inn* (1890), *The Filigree Ball* (1903), *The Millionaire Baby* (1905), *The House of the Whispering Pines* (1910), *Initials Only* (1911), *The Mystery of the Hasty Arrow* (1917), and *The Step on the Stair* (1923). In addition to *The Doctor, His Wife, and the Clock,* her books of short stories are *XYZ, a Detective Story* (1883), *7 to 12, a Detective Story* (1887), *The Old Stone House* (1891), *A Difficult Problem* (1901), *The Amethyst Box* (1905), *The House in the Mist* (1905), *Three Thousand Dollars* (1910), *Masterpieces of Mystery* (1913; republished, 1919, titled *Room Number Three),* *The Golden Slipper and Other Problems for Violet Strange* (1915), and *To the Minute, Scarlet and Black* (1916). Her materials were primarily those of mystery and suspense and surprise. Her plots are interesting and probable, leading usually to a pleasant solution. Notwithstanding her somewhat stilted and sometimes diffuse style and her artificial characterization, she is important in detective fiction for her careful construction of probable plots.

CORNELL WOOLRICH (1903-   )

Cornell Woolrich (other pseudonyms: George Hopley and William Irish; real name: Cornell George Hopley-Woolrich) was born in New York City, which has continued to be his home. He attended the DeWitt Clinton High School and Columbia University. Since leaving college he has devoted himself chiefly to writing. Beginning with his first novel in 1926, he has averaged publishing about a book a year. His first six volumes were love novels. When his seventh novel, *The Bride Wore Black,* appeared in 1940, he had changed from writing romances to producing books of mystery and detection. The mystery or detective novel is his dominant type of writing. His detective novels have well-sustained suspense, original and fast-moving plots, skilful and realistic characterization, sometimes irony, and sometimes pathos. He has often written on the theme of the seemingly impossible but terrifying disappearance of some lady. His short stories are nearly all of the mystery or detection type. His six books of stories deal with mystery or detection or action marked by strong suspense: *I Wouldn't Be in Your Shoes* (1943), *After-Dinner*

Story (1944), *The Dancing Detective* (1946), *Dead Man Blues* (1948), *The Blue Ribbon* (1949), and *Somebody on the Phone* (1950). "Wait for Me Downstairs" was first published in the *Detective Fiction Weekly* (June 22, 1940) with the title, "Finger of Doom." Anthony Boucher's anthology, *Great American Detective Stories* (1945) used the caption, "I Won't Take a Minute." Mr. Woolrich has suggested that in the present anthology the story be entitled "Wait for Me Downstairs." The theme is the vanishing of a woman who intended to deliver to an apartment a package and to return immediately and the clever deductions of a detective.

HARRIET PRESCOTT SPOFFORD (1835-1921)

Descended from Puritan stock, Harriet Elizabeth Prescott was born in Calais, Maine, and lived there until fourteen. Her next home was in Newburyport, Massachusetts, where she attended the Putnam Free School, graduating in 1852. For a short time she studied in the Pinkerton Academy, Derry, New Hampshire. Her Newburyport pastor, Thomas Wentworth Higginson, having been impressed by an essay that she wrote when fifteen encouraged her to write for magazines. Her clever adventure story, "In a Cellar," for which *The Atlantic* paid her one hundred and five dollars, appeared in 1859 and gave her a reputation as a short-story writer. In 1865 she married Richard S. Spofford, Jr., a lawyer. Her residence continued in Newburyport, except for winters in Washington, D. C., until her husband bought the five-acre Deer Island, near Newburyport, in 1874. On that island she made her home the remainder of her life, except for winters in Boston and two trips to Europe. To the hospitality of the Spofford home Whittier paid tribute in his poem, "R. S. S. at Deer Island on the Merrimac." Mrs. Spofford wrote essays, poems, novels, novelettes, stories, and miscellaneous works. Some of her most interesting essays, sincere and forceful, are in *A Little Book of Friends* (1916). Of her several volumes of verse, *In Titian's Garden and Other Poems* (1897) is the best known. Poetry was probably the form most congenial to her literary temperament. Her short prose fictions have been, however, more popular than her verses. The poems of *Titian's Garden,* despite their brilliant conceits and glowing adjectives, produce restful impressions of charming sights and sounds. Her first, and perhaps her most pretentious, novel, *Sir Rohan's Ghost* (1860), treating of crime and its retribution, shows influence by Poe. Some of her novelettes, *A Master Spirit* (1896), *An Inheritance* (1897), and *The Maid He Married* (1899) portray women's emotions. Probably her two best-known volumes of short stories are the first one, *The Amber Gods* (1863), primarily romantic, and the last, *The Elder's People* (1920), more strongly realistic. "In a Cellar,"

"The Amber Gods," and "Circumstance" have been placed among her greatest romantic stories; "Knitting Sale-Socks," "The South Breaker," "A Village Dressmaker," and "A Rural Telephone," among her most admired realistic stories. "Circumstance" is romantic in its main conception but contains many realistic details. Though Mrs. Spofford's writings have been criticized adversely for their glowing style, profuse in adjectives and images, they have been praised for natural dialogue, vivid description, and dramatic power especially in the climaxes.

HOWARD BLOOMFIELD (1900-   )

Howard Van Lieu Bloomfield, of Dutch ancestry, was born in Bloomfield, New Jersey, where he was reared. His interest in creating short stories largely arose from and was stimulated by his winning a prize for story-writing, while attending high school. To improve his writing ability, he studied in Harvard three years, 1918-19 and 1920-22, concentrating in the field of English and graduating with the Bachelor of Science degree. For a few years he was a newspaper reporter, then editor of a detective-story magazine, and from 1934 to 1940 editor of *Adventure*. Particularly from his magazine editorships he learned the importance of realism and suspense to good writing. From his hobby of sailing have been inspired several articles on yachting and oyster fishing and a book of travel, *Sailing to the Sun*, 1942. "My Wife Wants a New Spinnaker," published in *Yachting* (April, 1938), deals humorously with how a husband can cause his wife to enjoy sailing in a boat. The article, "Chesapeake Shell Game," *Saturday Evening Post* (February 3, 1945), describes oyster fishermen and treats of the oyster industry in Chesapeake Bay. The essay, "Those Oysters We Eat," *Good Housekeeping* (April, 1945), contains interesting information on types of oysters, the leading areas of production, and oysters as table delicacies. Besides his magazine articles, concerned chiefly with sailing and fishing and farming, Bloomfield has published a few rather striking pieces of fiction, in which characterization seems always prominent. His storiette, "Message to Dad," tells of a son away from home in a military camp writing a letter to his mother expressing admiration for his father's courage. The mystery story, "The Case on Turkey Point," characterizes a small-town policeman who solves a local murder. And the adventure story, "The Trap," while not neglecting to study character is perhaps even more interesting for the plot filled with perilous action. Bloomfield now lives on a farm on the Eastern Shore of Maryland, active with both farming and writing.